Ingleborough
Landscape and history

In memory of my brother Dennis who took me, aged ten,
up my first mountain.

Ingleborough
Landscape and history

David Johnson

CARNEGIE PUBLISHING
IN ASSOCIATION WITH

Of related interest from Carnegie

Professor David Hey: *A History of Yorkshire: 'County of the Broad Acres'*, hardback, £24.00
Professor David Hey: *Derbyshire: A History*, hardback, £24.00
Jan Wiltshire, *About Scout Scar: Looking into a Cumbrian Landscape*, softback, £7.95
Brendan Threlfall, *Birdwatching Walks in the Yorkshire Dales*, softback, £7.95
Colin Pooley (ed.), *Rivers and the British Landscape*, hardback, £18.00

Full details and secure online ordering at www.carnegiepublishing.com

Ingleborough: Landscape and history

Copyright © David Johnson 2008

First edition published in 2008 by
Carnegie Publishing Ltd
Carnegie House, Chatsworth Road,
Lancaster LA1 4SL
www.carnegiepublishing.com

in association with
the Yorkshire Dales Millennium Trust
Old Post Office, Main Street,
Clapham LA2 8DP
www.ydmt.org

ISBN 978-1-85936-187-0 (*hardback*)
ISBN 978-1-85936-188-7 (*softback*)

British Library Cataloguing-in-Publication data
A catalogue record for this book is available from the British Library

Designed, typeset and originated by Carnegie Publishing
Printed and bound in the UK by Cambridge University Press

Contents

Figures

Tables

Plates

Preface

This is the first book to adopt a fully holistic approach to Ingleborough, and arguably the first to consider in this way any individual upland bloc in the Pennine chain, with the exception of Rée's book on the Three Peaks, published twenty-five years ago.[1] The concept started from the premise that, in the real world, physical and cultural attributes cannot be separated, and this book proffers a synthesis of the physical and cultural. The ways in which people through the ages have made use of the mountain were a direct response to the opportunities and constraints embodied within it. Thus, past settlements were sited where conditions were at their optimal level, where soil, water and shelter were readily available. Wider land use patterns and activities through prehistoric and historic time reflect perceived, or empirically-derived, opportunities. It may be a gross simplification to say that human activity on the mountain is a result of physical conditions but there is a very strong element of this. To take a few examples from various time slots, parts of the mountain massif have been valued as turbary grounds, providing peat for domestic fuel; as moors dedicated to grouse management and field sports; as places of challenge and adventure, either by exploring its subterranean depths or by stomping to the summit; and, not least, by capturing in paint or photograph its varied moods. Geology and landscape processes are as central to the Ingleborough story as human settlement and activity.

The book also presents a synthesis of the most recent research in a broad range of fields from geology and geomorphology to archaeology, some undertaken by academics and some by dedicated amateurs. The style adopted is intended to be rigorous, erudite even, while still remaining accessible. In places it is necessarily technical, but jargon has been kept to a minimum and is explained as and when it appears. It is not directly aimed at academics, though hopefully it has something to offer them; rather it is meant to be of interest to a broad range of readers who have a 'stake' in Ingleborough or a feel for landscape interpretation, landscape history and landscape archaeology.

The list of bibliographic items is provided to guide the interested reader to more detailed material, with the emphasis being on academic research papers and books, as up to date as possible, rather than on popular-style books. A place-name glossary is also included: place-names can be an absolute minefield and gross errors of misinterpretation are not unknown, but successfully deconstructing them can help inform the understanding of a given landscape or locality.

Foreword

by Tony Robinson

One summer when my children were small, my partner and I took them on holiday to southern Turkey. Overlooking our campsite was a black mountain. We didn't know its name, it simply stood there large and triangular, like the mountains my children painstakingly drew in their primary school art books.

In the village cafe was a poster of it, and underneath in slightly ungrammatical English were the name and phone number of a man who, in exchange for a few dollars, offered to strap you to his body, then jump off the top of the mountain with a large kite attached to his back.

In retrospect I find it hard to understand why my partner and I decided to try this. Even more inexplicable is why we agreed that our two beautiful children should join in the fun. Maybe we were affected by the sun, the weather was particularly fine that year, or maybe the hippy blood which still coursed through our veins in the early eighties convinced us that communing with nature in mid-air was more important than health and safety. But whatever the long-forgotten reason, I made the phone call and we agreed to meet the man and his driver the following day.

It was only when the Mini-moke approached the lower slopes of the mountain that fear kicked in. From afar I hadn't realised how impossibly huge it was, and how complex its geography. Misshapen, rocky fields edged their way tentatively up it, only to peter out in a jumble of collapsed walls and boulders. Then the trees began, just a few at first – gnarled, twisted and stunted, but as we climbed higher we could see little clumps of them huddling nervously together, then woods revealed themselves, even a small forest. I'd lost sight of our village by now and was totally disorientated. We came out of the trees and found ourselves confronted by a deep valley which our vehicle butted its way around, sliding this way and that, along the dusty, barely discernible track. Even higher, and we were in a world of knife-edged peaks and impossibly sheer drops. My fear had turned to a swirl of absolute terror, although I would have been hard pressed to say exactly what I was frightened of; was it the thought of crashing, of being smashed to pieces when I jumped off the mountain, the look on the faces of my partner's parents when I told them what had happened to their grandchildren, or was it simply something to do with being confronted by the enormity of the mountain? Certainly by now it seemed to have acquired a terrifying personality – old, irascible, and entirely unmoved by my panic.

I don't remember much about the jump itself, other than my instructor telling me that I'd enjoy it more if I opened my eyes. I do remember how tedious the afternoon was though. We landed on a sandy beach next to a lagoon, and I then had to wait for hours while the driver shuttled our instructor back to the mountain so he could jump off again with the next sacrificial member of my family. And all the while it stood there, smaller now and maybe a little less daunting, while I sat on the sand with the occasional ice cream in my hand, waiting like Daedalus in the Greek legend, to see whether my son would float gently out of the sky, or plunge headlong into the sea.

It's hardly surprising that an encounter with a mountain should transform a fun, holiday jaunt into such a profound experience. High places have the unnerving knack of splitting us down the middle, scooping out our deepest emotions, and sending them spinning round us in fragments like a swarm of chattering gnats. I suspect that for as long as human beings have trod this earth they have climbed the cherry-blossom slopes of Fujiyama, the volcanic wastes of Popacatapetl and the scree-ridden hillsides of Olympus, drawn by a delicious feeling of fear and its attendant mysteries, to visit the shamans, witches and assorted seers who've pitched camp there.

Mount Shasta in North California is an ironic example of the longevity of our species' desire to invest the world's peaks with meaning. A sacred site for Native Americans since prehistory, at the end of the nineteenth century it became a magnet for the occult speculations of the emerging white middle classes. In the late 1920s Guy W. Ballard encountered a cosmic spirit there who showed him 'The luminous essence of divine love'. On the strength of this experience he started a religious movement whose rapid growth throughout the 1930s was only interrupted when he and his wife were convicted of fraud (the wise folk of the mountains have often been far wiser as spiritual teachers than as book keepers). Though the conviction was later overturned, the movement had lost its momentum; but others like the Church Universal and Triumphant replaced it, and even today, perhaps four millennia after humans first designated it sacred, UFO watchers, Woodstock renegades and those of a metaphysical bent meditate and drink herbal tea at the New Age resort that has been established there.

But what of our own little green island – are our hills and mountains mystic places too? Has a bearded prophet ever descended from an English peak with a check-list of God's commandments?

I have a friend, a surveyor who has walked our northern hills for thirty years, who thinks we are blind to the clues which indicate how intensely previous generations venerated them. All over their slopes are cairns, little ruins, and lumps and bumps which have continually been ignored or mis-

categorised. Ingleborough is the perfect example. It may not look as terrifying as my Turkish black mountain, and it hasn't got a drop-in centre for psychics and spiritualists, but it's still a place of wonder, and my friend thinks there's evidence that local people have always recognised this.

On a plateau close to Ingleborough's summit is a rubble rampart made of flat upright stones and drystone walling. Until a few years ago it was thought to be an Iron Age hillfort. It's certainly from the pre-Roman era, a time dimly remembered in the ancient Welsh name of its sister hill Pen-y-ghent. But present-day archaeologists are much more sceptical about whether this kind of structure really had a military function. It certainly wouldn't have been a very good fort; it could have withstood only the most cursory of attacks, and there's no permanent water supply. So what else could it have been? It would have been totally impractical as permanent settlement and it's far too elaborate to be a collection of shepherds' huts. It's when faced with conundrums like this that my friend's eyes go misty and he whispers the word 'ritual'!

It's impossible for us to know what arcane practices might have taken place on the slopes of Ingleborough two and a half thousand years ago; let's hope they weren't as bloody as the various forms of human sacrifice that seemed to have been in vogue just down the road in Derbyshire. But it would take someone with a singular lack of imagination not to see what an impressive location this so-called hillfort was built on, how powerful its occupants must have felt when their tribe had possession of it, how much closer to the sky than the earth they were, and how everything below them would have appeared tiny while the sky above seemed very close.

In these more practical and prosaic times, such glimpses of the sacred are too often reduced to nothing more than brief photo opportunity. But at the risk of sounding like the hippy I once was, let me gently remind you that though the geology of Ingleborough is fascinating, as are its fauna and flora, its location and microclimate, it's also a place of mystery and wonder where we can confront our innermost demons and angels – and long may it remain so.

Acknowledgements

The concept for this book originated in the Learning in Limestone Country Project (LiLC) which was jointly organised and promoted by the Yorkshire Dales Millennium Trust (YDMT), the Yorkshire Dales National Park Authority (YDNPA) and Natural England (NE). The objective was to widen knowledge of and interest in the special landscapes of the Yorkshire Dales' limestone country. As the writer of the book, I must express my gratitude to the project team for their vision and for the moral and practical support I have received during the book's gestation period. In particular I must single out Alex Barbour, of the LiLC Project, for her unfailing enthusiasm, guidance and patience. I must also express thanks to David Tayler of the YDMT and Paul Evans of NE.

Over time I have met and talked with many people who live around the mountain or whose work and personal enthusiasms have centred on it, including members of the Ingleborough Archaeology Group. There are too many to name here and it would be invidious were I to miss anybody out, so I will extend all-encompassing gratitude to all. I must, though, single out Yvonne Luke for sharing some wonderful ideas with me. I also readily acknowledge the assistance of staff in the various record offices named in Notes and References, and of the North Craven Historical Research Group.

Lucy Day has done a splendid job transforming my rough sketches into finished artwork throughout the book.

I value very much the input of Beryl Turner, David Turner and Robert White for their specialist comments on various chapters of the book, and I owe a debt of gratitude to Jill Sykes for meticulously reading the entire draft text, pointing out minor errors and inconsistencies, and suggesting alternative ways of making a point. Suggestions made by the anonymous referee are also gratefully acknowledged. The book is all the better for these inputs, though I must state that responsibility for any errors of fact or interpretation, or for any glaring omissions, must remain firmly mine.

·ONE·
Setting the scene

Ingleborough, Pendle-hill and Penigent,
Are the highest hills twixt Scotland and Trent.[1]

Type the word Ingleborough into the Google search engine and you will be presented with a bewildering choice of 66,000 options. Many of these are, predictably, personal blog-type entries or advertisements but there still remain huge numbers of 'worthwhile' entries, on geology, the so-called hill fort, its nature and wildlife, contemporary paintings and photographs, and so on. Do the same for Whernside and Pen-y-ghent and you will be offered 12,700 and 24,400 respectively. Just this one set of glib facts ably illustrates the pull that Ingleborough has, not just locally or even regionally, but nationally. It has an almost iconic status: and it can lay claim to possessing attributes that its neighbouring fells can only jealously regard. Its very shape, seen in profile, is perhaps paramount among these. It is not the highest of the Three Peaks – Whernside wins that accolade by being 13m higher at 736m OD though Ingleborough exceeds Pen-y-ghent's height by 29m. Technically they are all mountains rather than hills, being more than 610m OD, and in adverse weather conditions all three most certainly are, though many local folk would prefer just to call them fells.

It is easy to understand why Ingleborough enjoys such status and popularity. It dominates the horizon from afar and its looming presence is particularly commanding from the west, from Hornby and Claughton on the way to Lancaster, and from as far away as Yealand Conyers 24km to the west on the fringes of Silverdale and even Coniston Old Man. Seen from Newby Head in the east, especially under an atmospheric sky, its massive bulk takes on an almost sinister presence. The Arks, its almost sheer northern edge, soars out of and dwarfs the valley below, as if defying anyone to attempt a climb to the summit (Plate 1.1). The very summit, a level expanse of nothingness when low cloud levels mask the view, is in itself full of interest and detail with its 1km-long perimeter bulwark, the remains of the tower, and the twenty or so 'hut' circles. The view from the top on a clear day is unsurpassed in the western Dales: the whole sweep of the Lake District fells, the rolling moors of the Forest of Bowland, the Craven uplands from Warrendale Knotts above Settle northwards to Mallerstang, Morecambe Bay and, on days of exceptional clarity, even the Isle of Man, can all be picked out with precision.

It is not merely in our time that the mountain and its immediate environs have been perceived as special. For upwards of two centuries this has been a magnet for travellers and tourists of all kinds; it has drawn some of the country's well-known landscape painters and literary figures; and has been a focus for several hundred thousand walkers who have attempted the 37km-long Three Peaks Challenge. As the vast majority do it anticlockwise, attaining Ingleborough's top is, at the very least, a welcome sign that most of the remaining slog is downhill. No one can know how many thousands have climbed Ingleborough on its own, but the date of the first recorded Three Peaks circuit is known: two local teachers completed the round in 14 hours in 1887.

W. H. Auden's poem *In Praise of Limestone*, composed in 1948, though not specifically about Ingleborough, does provide a fitting and moving comment which can be applied to this mountain's limestone expanses, one which many would surely feel empathy with.

> ... but when I try to imagine a faultless love
> Or the life to come, what I hear is the murmur
> Of underground streams, what I see is a limestone landscape.
>
> (lines 91–93)

*   *   *

Of all those who have sat and committed the mountain to canvas or paper, two are going to receive special mention here. J. M. W. Turner visited the area and produced, on commission, three works, two of Ingleborough and the third at Chapel le Dale. All three were composed between 1810 and 1820. His *Ingleborough from the Terrace of Hornby Castle*, executed in pencil and watercolour on paper, is instantly recognisable as a Turner in its picturesque depiction of a rural pastoral scene in the fore- and middle ground with the mountain forming the backdrop under a cloud-laden but benign sky. In a similar mien is his *Ingleborough from Chapel-Le-Dale* which has the church as the centrepiece and the mountain, again as the backdrop, but this time under a heavy and threatening sky. Altogether different is *Weathercote Cave*, a watercolour like the others, which displays the full majesty and threatening power of the flood waters as they thunder into the chasm that is Weathercote (Plate 1.2). He captured the cave perfectly and left nothing to our imagination, even though he altered nature by including the top of Whernside in the view despite the fact it cannot be seen.

The Victorian, Leeds-born, painter Atkinson Grimshaw, less well known than his illustrious antecedent, chose White Scar, north-east of Ingleton, to commit his impression of Ingleborough to canvas, in 1868, in an oil painting entitled *Ingleborough from under White Scar* (Plate 1.3). Several of Grimshaw's works are full of drama and the power of nature and, to my eye anyway, this one is full of allegory. The mountain rises starkly into a wild sky with a stream foaming and crashing at its base, and a length of dry stone wall is the only suggestion in the entire scene of human incursion into the landscape as he perceived it. It is as if he is hinting at Creationism in what he depicts: it is not just any old mountain. It is a special place to be revered and respected. We shall return to this theme later.

William Westall also deserves consideration. A noted engraver, he was working in our area at the same time as Turner and, in 1818, published a collection in book form of views around Malham and Ingleton.[2] He was particularly drawn by caves, as were so many early travellers to the Dales, and the impression he wanted to give to posterity of Yordas Cave in Kingsdale, for example, is far from Romantic or Picturesque. He does focus on the drama but overall opts for a pleasing degree of realism choosing to emphasise visitors and their guide, dwarfed by the scale of the cave's interior.

From the time when the English gentry and minor aristocracy were prevented by Napoleon's machinations from undertaking their Grand Tour of continental Europe's cultural, historic and scenic splendours, the Ingleborough area has been firmly on the tourist map. It not only attracted the political and social elite but drew in the literati as well. William Wordsworth came this way and, in his epic poem *White Doe of Rylstone*, composed in 1807, he introduced the reader to the family vault of the de Claphams, of Clapdale Hall above Clapham, in the church at Bolton Priory in Wharfedale. In Wordsworth's own opinion this was his 'highest work' even though it was not an immediate success. In lines 246 to 254 of this 1,929-line poem, Wordsworth wrote:

> And, through the chink in the fractured floor,
> Look down, and see a griesly sight;
> A vault where the bodies are buried upright!
> There face to face, and hand by hand,
> The Claphams and Mauleverers stand;
> And, in his place, among son and sire,
> is John de Clapham, that fierce Esquire,-
> A valiant man, and a name of dread,
> In the ruthless wars of the White and Red;-

Local legend insists that the unfortunate de Claphams were buried in an upright position.

Wordsworth's friend and fellow Lakes Poet, Robert Southey, visited Chapel le Dale on one of his journeyings and, in his only novel *The Doctor*,[3] seven volumes long and published between 1834 and 1847, and described by reviewers as 'tedious' and tiresome,[4] he did provide some very useful local detail among the dreary padding. The story is set in the early eighteenth century and he described the interior of the yeoman farmer's house on a farm which was the birthplace and childhood home of the main character in the novel. He was Daniel Dove, who was to become the doctor in question. His home was in Chapel le Dale, very close to the church, and this section of the novel reveals much of their lives and gives detail which is as revealing as a probate inventory. It is a work of fiction but was patently written with local knowledge – Southey must have come here and seen the interior of the house which he described in the novel. The title of this chapter (IV, P.I) is entitled 'Birth and parentage of Doctor Dove, with the description of a yeoman's house in the West Riding of Yorkshire a hundred years ago'. He meant it to be factual.

In what Southey described as the 'kitchen', but in fact was more likely to have been the housebody, there were two oak benches that doubled as chests for storing oat bread out of reach of the vermin that would have been an inevitable part of life, a chest for household linen, a 'great' oak table, two 'uncomfortable' wooden chairs against the wall, an inglenook and a wicker chair. This all seems to suggest a prosperous household, a view strengthened by the presence of pewter dishes and silver items like a goblet, a saucepan and four apostle spoons, and religious pictures on the walls. This family had disposable income which they used to improve their level of comfort and, no doubt, to impress the neighbours, yet the size of the farm in the novel was only 26 acres (about 10ha). The fire was fed with peat, a further useful snippet of detail. Upstairs there were three rooms, all of which served a dual purpose as chamber and storeroom: one for the family, one for the yeoman's brother, and one for the maid, the latter an essential adjunct for a successful yeoman family.

The Doctor provides insights into other aspects of life at that time though Southey could, of course, have been writing from his own time, but was there much difference between life in 1730 and 1830? Of diet he says they made their own cheese and butter, the best milk being used for butter; young Daniel walked to school in Ingleton and took with him oat cake and cheese, with the occasional cold bacon or pork, for his lunch. They grew turnips, carrots and cabbages: potatoes were uncommon then; there was a herb garden and a few fruit trees; and bees were kept to provide their sole source of sweetness. Evenings were spent round the open fire: mother at the spinning wheel, maid knitting socks, father reading and musing silently, at times discoursing with his son and the boy's uncle. This was a small farm and Daniel was the only child, so presumably needed to help out on the farm, but his father had the presence and foresight to appreciate his potential and send him to school.

In one of the more lyrical passages in *The Doctor*, Southey paints a vivid picture of the churchyard at Chapel le Dale:

Plate 1.1
Ingleborough from the
East.
© R. F. White and
Yorkshire Dales
National Park Authority
AMY 260/23
(16 September 1986)

The turf was as soft and fine as that of the adjoining hills; it was seldom broken, so scanty was the population ... and the few tombstones which had been placed there were themselves half buried. The sheep came over the wall when they listed, and sometimes took shelter in the porch from the storm. Their voices and the cry of the kite wheeling above were the only sounds which were heard except ... on the Sabbath day ...

Yes, *The Doctor* is fictional but it was based around real people and it does hand down to us the detail of vernacular life which most writers of those times ignored, preferring to concentrate on the landowning classes. The book is difficult to read, and is utterly disjointed, but it is worth persevering to tease out the facts from the fiction.

Long before the time of Wordsworth and Southey, the poet Michael Drayton (1563–1631) had written about Ingleborough:[5]

> From *Penigent's* proud foot as from my source I slide,
> That mountain, my proud sire, in height of all his pride,
> Takes pleasure in my course as his first-born flood,
> And *Ingleborough*, too, of that Olympian brood,
> With *Pendle*, of the north, the highest hills that be,
> Do wistly me behold, and are beheld of me.

Was Drayton responsible, perhaps, for unintentionally generating the age-old couplet that appears at the head of this chapter, granting to the Three Peaks a status far in excess of what they deserve? Certainly, at that time, mountains were perceived as forbidding elements of a landscape which embodied horror and fear, and something to be avoided at all costs. Drayton was arguably among the first to see mountains in a rather different light, accepting their majesty and recognising the hold that they could have over the discerning observer or traveller. If this view has any credibility at all, then he was at the forefront of a literary movement that was to gain pace more than a century after his death.

We can usefully revisit Southey here. His novel is set in the 1730s and in one excerpt he recounts events from the lifetime of Daniel's father:

> Three or four times in his life it had happened that strangers with a curiosity as uncommon in that age as it is general in this, came from afar to visit ...

the natural curiosities that Craven had to offer. So, in the early eighteenth century tourists were a rare species but not so a hundred years later, and they came to feed their romantic ideas and ideals.

Daniel Defoe undertook a series of gruelling journeys, probably in the 1690s, across much of the country but did not venture into the heart of the western Dales, though this did not prevent him from saying that '... Penigent, which overtops all its neighbours' was a true mountain. Though he did not put this thought into words, he would no doubt have seen the Three Peaks in the same way as he had described neighbouring Westmorland as 'a country eminent only for being the wildest, most barren and frightful of any'.[6] Towards the end of that century diarists tended to adopt a more romantic and idealised attitude towards natural beauties stressing the attractions of the caves, gorges and waterfalls in the environs of Ingleton (and Malham). Among these diarists were John Hutton, in 1781, and John Housman, in 1802, who both published detailed guides for the new-age traveller of their day.

Housman adopted the true Romantic approach in his writing. Hurtle Pot at Chapel le Dale was of 'unfathomable depth';[7] the nearby Gingling Hole was a 'hiatus of profound depth'; and Weathercote Cave was 'perhaps the most copious and stupendous of any in England'.[8] Inclement weather prevented him from climbing Ingleborough but he ascribed masculinity and majesty to it:[9]

> ... with his steep rocky sides and heavy front, boldly rears his round highly-elevated head in full view before us.

Kingsdale was considered somewhat repellent having the 'appearance of a wild unfrequented desert',[10] in total contrast to the valley of Chapel le Dale which he perceived to be 'like a green strip of silk connecting two webs of the coarsest cloth' with 'pretty verdant fields,'[11] the two webs of course being Ingleborough and Whernside. These mountains, with their neighbour Pen-y-ghent, were 'noble eminences' but Ingleborough was supreme as it stood 'boldly forward as the surly sentinel of an army of hills encamped behind.'[12] He conceded that Pen-y-ghent was a 'towering and elegant mountain, standing pre-eminent among several lesser fells'[13] but Whernside had a 'much more humble appearance than his frowning neighbour' Ingleborough.[14] He may have been flowery, but one can hardly pick fault with his conclusions ... with one exception. He, too, grossly over-estimated altitude. He correctly recognised that Whernside was the highest and Pen-y-ghent the lowest, but all three were considerably higher than Helvellyn! Whernside, in fact, was estimated to be almost as high as Ben Nevis, set at 4,050 feet (1246m).[15]

This is not the most wayward height ascribed to that mountain, however; J. S. Fletcher set its summit at 5,340 feet (1,643m) with Ingleborough at 5,280 feet, which is exactly one mile (1,624m).[16] If only. At least Fletcher had his priorities right: there was 'nothing to gain'[17] in climbing Whernside whereas of its southern neighbour he believed there was 'probably no mountain summit in England so full of interest as this.'[18] No doubt many Cumbrians would beg to disagree. Fletcher was really a hundred years behind the times in his use of over-dramatised and romantic language. Trow Gill above Clapham is a splendid spot but is it really as 'fearsome and awe-compelling' as he says?[19]

The Hon. John Byng, later to be Viscount Torrington, undertook a series of mammoth journeys across the nation during which he crisscrossed this part of the Dales in 1792. He was often less than complimentary about the state of our roads and the degree of hospitality offered in our inns, but his account is down to earth and, on the whole, eschewed floweriness, in contrast to Housman and Fletcher. Byng could be very descriptive in a factual way providing half-hidden, almost subliminal, insights into the way things were. Of Ingleborough he wrote 'All the Yorkshire around, tho' black, seem of small account in the comparison ...' telling us, perhaps, that he did see this mountain as being special and to be revered for its height and scale.[20] He hired a guide to venture into Weathercote Cave, that unmissable stop on every early traveller's itinerary, and here he did lapse into the Romantic when he said 'These cascades fall with a horrid din, filling the mind with a gloom of horror,'[21] a sentiment that is mirrored in Turner's painting of the same scene. His descent was made in the middle of June and this description provides useful anecdotal evidence of the dreadful weather conditions that prevailed in England year on year during the 1790s. On his journey through Chapel le Dale he had endured '... many storms of rain; and these came upon you, in a mist, from the mountains, without giving the least warning,'[22] which backs up the accepted assessment of that decade's weather.

On an early spring day in 1859 Ruskin had felt the full power of

Ingleborough's unpredictable weather 'between Hawes and Settle, just on the flat under Whernside' where he described in a letter the 'vague sense of wonder with which I watched Ingleborough stand without rocking', such was the ferocity of the wind which he felt sure 'seemed as if it would blow Ingleborough into Lancaster Bay'. Ingleborough – and Pen-y-ghent – were to him both "really fine" hills.[23]

* * *

Just as the bulk of Ingleborough commands the landscape from all around so, too, is its summit plateau the obvious place to command the view. In turn, this made it an ideal spot for use as a signal station in the days when bonfire beacons were used to communicate urgent messages across the land in a kind of pyrotechnic telegraph system. There was definitely a beacon on Warton Crag near Yealand, and this has a direct line of sight to the top of Ingleborough. The last time this was done on the mountain was to celebrate the Queen's Golden Jubilee in 2002 but it must have served this purpose for centuries, and this particular beacon was sited on Little Ingleborough rather than on the summit. Beacons were certainly used to prepare the country for possible invasion by the Spanish Armada in 1588 and it is not beyond the bounds of reason to postulate that Ingleborough may also have been pressed into service on that occasion. In more recent times fires have been lit on the summit to mark royal occasions such as the Golden Jubilee of Queen Victoria in 1887, the coronation of George V in 1911 and the Silver Jubilee of his accession in 1935. On this occasion a tractor was used to haul old tyres and other combustibles and someone even tried – and almost succeeded – in driving a large open-top car to the top. In an act that appeals to my darker side, persons unknown took it upon themselves to roll some of the tyres back down the steep side of the mountain before the bonfire was secured!

The next beacon was lit only two years later, to mark the coronation of George VI, and this time the tractor made it all the way to the top. The prime mover behind this fire took the precaution of camping on the summit to ward off any potentially mischievous elements. Further fires were built for Queen Elizabeth's coronation in 1953 and Silver Jubilee in 1977.

A 'Hospice Tower' was erected in 1830 by a local eminent citizen as a shelter for those who had made it to the top and as a shooting cabin for grouse shooting parties.[24] It was circular, with door and windows, it had a domed and battlemented top, and was raised on a stone dais. An inaugural programme of events was organised on one particular summer's day, with races around the summit perimeter, athletic competitions and food galore. A large crowd attended and, in a scene that would surely resonate in today's seemingly anarchic and vandal-laden society, the demon drink began to dominate the proceedings, once the dignitaries had left, as the throng vented their pent-up frustrations on the tower and comprehensively wrecked it. History does record the reaction of the tower's sponsor: he was so furious he vowed it would not be rebuilt and it very quickly disintegrated into the heap of stones on the western edge of the summit plateau that can still be seen today.

*   *   *

Plate 1.3
Ingleborough from under White Scar by J. A. Grimshaw. Bradford City Art Galleries

Let us consider for a moment what the name Ingleborough might signify. One suggestion translates it as 'the fortified camp on the hill or peak', the 'ingel' being postulated as Old English (Anglo-Saxon) for hill and the 'borough' as Old English *burh* meaning fortification or earthwork of a defensive nature.[25] Take this a step further and it could, perhaps, be concluded that the name refers to the supposed Iron Age fort on the summit plateau. Go down an alternative route and 'borough' could derive from the Old West Scandinavian (*ie* Norse) word *beorg* or Old English *berg*, both of which mean hill. In this case, Ingleborough would mean 'hill hill'.

However, there is a totally different route to the origin of the place-name, one that requires a completely new mindset and a willingness to cast off the twenty-first century way of perceiving the distant past in favour of a radically different approach.[26] There is a prominent hill, complete with summit defences, in the Preselli Hills in the Pembrokeshire National Park. It is called Carn Ingli. Carn is the Welsh equivalent of the word cairn, both of which were applied either to archaeological piles of stones or to a natural boulder field mistaken for anthropogenic piles. The second element in the name means angels and ingli is a corruption of an early Welsh word which has appeared in various forms over the centuries: Carn Engylau or Carn yr Ingli which were transmuted into Carnengli and Carn Yengly before taking on their present form. They all mean cairn of the angels. In medieval times the hill was known in Latin as *Mons Angelorum*, which means the same.

In the late fifth or early sixth century this Welsh hill was the home of a missionary hermit, one of the pioneers in mainland Britain of the Celtic church. He was called St Brynach, and he was renowned through the Middle Ages because he had often communed on that hill top with the angels – hence the name given to the hill. We can hypothesise – some might say fantasise – that he was fully aware that the hill had symbolic significance to the area's pagan inhabitants and that he was consciously trying to adapt this form of ritualism to a Christian form to make the latter more acceptable. After all, many aspects of Christian ceremonial derive directly from pagan practices. If a hill as prominent as the one St Brynach had chosen meant so much to the old religious, why could it not be 'baptised' into the new religion just as pagan folk were welcomed into Christianity?

What has all this to do with Ingleborough, though? There are no links here with St Brynach but there are interesting parallels, and this is the point where the reader may need to suspend modern logic and reason. A stream rises on the south-west slopes of Ingleborough. It is called Green Springs now but in the not too distant past the main source, the main spring, was called St Anthony's Well.[27] He was one of the most revered holy men of his time. He lived as an ascetic, somewhere between AD 250 and 350, in the Egyptian desert, and was counted among the founders of the monastic ideal and his lifestyle became very influential in the development of early Celtic Christianity. He is said to have spent much of his hermitic life in the mountains fending off demons and battling with the devil. This brings us neatly to a second link. The northern face of the summit plateau, The Arks, is a tumult of rocks and boulders with sharp prominences and narrow gullies: one of these was formerly called the Devil's Gulch and local legend had it that the devil was cast off the mountain here. The commotion caused by the devil's desperate attempts to save himself brought about the rocky havoc below.

Our circular argument is nearing completion now. Did early missionaries view our mountain in the same manner as St Brynach perceived Carn Ingli? Was the association with St Anthony a carefully thought out way of changing whatever Ingleborough was originally called, of baptising it to bring it and the people who saw it as a major symbolic part of their everyday lives into the new faith, and to rid it of its pagan associations for ever? It may be that the 'ingle' derives not from 'ingel' at all, but from 'ingli', that it did not simply mean hill but instead alluded to the angels who protected it and the surrounding area.

*　　*　　*

Returning firmly to earth now, it might be useful for the reader to have the area encompassed by this book defined, because it extends beyond the mountain itself. No feature – be it geological, geomorphological, archaeological or cultural – exists in isolation. I am a great believer in symbiosis, in the interaction between and interdependence of different variables. The mountain has influenced what has gone on around it, in natural and human terms, and in turn people over the millennia have modified and shaped the fine detail of the mountain. Thus, everything within the road triangle has been included, as well as the valleys which surround the massif: Chapel le Dale[28] to the north, upper Ribblesdale to the east, and the fringes of the Wenning valley to the south (Fig. 1.1). I have not strayed too far, though. Gearstones is here because that should not be amputated from the valley of Chapel le Dale; Kingsdale also appears here and there, despite its being detached from Ingleborough by the limestone plateau of Scales Moor; but in Ribblesdale we go no further south than Helwith Bridge.

Four modern civil parishes extend nearly to the top of the mountain (Fig. 1.2): Ingleton which takes in all the dale through Chapel le Dale with Ribblehead and Gearstones; Horton in Ribblesdale incorporating much of Sulber and Park Fell as well as the eastern part of Moughton; Austwick extending over the rest of Moughton, Crummack Dale and The Allotment; and Clapham cum Newby which takes in Newby Moss, Clapham Bottoms and Clapham Bents. All four have a common boundary on Simon Fell, Ingleborough's eastern outlier; only Ingleton and Clapham meet on the summit plateau. There used to be a further parish, Newby having been a separate entity through most of recorded history. The 1:25,000 Ordnance

Survey map marks 'BS' on Grey Scars on the current Ingleton-Clapham cum Newby boundary (SD7287 7228) and the boundary stone has the letter 'I' carved on the west side and 'N', for Newby, rather than 'C' on the opposite (Plate 1.4).

The book has been divided into two parts. The first deals with natural forces and processes, focussing on Ingleborough's geological foundations and the tectonic events that modified what geology intended, in Chapters 2 and 3. It then goes on to consider, in Chapter 4, how geomorphological processes (geomorphology is the study of landforms and landform processes as opposed to geology which is about rocks and rock forming processes) have shaped and modified the landscape through time, be they the result of direct ice or water action or less perceptible and slower-acting atmospheric conditions. Part 2 moves on to look at the landscape in terms of the human input, for example how mankind settled and exploited nature's bounty, either in the distant past (Chapters 5 and 6) or in more recent times (Chapters 8 and 9). Finally, modern developments and influences are visited, in Chapter

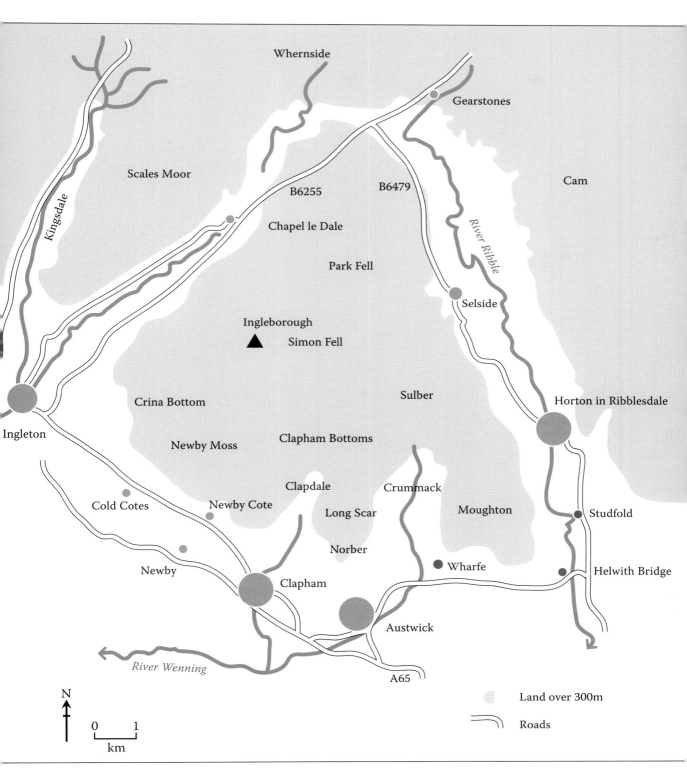

Whernside

Gearstones

Scales Moor

Cam

Kingsdale

B6255

B6479

River Ribble

Chapel le Dale

Park Fell

Selside

Ingleborough
▲ Simon Fell

Crina Bottom

Sulber

Horton in Ribblesdale

Newby Moss

Clapham Bottoms

Clapdale

Crummack

Studfold

Cold Cotes

Newby Cote

Long Scar

Moughton

Newby

Norber

Wharfe

Helwith Bridge

Clapham

Austwick

River Wenning

A65

N

0   1
km

Land over 300m

Roads

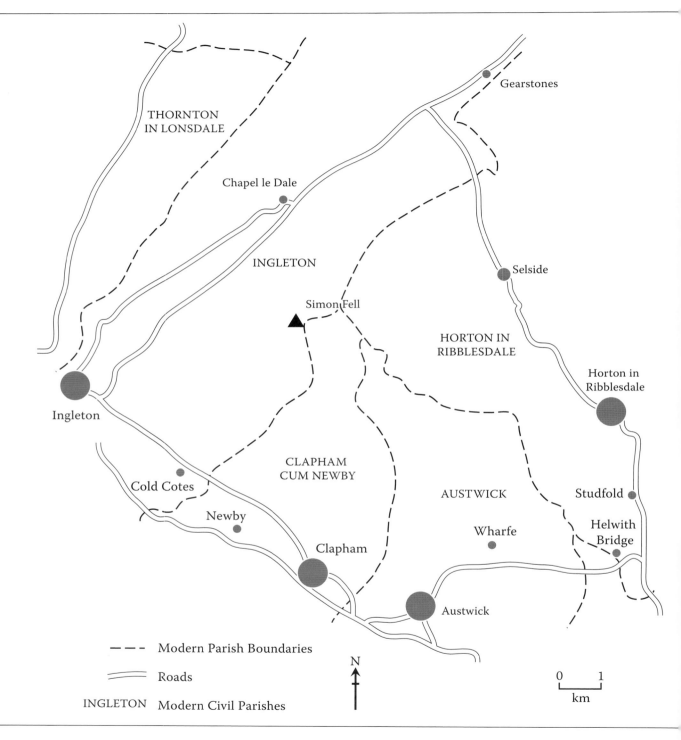

THORNTON
IN LONSDALE

Chapel le Dale

INGLETON

Simon Fell

Gearstones

Selside

HORTON IN
RIBBLESDALE

Horton in
Ribblesdale

Ingleton

Cold Cotes

Newby

CLAPHAM
CUM NEWBY

Clapham

AUSTWICK

Wharfe

Studfold

Helwith
Bridge

Austwick

- - - Modern Parish Boundaries

===== Roads

INGLETON Modern Civil Parishes

N

0   1
km

Figure 1.2 Ingleborough: Modern Parishes.

10, to bring the story of the development of Ingleborough's landscape up to date.

Further to this separation of physical and cultural attributes, the geographical area has also been divided into two more or less equal parts in Part 2. The rationale for this is a perception that the northern side of the mountain (Ingleborough North), facing Chapel le Dale and Ribblehead, is arguably different in the ways past peoples have responded to opportunities from Clapdale and Crummack Dale and the Helwith Bridge area which, obviously, look to the south. Even if this division is not real, it is convenient. Chapter 7 ties the two geographical areas together, physically and culturally, by looking at how people through the ages have moved across the landscape and how the 'natural' landscape has impacted on such movements. Wherever appropriate, a cross-referencing system has been applied to refer the reader to other sections of the book in the hope that this will aid understanding, while hopefully not interrupting the narrative.

No book could ever hope to be all-encompassing and it is always necessary to be selective in what is included. Whatever aspects of Ingleborough might have been omitted, it was purely down to chance, and there has been no intention to suggest such are not important.

* * *

Much of the Ingleborough massif is open access land under the Countryside and Rights of Way (CRoW) Act 2000 but inclusion of any site or mention of any specific grid reference in the text does not imply any rights of access whatsoever. Permission, as always, should be sought from landowners or tenants where access is not enshrined by law. It should also be noted that access under the CRoW Act only applies to walking. Any readers who might wish to seek out sites mentioned in the text are referred to the Countryside Code as revised under the CRoW Act.

Many of the sites mentioned in the text are environmentally or archaeologically sensitive and not able to withstand more than the occasional set of feet. It is for this reason that such sites have not been identified with a grid reference.

PART 1
THE PHYSICAL LANDSCAPE

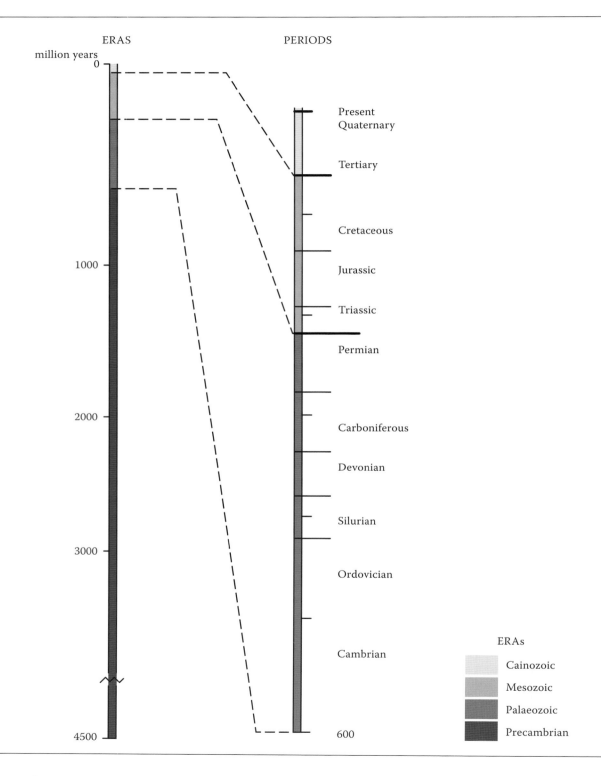

ERAS   PERIODS

million years
0

Present
Quaternary

Tertiary

Cretaceous

1000   Jurassic

Triassic

Permian

2000   Carboniferous

Devonian

Silurian

3000   Ordovician

Cambrian

ERAs

Cainozoic

Mesozoic

Palaeozoic

4500   600   Precambrian

· T W O ·

Geology of the Western Dales

The Geological Time Scale

Before looking in detail at the geology of the Ribblehead area, or even of the western Yorkshire Dales, it might be useful to gain an appreciation of the geological time scale (Fig. 2.1). This is a sequence of geological periods from the very beginning of our planet's life to the present time. Geologists are generally in agreement that the earth was formed more than 4500 million years ago and they have divided geological time since then into long periods called eras. Eras are subdivided into periods, and these are further subdivided into epochs. Science is fond of using terms and abbreviations, and geology is no exception.

The first 4000 million years or so fall within Precambrian time. This is obviously an enormous length of time and being so distant from us is full of unknowns. The oldest sections of the earth's crust (its superficial skin) are made up of Precambrian rocks, as across the Canadian Shield, around parts of the Baltic Sea and in parts of northern Scotland. There are no rocks from this period in the Yorkshire Dales.

The next 370 million years make up the Palaeozoic (Ancient Life) era and this differs from the Precambrian by having a richer fossil record: no life forms are known from the earliest Precambrian but fossils become progressively more common and more divergent with almost an explosion of life forms at the beginning of the Palaeozoic. Most of the rocks in the Dales fall within three geological periods of this era while rocks from three other Palaeozoic periods are missing. In order of decreasing age the six are the Cambrian, Ordovician, Silurian, Devonian, Carboniferous and Permian. It is the Cambrian, Devonian and Permian that are missing. Anyone who has read anything about the physical background of the Dales will immediately recognise the word Carboniferous as most of our rocks are from this one period.

The Mesozoic is absent from the Dales and this was followed by the Cainozoic (New Life) era which lasted for 65 million years and is subdivided into the Tertiary and Quaternary periods which, in turn, are further broken down into epochs including the Pleistocene (corresponding to the most

Figure 2.1
Geological Time Line

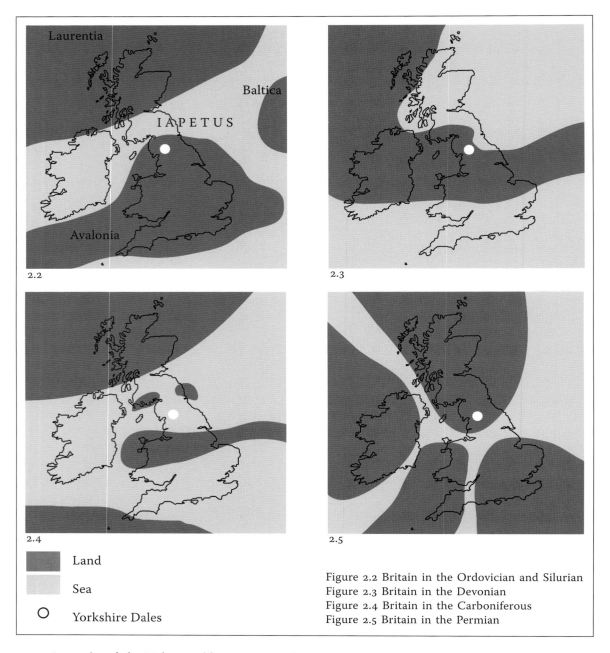

Land

Sea

○ Yorkshire Dales

Figure 2.2 Britain in the Ordovician and Silurian
Figure 2.3 Britain in the Devonian
Figure 2.4 Britain in the Carboniferous
Figure 2.5 Britain in the Permian

recent ice age) and the Holocene (the time since the most recent ice retreat).

In 2002 a scientist put forward the then highly controversial notion that we are no longer living in the Holocene and that a new epoch had dawned. In 2008 twenty-one earth scientists, including Mark Hounslow of Lancaster University, signed their names to an article in which they put forward a strong argument that the Holocene has indeed been replaced by the

Anthropocene (meaning man-influenced).[1] They cite global climate change, the reality of which surely no one can doubt; increases in ocean temperatures with the inevitable increase in the volume of oceanic water and the knock-on effect of sea level rise; an increased rate of extinctions and changes to habitat distribution; and, perhaps least well known, changes to sedimentation regimes across the world as rivers are dammed thereby altering natural erosion-sedimentation patterns, and as human activities impact on river flow. These changes will undoubtedly have insidious effects on Ingleborough and its habitats over the ensuing decades.

Geological processes of the Palaeozoic Era

We need to think of rocks initially being formed and then transformed over millions of years into features such as mountains and ridges and cliffs. We must then visualise these features and the rocks that underlie them being ever so slowly worn away by a wide range of natural processes such as glacial or river or wind erosion, or deposited in a different form elsewhere to give us the physical landscape we enjoy today. In this section we will concentrate on how mountains and major landform features come to be created in the first place within the Palaeozoic, as relevant to our area.

Ordovician and Silurian: 488–416 million years ago

From the Cambrian era much of what is now Britain was a deep ocean, called the Iapetus Ocean, the proto-Atlantic, if you like (Fig. 2.2). Sediments from the extensive Laurentian landmass to the north (now North America, much of Scotland and north-east Ireland), a smaller northern landmass referred to as Baltica (now Scandinavia and Baltic Russia), and a southern landmass referred to as Avalonia, were being washed into the ocean by rivers and they slowly built up successive layers of coarse sands and fine mud on the ocean floor with the skeletal remains of life forms settling within the accumulating sediments. The total thickness of all these Ordovician sediments has been estimated at several kilometres. Throughout the Ordovician, Avalonia and the two northern landmasses were slowly converging, squeezing Iapetus between them, forcing the undersea sediments into a series of tight folds and creating an island arc (like the West Indies today) from volcanic activity: the Lake District is a remnant of this island arc. As the weight of sediments built up into hundreds of metres, the pressure of overlying material gradually compressed the underlying sediments into layers, or strata, of solid rock by a process known as diagenesis. The mud became shale or mudstone, the coarse sands became gritstone and sandstone.

In the Silurian there was a further marine advance with more sediments being laid down 1600m thick in the Dales, though more than twice as thick in the Lake District. Rocks from the Ordovician and Silurian periods are referred to as Basement rocks in geology.

Devonian: 416–359 million years ago

Towards the end of the Ordovician and into the early Devonian a long period of progressive deposition and uplift came to an end as tectonic plate movements closed Iapetus and uplifted the strata into a range of mountains, in a process geologists term an orogeny, which was attached to the 'North American' landmass rather than to 'Europe' (Fig. 2.3). This uplift led to complex folding within the rocks of these new mountains which would have dwarfed today's Alps.

This mountain building phase – the orogeny – is referred to as the Caledonian orogeny, and the folding was on a massive scale with many of the rocks in our area being affected by the resulting heat and pressure exerted by these earth movements.

As the Devonian progressed the processes of erosion wore these mountains down to a level, and arid, plain: no new deposits were laid down in the Dales during this period, though some igneous dykes were pushed through the rock strata, and a granite mass rose up, about 400 million years ago, from below the crust to underlie much of what is now the Dales. This mass of Wensleydale Granite underlies what is known as the Askrigg Block.

Carboniferous: 359–299 million years ago

The geological record now starts to become very complex. At the start of this period 'Britain' was sitting astride the equator and the old Devonian land surface was slowly drowned by a warm and shallow sea (Fig. 2.4), so conditions in the southern part of the Dales would have been similar to parts of the Caribbean nowadays. Deep deposits of mud, with shelly inclusions, developed on this sea floor which diagenesis turned into Bowland shales rock. The now subsiding Askrigg Block was much more stable tectonically than the more rapidly subsiding area of the Craven Basin within which a much greater thickness of deposits built up than on the Block. Along the divide between the two a major fault (the Mid Craven fault) developed as a submarine feature, and reef knolls formed along its length (the Craven Reef Belt), formed of rich fossil remains, but not pure coral as sometimes written. As the Carboniferous period progressed the Askrigg Block was also enveloped in warm sea and the limestones which typify much of the Dales formed from the remains of countless generations of marine creatures.

Sea level fluctuated markedly during this period leaving alternating strata of shales, sandstones and limestones in a repeated sequence or cyclothem. We know these combined cyclothem strata as the Yoredale Group or Wensleydale Group of rocks. During the later Carboniferous the sea deepened and a different set of sediments was laid down in the form of mud, eventually becoming shales. As sea level decreased again sands were also laid down, later becoming sandstones, with limestones forming intermittently.

Towards the close of the Carboniferous there was marked uplift of the

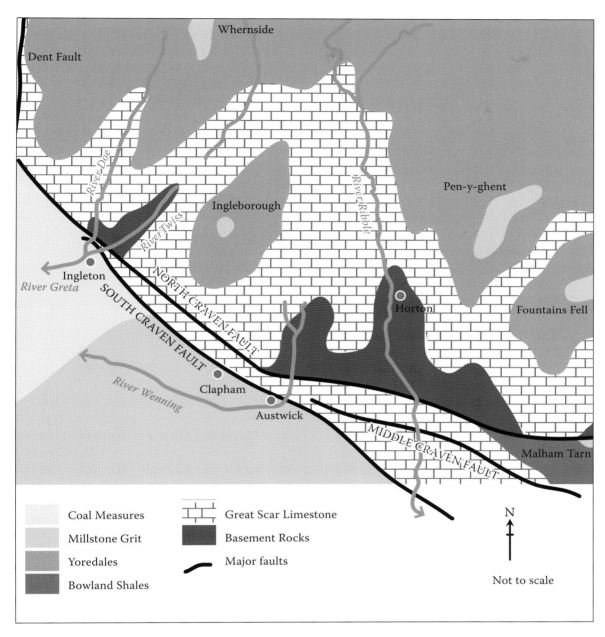

Figure 2.6
Solid Geology of the
Three Peaks.
Source: compiled from
British Geological
Survey mapping and
map memoirs

Legend:
- Coal Measures
- Millstone Grit
- Yoredales
- Bowland Shales
- Great Scar Limestone
- Basement Rocks
- Major faults

N

Not to scale

landmass in what is now Scotland making the sea over the Dales even shallower. Rivers from that northern land mass poured sands and gravels over a vast area in deltas where these rivers entered the sea, giving us the coarser sandstones and Millstone Grits that form the highest parts of the Three Peaks. As these deltas silted up and became more muddy swamp than gravel expanse, thick deposits of decaying organic matter built up to ultimately create the Coal Measures that outcrop in parts of our area.

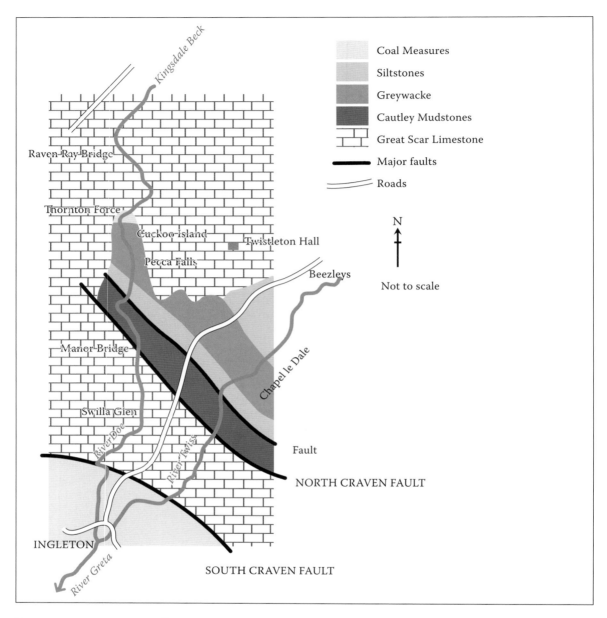

Legend:
- Coal Measures
- Siltstones
- Greywacke
- Cautley Mudstones
- Great Scar Limestone
- Major faults
- Roads

N

Not to scale

Labels on map: Kingsdale Beck, Raven Ray Bridge, Thornton Force, Cuckoo Island, Twistleton Hall, Pecca Falls, Beezleys, Manor Bridge, Chapel le Dale, Swilla Glen, River Doe, River Twiss, Fault, NORTH CRAVEN FAULT, INGLETON, River Greta, SOUTH CRAVEN FAULT

Permian: 299–251 million years ago

The gentle rhythmic ebb and flow of the Carboniferous gave way to a more geologically unsettled period during the Permian (Fig. 2.5). A further major orogeny (the Hercynian) occurred at this time uplifting the entire Dales area and shattering the boundary between the Askrigg Block and the Craven Basin with a series of major tectonic faults and the development of lines of mineralisation, though there is some doubt as to whether the major faults were formed in the Permian or late Carboniferous.

Figure 2.7
Solid Geology of the Ingleton Glens.
Source: Brumhead (1979), p. 27

Post-Permian: 251 million years ago to the present

Since the Hercynian orogeny the Dales were mostly above sea level, except during parts of the Jurassic and Cretaceous, and the dominant physical processes have been denudational as ice or water in repeated glacial and interglacial episodes have left their mark on the landscape. There was more movement along the faults in the Tertiary and some very spasmodic activity since then, with the most recent 'serious' movement in 1944.

Rock Forming Processes and Tectonics

Rocks fit into one of the following categories: igneous, sedimentary or metamorphic. The western Dales contain examples from all three though sedimentary rocks are dominant. We have seen above how rivers from previous landmasses brought vast amounts of sediments of all kinds into archaic oceans and seas, sediments that became mixed up with skeletal and faunal remains. We have seen that sea level fluctuated many times resulting in repeated periods of deposition under water and denudation when exposed above sea level. It might follow logically that the various bands, or strata, of sedimentary rock are in horizontal and parallel bands. Indeed this is often the case and it can be seen on the northern slopes of Ingleborough where the different, and stepped, bands stand out clearly as they seemingly march up to the summit plateau.

It is not always the case though as episodes of tectonic instability have confused the picture. In the Devonian period a huge mass of Wensleydale Granite was thrust up from the depths uplifting the sedimentary strata above it. Granite is an igneous rock, very coarse grained and containing a high proportion of quartz crystals of varying colour, and it cooled down very slowly causing it to remain at depth rather than reach the surface. This granite intrusion is not totally level along its upper surface but is inclined slightly to the north-north-east, so the sedimentary strata overlying the granite are also slightly tipped that way.

To summarise the story so far, the Askrigg Block forms much of the Dales and it consists of layers of sedimentary rock from the Carboniferous (shales, sandstones, and limestones) lying on a subterranean igneous (granite) mass intruded in the late Devonian (Fig. 2.6). In the south-west of the Dales, however, the geological picture is infinitely more complicated than this. Below Chapel le Dale (Figs. 2.7 and 2.8), as well as in Clapdale, Crummack Dale and Ribblesdale around Helwith Bridge, earlier rocks have been exposed by millions of years of denudation. These inliers, as geologists call them, consist of Ordovician and Silurian shales, siltstones, sandstones, flagstones (narrow-banded sandstones) and limestones, but these are all very different from their Carboniferous equivalents. They have been subjected to extremes of pressure for many millennia more than the Carboniferous rocks so they tend to be rather more dense. In short they underwent a certain degree of

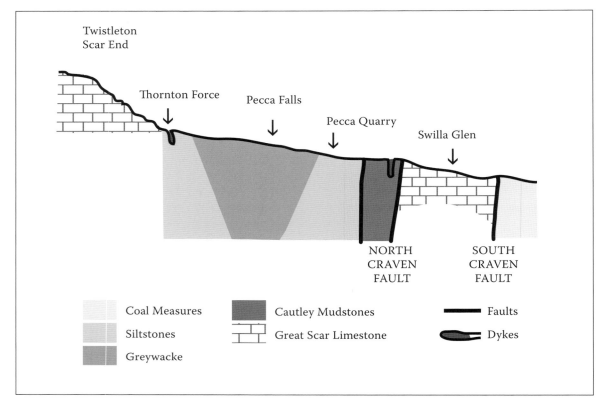

Twistleton
Scar End

Thornton Force

Pecca Falls

Pecca Quarry

Swilla Glen

NORTH
CRAVEN
FAULT

SOUTH
CRAVEN
FAULT

Coal Measures   Cautley Mudstones   Faults

Siltstones   Great Scar Limestone   Dykes

Greywacke

metamorphism (chemical and physical change caused by intense heat or pressure) during the Caledonian orogeny. Because these rocks lie at the bottom of the entire geological sequence they are referred to as Basement rocks.

Figure 2.8
Geological Section through the Ingleton Glens.
Source: Brumhead, p. 31

Greywackes and Turbidites

Below Chapel le Dale there are also exposures of a type of rock called the Ingletonian. Unlike all the other rocks in the area, this contains no fossils and until very recently it was assumed the Ingletonian was Precambrian in age, or at the latest Cambrian. Recent work has tentatively reclassified it as early Ordovician.[2] These are the rocks currently being exploited at Ingleton Quarry. They can also be seen at various points along the Waterfalls Walk. They have a definite greenish hue, especially clear when wet. The Ingletonian is made up of three discrete elements: very thin beds of siltstones and mudstones, coarse bands containing a high proportion of feldspar and quartz (the quarrymen's 'Ingleton granite' though it is not granite at all), and thicker bands of a rock called greywacke, which is actually greenish rather than grey. This is made up of grains of quartz in a clay cement matrix and through a magnifying lens appears as a jumble of tiny and completely unsorted (*ie* unlayered) fragments. Because of its great age, its original composition has been changed. Close examination of these rocks would clearly demonstrate the alternating nature of the thin and thick bands of the Ingletonian.

These beds illustrate what is called in geology graded bedding. In a river coarser and heavier particles of sediment quickly settle on the bottom and the finer and lighter material settles later: this enables us to work out which rock layers were deposited first. Coarser particles become the thicker beds; finer ones the thinner. If the beds remained horizontal, as laid down, the job would be easy but here they have been turned on their sides by tectonic forces. In the Beezley Falls sequence the falls themselves are in the thickly bedded sandstones while the force of falling water has created the plunge pools in the thinner siltstone beds.

To confuse the issue further, greywackes are turbidites laid down in turbidity currents. Greywackes can contain evidence of several different turbidity currents and, though in a given piece of rock they may appear to be linked and thus broadly contemporary, in reality each turbidity event may have been separated by thousands or even tens of thousands of years. To comprehend turbidity currents firstly visualise a steep slope somewhere in the mountains, with the surface material being soft clays or muds. Introduce a prolonged period of heavy rain which would saturate the material and leave it unstable, on the brink of collapse. Now add the ingredient that will cause that slope to fail, maybe an earth tremor or even more heavy rain, and see in your mind what happens. The failing part of the slope will suddenly and quite dramatically cascade down the slope at high speed, tumbling as it goes while at the bottom of the slope the material will come to rest as a chaotic unsorted mass of clay, mud and who knows what. What you would have just witnessed is a classic landslide. Now transfer that whole sequence of events, on a grander scale, to a steep slope deep in the ocean, a slope long enough for the material to pick up considerable speed. The flow of water and material is the turbidity current; the end result material at the base of the slope is the turbidites. Allow them to be transformed into solid rock by diagenesis and you have the greywacke.

Faulting

The Askrigg Block is bounded on its southern edge by a series of tectonic faults, the Craven faults. According to many accounts there are three Craven faults – the North, Middle and South. It will probably come as no surprise now to learn that this picture is far too simplistic. We must think in terms of a fault zone rather than individual string-like faults. Within this zone there are a number of parallel faults, running broadly north-west to south-east, of which the Craven faults are but three. The fault zone should be seen as a shatter belt with countless short faults linking one prime fault with another and criss-crossing the whole belt like a crazed spider's web. Along the northern edge of this zone is the North Craven Fault, and this makes a very distinct break, while the southern edge is rather less obvious. In the western Dales this is not bounded by the South Craven Fault, however, but by the Holm Fault (Fig. 2.9).

Let us not consign the South Craven Fault to the background though as, along with the North Craven Fault, it is very long and produces the most dramatic effect on the present landscape in the form of cliffs or scars, as they are locally known, especially given the impact of glacial erosion on them.

On some faults the movement is lateral whereby two plates or landmasses glide slowly past each other, either in the same or opposite directions. Movement on these transform faults tears the crust apart. On other faults the direction of movement is vertical. One side is either thrust upwards or downwards in relation to the other depending on the strength of respective forces. This is what happened along the Craven faults. The general land surface drops in a series of pronounced steps: from the Askrigg Block proper the surface drops as you cross the North Craven Fault, drops again over the Middle Craven Fault near Settle, and yet again over the South Craven

Figure 2.9
Tectonic Faults in Craven.
Source: Arthurton et al. (1988), p. 97

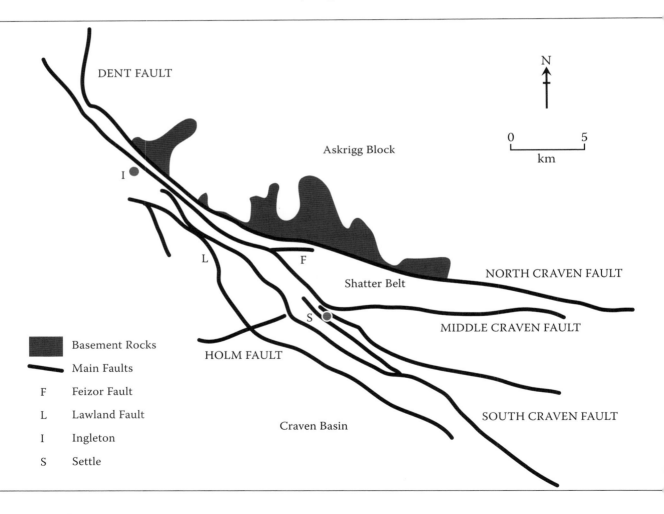

Fault, especially along Buck Haw Brow west of Settle. The vertical drop, the downthrow, on the North Craven Fault near Ingleton is about 100m but on the South Craven Fault it is far greater.

The precise line of a fault – the actual break between one side and the other – is rarely clear on the ground as subsequent erosion has masked the divide. A glimpse of the North Craven Fault can be seen, however, on the Waterfalls Walk a short distance north of Manor Bridge where a wall of limestone on one side is separated from the Ordovician mudstones on the other by a narrow band of a rock type called breccia which is made up of angular fragments of shattered rock. A small exposure of the South Craven Fault can be seen from the road in a private garden in Giggleswick.

The western edge of the Dales is marked geologically by the north-south Dent Fault that runs nearly 40km from the South and North Craven Faults at Leck, west of Ingleton, through Barbondale to Kirkby Stephen. To the east of this fault is the Askrigg Block; to the west are Ordovician and Silurian strata with Silurian greywackes in the southern parts of this zone. As with the Craven faults there was post-Triassic movement along the Dent Fault.

Folding

Faulting is part and parcel of tectonics. So is folding, and this has also had a profound impact on the landscape particularly around Ingleton (Fig. 2.8) and at Helwith Bridge in Ribblesdale.

Tectonic movements lead to existing layers of rock being deformed through a 'squeezing' action as the horizontal strata are pushed up into a series of folds. The steepness of the folding will depend on the forces being exerted and the symmetry of individual folds will be determined by the relative strength of opposing forces. Gently dipping limestone strata, at an angle of no more than 20 degrees, are to be seen on the old working faces of Mealbank Quarry at Ingleton, from the footpath on Storrs Common on the opposite side of the river. This outcrop is the south-west side of a gentle anticlinal fold (ie an upfold). This quarry, incidentally, lies between the North and South Craven Faults.

Further up the river from Storrs, north of the North Craven Fault, are Basement rocks where the greywacke beds are in places almost vertical. It taxes the mind greatly to imagine the scale of forces needed to deform horizontal beds of solid rock into near vertical isoclinal folds. Detailed work has demonstrated that these tight folds are superimposed on earlier more gentle folds, suggesting that various orogenic episodes have been experienced here. In contrast the Silurian rocks are more openly folded. A narrow and deeply cut side valley in Twistleton Glen lies along the line of the bottom of a tight syncline (ie a downfold), dipping at an angle of 70 degrees, which has been enhanced by faulting.

Tectonic instability also causes localised igneous activity. The subterranean granite mass mentioned earlier is an igneous intrusion but there are signs of igneous extrusions in the waterfalls area. An extrusion here is the result of igneous material pushing to the surface along vertical joints and horizontal bedding planes in existing sedimentary rocks, in a molten form, to create linear features called dykes and sills. On the northern edge of the plunge pool below Thornton Force there is a narrow band of clearly different rock, no more than 600mm wide: this is a dyke consisting of a type of igneous rock called lamprophyre. Two other dykes can be seen cutting up the old quarry face just below Snow Falls on the eastern side of the Waterfalls Walk.

Mineralisation

Tectonics also leads to mineralisation. During the Carboniferous period cooling of granite at considerable depth may have released energy in the form of heat which changed solid minerals into a solute (liquid) form. As these rose within the strata, relative cooling would have resulted in these solutions crystallising and solidifying as mineral veins throughout the limestone areas of the Dales. Brine from sea water trapped within the sedimentary layers also transformed metals into a solute form. The most common minerals include lead (galena), zinc (sphalerite and smithsonite) and copper (chalcopyrite) all of which have been mined, as well as other less valuable minerals like barite, calcite and fluorite. In the Ingleborough area lead was worked on a not too successful basis on Lead Mine Moss (SD726 745): in 1703 Henry Bouche of Ingleton leased to John Blackburn the right to prospect for lead and to work it around Ingleborough.[3] It was also trialled unsuccessfully near Manor Bridge on the Waterfalls Walk. East of Gearstones the Cam Vein was worked from a series of shafts centred on SD819 830 and there are discarded samples of galena and calcite lying around the main shaft. The dates when this mine was worked are unknown but it was probably during the eighteenth or nineteenth century.

A Geological Unconformity

There is one last element to make the general geological picture complete. There is a gap between the Silurian and Carboniferous of over 50 million years during the Devonian period. No rocks were laid down here during the Devonian because what is now the Dales was above sea level. This means that Carboniferous rocks lie directly above Basement rocks and there is what geologists call an unconformity between the two. Thus, the junction between the older Basement rocks and the younger Carboniferous rocks represents a long break in depositional processes: there is a gap in both years and rocks though not, obviously, in space as you look at an unconformity. The unconformity in our area can be seen very clearly at Thornton Force on the Waterfalls Walk. The upper part of the falls is made up of horizontal strata of Carboniferous limestone sitting on top of steeply dipping basement rocks. These have been cut back leaving a pronounced lip beneath the limestone because they are less resistant than the limestone. If you were to place your hand across the unconformity, you would be spanning millions of years of geological history, millions of years of missing deposits.

Unconformities can also be seen at Crummack Dale and Helwith Bridge, as we shall see in the next chapter.

*   *   *

Chapter 3 will explore the geology of the Ingleborough massif to illustrate more fully certain geological themes.

THREE

Geology of Ingleborough

Overview

Basement (ie pre-Carboniferous) rocks do not outcrop to the north of Ingleborough, and it is Carboniferous limestone, the Wensleydale (or Yoredale) Group of rocks, and Millstone Grit strata that make up the bulk of Ingleborough and Whernside and underlie the valleys in between. What distinguishes the geological make up of the southern part of the mountain from the northern are the extensive exposures of Basement rocks around Ingleton, in Crummack Dale and between Helwith Bridge and Horton in Ribblesdale. However, much of what we can see on the ground surface, especially around Ribblehead and in Ribblesdale, is not solid rock at all: it consists of glacial deposits which are considered 'drift' geology rather than 'solid' geology.

Viewed from the north or north-east the changes in the geology of Ingleborough from top to bottom are clearly displayed in its stepped profile (Fig. 3.1). The picture is less clear on Whernside partly because there has been more land slippage which has masked much of the underlying rock layers. These variations in rock type with increased altitude can also be mapped, as shown on Figure 3.2. It should be noted that a solid geology map like this one shows rocks with all surface deposits stripped off: it is in fact looking under the skin of glacial material.

The southern side of Ingleborough cannot be described as physically dramatic, as the stepped nature of the beds is less apparent than on the northern side, and the average angle of slope from summit plateau to valley bottom is far less here. The vertical height difference between summit and valley is 500m on both sides but the horizontal distance on the north is only 2km compared with 5km to the south.

Ordovician Outcrops in Clapdale

The North Craven Fault (see later) cuts across Clapdale, above Clapham, immediately north of the lake and processes of erosion over the millennia have peeled off the Carboniferous strata upstream of the fault line to expose underlying Lower Palaeozoic (Basement) rocks. This exposure is very limited in extent but is to be seen at close quarters in the bed of a small tributary stream called Cat Hole Sike. The dominant geology all around is Carboniferous limestone, appearing in horizontal layers, but within the stream the thinly bedded rocks are inclined at a very steep angle. These are part of the late Ordovician Norber Formation which, in turn, is part of the wider Coniston Limestone Group (named after Coniston in the South Lakes). These rocks consist of dark-grey calcareous siltstones which are composed of consolidated silts or muds containing a high proportion of calcium-based material with fine-grained clay particles. Even though rocks such as these were formed in marine conditions, they contain few fossils which may reflect the fact that the Coniston Limestones were the earliest Ordovician deposits apart from the Ingletonian.

A further very small Ordovician inlier of Coniston Limestone occurs in the valley of Jenkin Beck, just south-east of Ingleton, but the bedrock here is largely masked by glacial deposits.

The Geology of Crummack Dale

Whereas the Ordovician outcrop in Clapdale is a very minor inlier of Basement rocks, Crummack Dale forms part of a much more extensive inlier that extends across and up Ribblesdale and further east to Malham Tarn.[1] This inlier is exposed in the same ways as in Clapdale, though on a much grander scale and it, too, is bounded along its southern edge by the North Craven Fault. The complex shatter belt south of this inlier, between the North and South Craven Faults, weakened the basic structure thereby contributing to increased erosion rates and a more rapid and sustained exposure of Basement rocks.

Crummack Dale is surrounded on its western, northern and eastern sides by beds of Carboniferous limestone above 300m. The contrast between these beds and the ones below is stark and unmistakeable. The limestone is dominantly light-grey in colour and the individual beds appear to have been little disturbed since they were laid down. The earlier rocks are much darker in hue, in places can be seen to have been contorted by folding, and a number of localised faults have added complexity to the general picture. Within Crummack Dale both Ordovician and Silurian rocks are to be seen.

Basement strata within Crummack Dale are best exposed in the valley bottom as much of the lower valley sides has been masked by scree aprons beneath the limestone scars, though there is one major exception to this. On

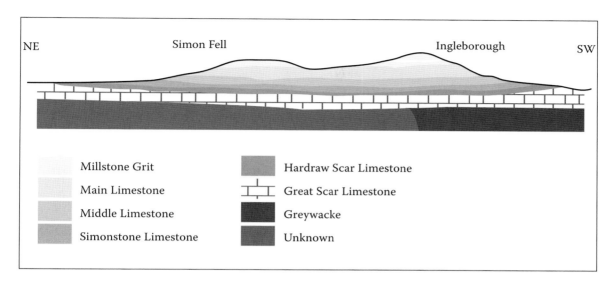

NE   Simon Fell   Ingleborough   SW

Millstone Grit

Main Limestone

Middle Limestone

Simonstone Limestone

Hardraw Scar Limestone

Great Scar Limestone

Greywacke

Unknown

Figure 3.1
Geological Section
through Ingleborough.

the eastern side the Basement is clear of scree below and just north of the impressive Studrigg Scar. The junction between Carboniferous and Basement rocks shows as an almost ruler-straight line in the sheer cliffs (SD781 708). Above this line the limestone lies in horizontal layers while below it the Basement Silurian beds are very steeply dipping. The dividing line marks a major break in the geological succession. If the succession was intact and undisturbed, the Carboniferous would lie on Devonian and not Silurian, and they would both be broadly horizontal. This is clearly not the case here as the Devonian is missing and the Silurian beds are not horizontal: Studrigg is a particularly fine example of a structural unconformity.

The term unconformity needs to be approached from several directions and understood in several dimensions. Firstly, there is a time element. An unconformity represents a period of unrecorded time during which it is not known what was happening geologically. Secondly, it represents a break in deposition, a period when the surface in question was not under water and no sediments were being laid down, as in the Devonian. Thirdly, the unconformity could mark a palaeo surface which had been planed down by erosional processes and upon which later sediments were deposited. For example, Carboniferous rock could 'unconformably' overlie Ordovician strata with the Silurian absent from the geological record. As it is known that there was sedimentation during the Silurian, it must mean that rocks of Silurian age had been worn away before the limestone was laid down.

There is a classic example of an unconformity between the Ordovician and the Carboniferous at Nappa Scars at the south end of Crummack Dale (SD768 697). Rocks of the Ordovician Norber Formation – the same as in Clapdale – make up the bottom of the lower scar at Nappa with layers of calcareous siltstone dipping at an angle of up to 70 degrees. The upper scar is composed of massive horizontal beds of Carboniferous limestone but between the two is a sandwiched layer, 500mm to 1.50m thick, which consists of basal conglomerate (Plate 3.1). This means an unsorted, jumbled mixture of boulders and pebbles of Ordovician age, with some much larger and angular Silurian boulders, cemented together by a later limestone mixture. Nappa Scars are a geologist's paradise, given the clarity of the unconformity and the scale of the conglomerate, and it has the added advantage of lying on a right of way.

The same pre-Carboniferous land surface, the same unconformity, reappears further north at Austwick Beck Head where conglomerate is also apparent.

In geological terms, Crummack Dale is noted for more than its unconformities: the details of pre-Carboniferous sedimentation and folding can be read in the landscape. It is a complex picture (Figs. 3.3 and 3.4). Let us start by laying out the constituent parts. Rocks from the Ordovician and Silurian periods are represented here; they are both sub-divided in Crummack Dale into series and formations; each formation is further broken down into rock types, as shown in Table 3.1.

Table 3.1 Geological Succession in Crummack Dale and Ribblesdale

Period	Series	Group	Formation	Rock Types
Silurian	Ludlow		Neals Ing	sandstones
			Horton	sandstones, siltstones
	Wenlock		Arcow	calcareous silts and
			Austwick	sandstones, siltstones
	Llandovery		Crummack	silts and mudstones
Ordovician	Ashgill	Coniston Limestone	Sowerthwaite	mainly sandstones
			Norber	calcareous siltstones, limestones
	Arenig	Ingleton		greywackes*

* these do not crop out in Crummack Dale but there is a small exposure in Ribblesdale.
Source: K. C. Dunham and A. A. Wilson (eds), 1985, *Geology of the North Pennine Orefield, Volume 2 Stainmore to Craven*, London: HMSO.

In addition to the rocks themselves, there are three recognisable folds running west-north-west to east-south-east: two anticlines (upfolds) with a syncline (downfold) in between;[2] and a number of very small and localised

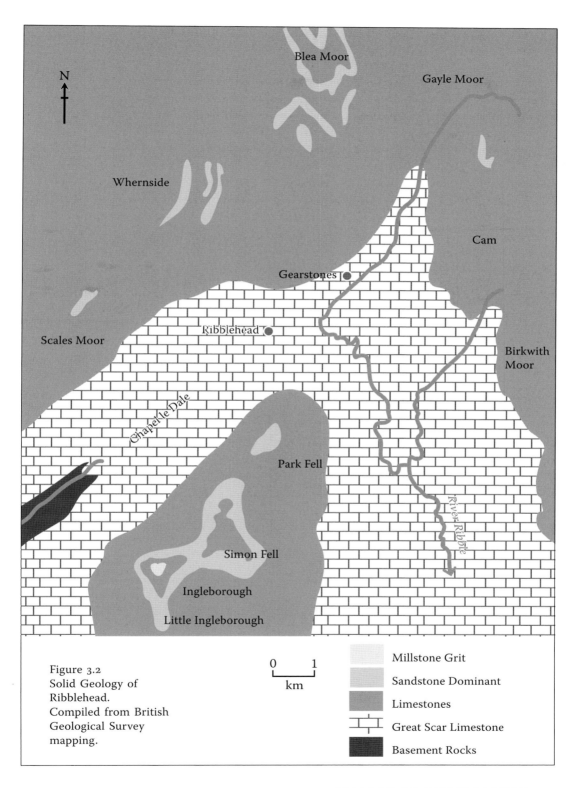

N

Blea Moor

Gayle Moor

Whernside

Cam

Gearstones

Ribblehead

Scales Moor

Birkwith Moor

Chapel'le Dale

Park Fell

River Ribble

Simon Fell

Ingleborough

Little Ingleborough

Figure 3.2
Solid Geology of
Ribblehead.
Compiled from British
Geological Survey
mapping.

0   1
km

Millstone Grit

Sandstone Dominant

Limestones

Great Scar Limestone

Basement Rocks

faults. These folds and faults were integral elements of prolonged tectonic movements long before the Carboniferous period, mainly during the Devonian.

From the Ordovician period most of the rocks within Crummack Dale belong to the Coniston Limestone Group which is mainly made up of rocks within the Norber and Sowerthwaite Formations. These outcrop at the southern end of the valley, and it may be helpful to describe their location in relation to easily recognisable ground features, particularly the road into the dale. Austwick lies on Carboniferous limestone and this stops abruptly at the head of the village at the North Craven Fault: north of Austwick Hall Ordovician rocks outcrop. Initially, it is Jop Ridding Sandstones, which are part of the Sowerthwaite Formation.[3] At the foot of the long slope north of the cross-roads with Thwaite Lane, where the road turns sharply to the east, these give way to the limestone and siltstone of the Norber Formation. These extend as far north as the junction with the access track to Sowerthwate Farm where there is a very narrow band of tuffs, the remnants of volcanic activity, and then another band of sandstones of the Sowerthwaite Formation. Part way up the hill known as Norber Brow, still within the Norber Formation, the crest of the east-south-east Austwick anticline cuts across the road. As Figure 3.4 shows, the upper strata of the anticline have long since been eroded away so what is to be seen now is the stump of the much reduced upfold. Either side of this crest the Ordovician layers dip downwards, to the south to be truncated by the North Craven Fault, to the north to run under later Silurian rocks. Norber Brow is interesting in its own right as it is a fossilised pre-Carboniferous cliff line where younger limestones had encroached on an older land surface. All the Ordovician beds are fossil-rich with trilobites, graptolites and brachiopods in localised abundance.

If we continue the journey northwards from the Sowerthwaite sandstones, we would be transferring from Ordovician to Silurian rocks, at first onto the siltstones and then the sandstones of the Austwick Formation. The roadside walls are built of the sandstones, locally known as grits but technically greywackes. For the dry stone waller they can be a nightmare as no two stones have matching straight edges (Plate 3.2). Beyond the junction of Crummack Lane and White Stone Lane the road crosses the base of the Studrigg-Studfold syncline. This cuts across the valley, again running east-south-east, and crosses Hunterstye Lane on the east side of the valley where this turns sharply to head eastwards for a short distance. One small section of rock from the southern limb forms the bed of the lane immediately west of the Wash Dub on White Stone Lane. Continuing further north Hunterstye Lane traverses the northern limb of the syncline within which the slightly older Austwick 'grits' and younger Horton formation siltstones outcrop at the surface, as well as calcium-rich silts of the Arcow Formation. The dry stone walls lining Hunterstye Lane emphasise the basic differences between the grits and silts: where the walls still stand to full height, the building material

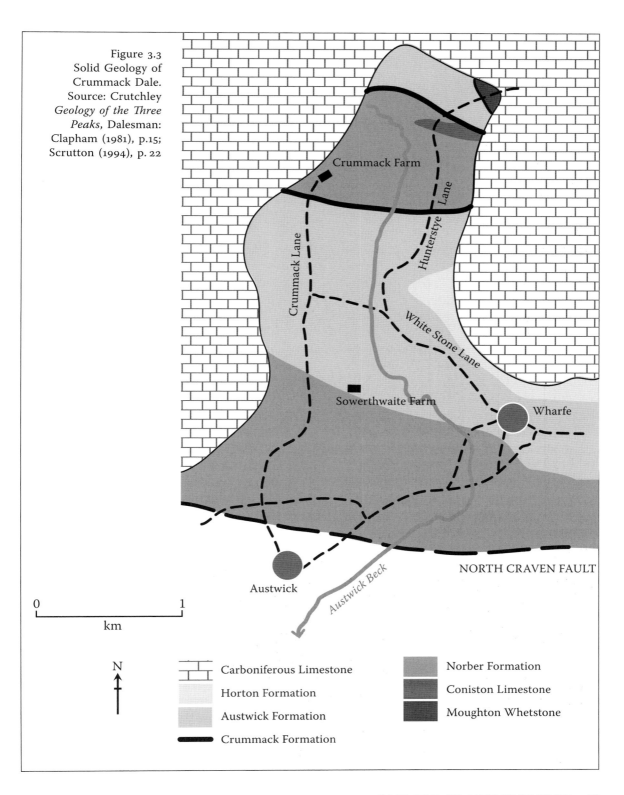

Figure 3.3
Solid Geology of
Crummack Dale.
Source: Crutchley
*Geology of the Three
Peaks*, Dalesman:
Clapham (1981), p.15;
Scrutton (1994), p. 22

Crummack Farm

Crummack Lane

Hunterstye Lane

White Stone Lane

Sowerthwaite Farm

Wharfe

Austwick

Austwick Beck

NORTH CRAVEN FAULT

0   1

km

N

Carboniferous Limestone

Horton Formation

Austwick Formation

Crummack Formation

Norber Formation

Coniston Limestone

Moughton Whetstone

Plate 3.1
Basal Conglomerate at
Nappa Scar, with Great
Scar Limestone forming
the upper bed.

Plate 3.2
Dry Stone Wall in
Austwick 'Grits'. 'No
two stones are the same
shape'.

Plate 3.3
Silurian Strata exposed in Dry Rigg Quarry, horizontal beds of Great Scar Limestone above. The North Craven Fault is of the picture to the left (south).

was the dense and resistant grit; where they have all but disappeared as the stone has flaked away to dust, silt was the choice.

Progressing further north updale leads onto the southern limb of the Crummack anticline, over Crummack Formation silts and mudstones and Ordovician Coniston limestones, and finally back onto Silurian Austwick Formation sandstones at the head of the valley where Hunterstye Lane begins its final ascent out of the valley bottom. At this point Crummack Dale reveals yet another aspect of its geological complexity.

Tucked away close to the last gate on Hunterstye Lane, in the stream bed below the rising called Moughton Whetstone Hole at SD784 719, is a scatter of rock fragments coloured green and dark-red to purple, seen at their best when wet. These fragments are called whetstones because they were once used for sharpening stones. They are in fact Austwick Formation siltstones that naturally outcrop near the wall on Capple Bank just to the north.

The alternately coloured bands are known to geologists as liesegang rings. The green banding is the natural colour of this rock while the purple colour derives from oxidation. This is a process of weathering whereby metal ions within sediments react chemically with atmospheric oxygen to break down the rock as the minerals are transformed from a ferrous state into a ferric state. This is essentially the same as rusting in metal and the outcome is the same: the rock slowly decomposes. The original colour – in this case green – becomes reddish-purple. The green and purple bands were not formed as layers during the sedimentation process: in fact, they cut across sedimentary layers. The bands originated within solid rock from weathering and oxidation, probably as groundwater levels within the pre-Carboniferous rock fluctuated. This indicates that the rings formed during the Devonian or very early Carboniferous.

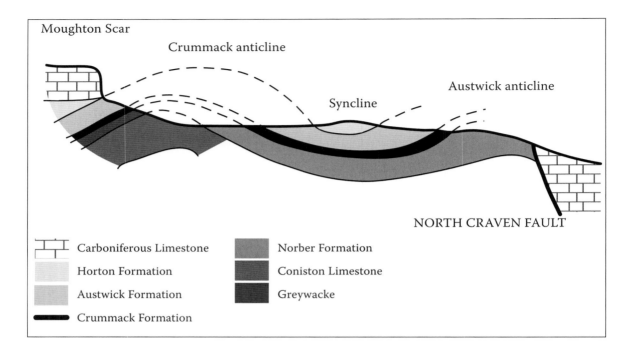

Moughton Scar

Crummack anticline

Austwick anticline

Syncline

NORTH CRAVEN FAULT

Carboniferous Limestone

Horton Formation

Austwick Formation

Crummack Formation

Norber Formation

Coniston Limestone

Greywacke

Silurian Geology at Helwith Bridge

The Basement inlier bordering the North Craven Fault reaches its maximum geographical extent in Ribblesdale between Helwith Bridge and Horton (Fig. 3.5). Here, though, the Ordovician crops out at the surface to a limited extent, and the geological map is a little less complex than in Crummack Dale, even if the structure in cross-sectional view is not. However, more than two centuries of quarrying have opened up the geological picture book here making it easier to observe, read and interpret (Plate 3.3).

The Ordovician is represented by the Crag Hill Limestone, part of the Norber Formation (see Table 3.1), and it reaches the surface across the northernmost part of the inlier, especially just west of Cragghill Farm (SD806 709) and in Douk Ghyll east of Horton. These limestones are very similar to those seen in Crummack Dale; at Cragghill they are 30m thick at the most, highly fossiliferous, and are seen here in the core of an asymmetrical anticline with its steepest limb dropping to the north.

The Silurian sequence consists of three formations: the Austwick Formation is the oldest (see Table 3.1); this is overlain by rocks of the Arcow Formation; which, in turn, is overlain by Horton Formation strata. All were massively folded during the Caledonian orogeny, and the position here is not just that of alternating anticline and syncline. Small, parasitic, anticlines are found on the limb of the main syncline, indicating repeated episodes of tectonic pressure. Just north-east of Dry Beck Farm (SD815 715), for instance, there are ten parallel small-scale folds within a horizontal distance of less than 600m,

Figure 3.4
Long Profile showing the Solid Geology of Crummack Dale.
Source: Crutchley (1981), p.14; Scrutton (1994), p. 22

Figure 3.5
Solid Geology of the
Ribblesdale Inlier.
Source: British
Geological Survey
1:50,000 Series, Sheet
60, Settle Solid Geology

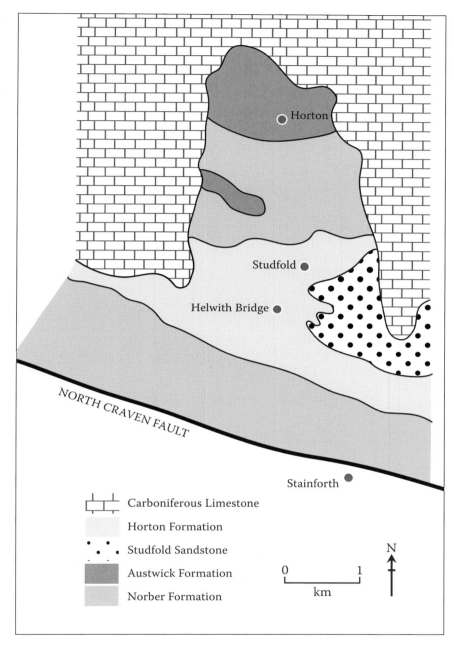

Horton

Studfold

Helwith Bridge

NORTH CRAVEN FAULT

Stainforth

Carboniferous Limestone

Horton Formation

Studfold Sandstone

Austwick Formation

Norber Formation

0   1
km

N

and minor folds could be seen in earlier working faces of Arcow and Dry
Rigg Quarries (Plate 3.4), and in the slopes between Dry Rigg Quarry and
Foredale Farm where a small anticline and small syncline run down the field
while the ribs of the northern and southern limbs of a syncline are prominent
just above the farm, the axis being seen as a linear depression. An anticline is
also prominent below the terrace of cottages. The main syncline is the same

Studrigg-Studfold syncline already seen in Crummack Dale. It cuts across Ribblesdale from Foredale Cottages through the farm of that name to run just north of the junction of Moor Head Lane and Long Lane.

Beds within the Austwick Formation reach a maximum thickness of 600m though 300m is more common at the north end of the inlier towards Horton, and they consist of alternating sandstones and siltstones. Each layer of sandstone is about 2m thick with the interspersed siltstones being very fine in comparison. The former resists erosion and stands proud of the weaker silts.

The Austwick Formation beds at Helwith Bridge are renowned as they contain exposures of what are said to be England's finest flute casts (Plate 3.5), the imprint of archaic oceanic turbidity currents.[4] They can be seen from the road in several minor rock outcrops to the west of the entrance to Dry Rigg Quarry. What you would be looking at is the underside of the base of that particular sandstone bed, and you would see a series of ripple marks (the flutes and flute casts), at first glance remarkably akin to what you would see on a sandy beach today. However, while sand ripples are positive features resulting from deposition, flutes are negative features and are the product of erosion by turbidity currents on the sea floor. The grooves carved out by the currents are called flutes, the deposits within the grooves are the flute casts. Definitely less noteworthy, though, is a small outcrop of liesegang rings at the north end of Moughton Plantation, the same as we have seen at the head of Crummack Dale.

Lying above the Austwick Formation is a narrow band of Arcow Formation calcareous siltstones, too narrow to effectively map on Figure 3.5, but visible in the section (Fig. 3.6). These do not exceed 35m in thickness, and 10m is more common, but they are thickly-bedded and have a grey colour when freshly exposed by quarrying. These, too, can be seen in the southern part of Arcow Quarry and there are a few small outcrops in the same fields as the flute casts.

The Arcow beds separate the older Austwick Formation from the younger

Plate 3.4
Anticline in Dry Rigg Quarry, exposed in a working face and showing a steeper north limb.

Plate 3.5
Flute Casts near Dry
Rigg Quarry.

Horton Formation. These are dominantly siltstones – flagstones to the quarrymen of old – with a distinctly bluish hue when wet, though they very quickly dry and weather to a uniform dark grey, and they differ from most of the Silurian rocks by being fossil-poor. These beds can be seen in the disused Helwith Bridge and Combs Quarries: the working face in Combs is magnificent and has appeared as a type-example in a number of geological texts because its beds are so steeply-dipping and so clear to read and map (see Plate 3.6). Within the more massive siltstone strata there are thinner, more shaley beds as well as traces of minerals such as lead, copper and iron pyrites, though not in commercially-viable quantities. Also visible in the face of Combs Quarry are very narrow bands of lighter coloured material. These are made up of solidified volcanic clay and each band represents a separate thin veneer of deposits from separate volcanic events during the Silurian. Because these bands are so fine they are less resistant to erosion and thus are slightly recessed between the beds of siltstone.

Integral to the Horton Formation is the Studfold Sandstone which consists of thickly-bedded sandstones, up to 80m in total thickness, best seen from the gate into the disused Studfold Quarry. Like the Horton siltstones, these beds were also deposited by turbidity currents.

There is a further element of the structural geology visible in the quarry faces at Helwith Bridge. While faulting or folding is underway, one layer of rock will slide over its adjacent layer and, as both layers are under extreme pressure, an impression will be left on the two contact surfaces in the form of scratch marks parallel to the direction of movement. This is a process known as slickensiding. When a quarry blast exposes a bed for the first time since the movement and slickensiding last occurred, the scratch marks can be identified.

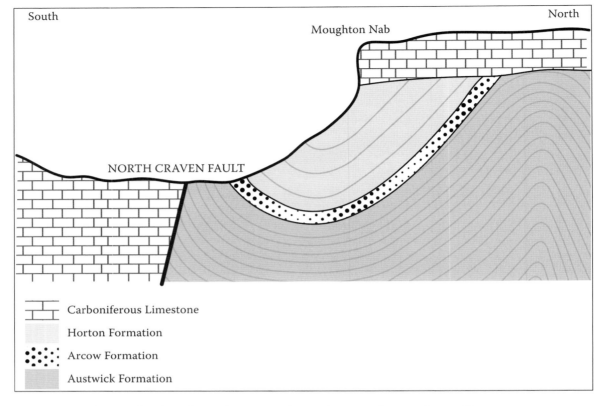

Moughton Nab

NORTH CRAVEN FAULT

Carboniferous Limestone

Horton Formation

Arcow Formation

Austwick Formation

We cannot leave Helwith Bridge without considering the unconformity that can be seen so clearly here (see Plate 3.6). In Combs Quarry and at Moughton Nab the unconformity can be viewed at close quarters. The topmost layers of rock are in the more or less horizontal Cove Limestone which sits directly on top of steeply-dipping Silurian. The Devonian succession is absent. The junction between the two is the palaeo wave-cut platform onto which marine deposits were laid during the Carboniferous. Unlike the Nappa Scar unconformity, there is no intermediate layer of conglomerate at Helwith Bridge: it is a direct interface between Silurian and Carboniferous.

Figure 3.6
Sketch Section to
show Solid Geology at
Helwith Bridge.

Great Scar Limestone

Away from the Basement inliers, the geology of much of the Ingleborough massif is dominated by Great Scar Limestone which forms vast expanses of exposed bare rock, especially in the south-eastern parts. The Great Scar beds are seen all around Crummack Dale as prominent vertical scars that bring to an abrupt end the horizontal layers of limestone. From the North Craven Fault to the north end of Thwaite Scars the beds are almost perfectly level but northwards from there they dip ever so gently towards the north-east, though not uniformly so. On Sulber and Moughton Scars, and on the

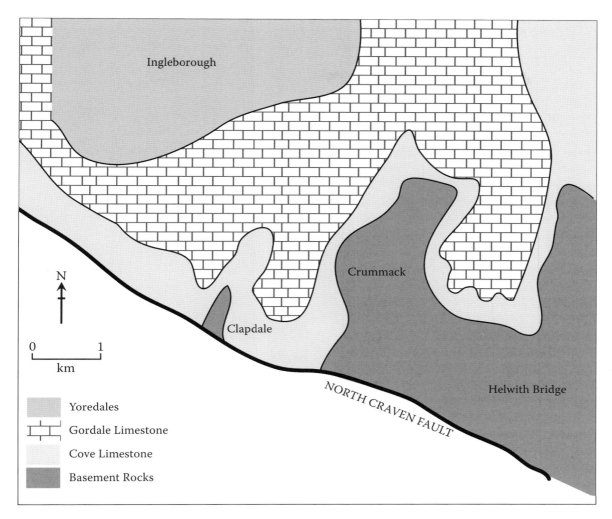

Ingleborough

Crummack

N

0   1
    km

Clapdale

NORTH CRAVEN FAULT

Helwith Bridge

Yoredales

Gordale Limestone

Cove Limestone

Basement Rocks

Figure 3.7
Carboniferous Geology
on Ingleborough South.
Source: British
Geological Survey
1:50,000 Series, Sheet
60, Settle Solid Geology

northern side of the mountain, they are once more broadly horizontal. In the scars of Twistleton and Scales Moor on the northern side of the Chapel le Dale valley the horizontal bedding is especially clear (Plate 3.7).

Geology is a very complex discipline and terminology tends to change when new surveys are undertaken.[5] This is certainly so for Ingleborough. There was a time when all the limestones were simply designated Carboniferous limestone but later re-evaluations introduced the terms Horton Limestone and Kingsdale Limestone, terms which can still be met in some publications. The most recently completed and very comprehensive survey, in 1988, preferred to use the terms Kilnsey Formation and Malham Formation for different beds within the Great Scar Limestone.[6] As if that is not complicated enough, the Malham Formation is further subdivided into older Cove Limestone and younger Gordale Limestone, named after prominent localities where the different types of rock outcrop.

All these are limestones and they form the scars and pavements that are seen so prominently around Chapel le Dale and the expanses of limestone pavement surrounding Ingleborough and topping Scales Moor. Cove Limestone tends to form major scars with associated screes whereas the Gordale beds are more exemplified by smaller stepped scars and limestone pavements. The differences are in the detail of mineralisation, of the fossil record and of purity. Limestones of the Kilnsey Formation, for example, consist of approximately 97 per cent calcium carbonate ($CaCO_3$) while the Malham Formation rocks exceed 98.50 per cent. What all the limestones have in common is their grey colour but, alas, there is grey and grey. Kilnsey Formation rocks tend to be distinctly darker in hue than the Malham Formation, though light conditions and the amount of moisture can distort natural colours.

Plate 3.6
The Silurian-Carboniferous Unconformity in Combs Quarry. Two massive beds of Great Scar Limestone overlie the Silurian strata.

The Wensleydale or Yoredale Group

Until a 1976 re-survey these rocks were known as the Yoredale Series and this terminology is still widely used.[7] They lie above the Great Scar Limestone, meaning they are younger. Their total thickness is less than the Great Scar Limestone, averaging 150m, and they form the bulk of Ingleborough and

Whernside above the limestone plateau level. Wensleydale Group rocks outcrop on Whernside, on Simon Fell and Park Fell, outliers of Ingleborough; on Blea Moor and Gayle Moor; and on Cam Fell and Cosh. Approximately half of the total area encompassed by the National Park is underlain by these rocks.

The Wensleydale Group consists of a repeated sequence – or cyclothem – of sedimentary rocks, generally horizontal in form with bands of limestone, mudstone and sandstone, the mudstone often being written up as shale. In the Ribblehead area the top of the lowest layer of limestone (the Hawes Limestone) within the Wensleydale Group is marked by a distinct and narrow band of almost almond-shaped algal nodules known as the 'Girvanella Band'. It can be seen in the stream bed just above Yordas Cave in Kingsdale. Within the total sequence there are nine layers of *named* limestone and several unnamed ones and at least thirteen sandstone layers, though the whole sequence does not necessarily occur in any one locality. There are alternating bands of limestone, sandstone and shale with all three rock types repeated time and again, but not necessarily absolutely so as mudstone (shale) and sandstone layers do not always occur.

Plate 3.7
Carboniferous Limestone Strata on Twistleton Scars. Each step represents a discrete limestone bed.

Some of the limestone bands were named by nineteenth-century geologists; others by lead miners from the same century. Their relative thickness varies from 1m to 60m, as does the thickness of individual layers from one locality to another. For example, on Ingleborough the succession of limestones passes from the Hardraw Scar above the Great Scar Limestone plateau, through the Simonstone, Middle, and Five Yard Limestones to the Main Limestone (highest and youngest). Most of the limestone beds are fossil-rich, especially in corals, crinoids and brachiopods. The Main Limestone varies from 21m to 24m and forms Greensett Crags on Whernside and the most prominent scars high on Ingleborough.

Part of the Wensleydale succession can be seen clearly in the bed of Mere Gill on the flanks of Ingleborough (SD7458 7503) where the Five and Three Yard beds can be seen in close proximity to shale bands (Plate 3.8). A similar succession can be seen in the bed of Force Gill on Whernside (SD759 819).

The layers of sandstone are unnamed and they, too, vary in thickness as well as in grain size and consistency. Some take the form of thin flagstones and it is quite common to see on the surface of these flags what resemble thin, linear and curving strips of solidified plasticine moulded on to the rock. They are fossilised worm casts, the imprint of where worms had long ago burrowed through the deposits before they were transformed into rock. Massive beds of sandstone form much of the pedestal of Ingleborough and Whernside, The Arks and Black Shiver in particular dominating the brooding presence of Ingleborough.

The shales are very soft and tend to readily crumble when exposed on the surface. They appear on the ground, often in gills, as dark grey to black, paper-thin flakes of rock.

The later Carboniferous saw dramatic changes in sea conditions as the clear ocean in which the Great Scar Limestone was formed gradually became ever shallower. This was not a continuous process, though, as sea levels fluctuated, hence the cyclothem, leading to variations in sea conditions. The limestone beds of the Wensleydale sequence were formed in clear seas, but falling sea levels in relation to the dominant land surface slowly gave way to muddy lagoon conditions in which mudstones formed or to extensive sand banks which eventually became consolidated and cemented to form sandstone.

Millstone Grit

The youngest and highest Carboniferous rocks in the Ribblehead area consist of Millstone Grit, a term first applied because their toughness made them suitable for use as stones for grinding grain into flour. Some grits were also used locally in previous centuries for making bakestones, or backstones, if the stone was sufficiently fire-resistant, as well as lintels, quoins and gate stoops. The topographic place-name Backstone Gill (SD704 800) in Kingsdale is a clue to this long-lost activity. The name Whernside means in Old English 'the hill where millstones were obtained' and a quernstone (hence 'whern') is the name given to a grinding stone.

Millstone Grit was deposited where a huge river flowing from the north-east entered the shallow sea that covered what is now the Dales through an enormous delta. This river's load mainly consisted of sands: the coarser and heavier grains settled first to make up the lower layers of the delta; the less coarse grains settled above these to become the upper layers, though all Millstone Grit is coarse grained compared to sandstones. These differences in sediment are reflected in the gritstones which consist of beds of either very coarse-grained or fine-grained rock, sometimes with siltstone layers, and all interbedded. The coarse layers contain variable quantities of rounded quartz pebbles. Some rocks containing evidence of turbidites that were created from rapid sediment flows down the front edge slopes of the delta.

In some exposures there is clear evidence of cross-bedding: this is where sediments were being swept along in fast-flowing distributaries within the delta. Water flow was so dynamic in these river branches that the dominant current changed constantly, laying down sediments this way now and that way later.

Differences of stratigraphy have led to geologists classifying gritstones into various categories. In the Ribblehead area they are the Lower Howgate Edge Grit forming the 18m thick summit capping of Ingleborough as well as occurring on top of Widdale Fell and on Whernside; and the Upper Howgate Edge Grit forming the higher parts of Whernside. There are no other outcrops of Millstone Grit within this area.

The Craven Fault System

The network of faults bounding Ingleborough to the south is shown in Figure 3.8. The situation between the Middle and South Craven Faults is particularly complex and maps tend to simplify the faults westwards from Austwick, which is roughly where the North, Middle and South Craven and Feizor Faults come together tangentially.[8] Reality though is somewhat different as there are not just two parallel faults (North and South) but, in places, minor faults and cross faults as would be expected in a region which had experienced such massive and prolonged tectonic disturbance.

The North Craven Fault follows Old Road very closely from Ingleton to Newby Cote, which is bisected by the fault, then cuts across just north of the lake in Clapdale over to Town Head in Austwick before describing a gentle arc through Wharfe Wood to Stainforth and beyond. The South Craven Fault runs broadly parallel to its counterpart but south of Old Road, runs through Cold Cotes, under Clapham churchyard and through the western end of Austwick. It then swings slightly southwards towards Settle before which Buck Haw Brow is the actual line of the fault. At Newby Cote the two faults

Plate 3.8
Yoredale Shales in Mere
Gill, Ingleborough.

are separated by a distance of only 100m but between Clapham and Austwick the gap widens to 400m; east of there the two diverge completely.

Because the minor faults north of the North Craven Fault are small-scale features they tend not to have specific names, but they do leave a very distinct imprint on the ground. One such fault runs south-eastwards from Newby Moss (see Fig. 3.8) where Grey Wife Sike disappears underground. At first its line does not leave much of a surface impression but to the east of the enclosure wall by Little Knott it begins to leave more of a mark. Between this wall and Clapdale farm there is a group of very large shakeholes, which have opened up where the limestone beneath the glacial veneer has been dissolved along the line of the geological weakness that the fault represents, and it continues as a deep and broad dry valley, opened up by glacial meltwater, clearly visible south of Rayside Plantation and just north and east of the farm. This fault then cuts across to the foot of the rocky hill called Thwaite where it divides into three branches: the northern line is seen on the ground as a deep gash that almost slices Thwaite in two; the southern line marks the lower scars, including Robin Proctor's Scar; while the middle branch cuts across Norber where it further sub-divides into two, showing as distinct, stepped limestone scars between Robin Proctor's Scar and the north boundary wall of Norber.

One tectonic feature is known as a fault block and these often form steep-sided upland blocks. The lower, southern sections of Thwaite and Norber enclosure are upstanding fault blocks caused by down-faulting along this series of faults, leaving the area in between higher, but this faulting is so ancient that present differences in relative height may result from variable rates of resistance to erosion rather than to actual faulting disturbance.

Another small fault (Sulber Fault) describes a ruler-straight line to form Sulber Nick (Plate 3.9). East of the north-south boundary wall, at the eastern end of the Nick, the fault leaves the path and curves away to the south-east before petering out. This fault is also responsible for the development of the major Nick Pot-Hangman's Hole cave/pothole system at the western end of Sulber. Short faults like this one are the result of localised tectonic movements caused by more significant disturbance elsewhere, possibly along the main Craven fault zone. It is also worthy of note that the total down-faulting along the Craven Faults approaches 600m whereas along the minor faults it is just a few metres.

Drift Geology

Much of the bedrock has been masked by a veneer of later deposits. This veneer is not uniform in origin, thickness or composition. The geological map of the area classifies the various deposits that make up the veneer as drift and the map breaks it down into peat, alluvium, and boulder clay.[9] Strictly speaking though, the term drift should only be applied to deposits with a glacial origin, either from the actual ice or from meltwater. The map does not differentiate deposits found on old lake beds (technically known as lacustrine deposits), nor does it recognise areas where the surface layer consists of loess.

Plate 3.9 Fault-guided Sulber Nick, with Fountains Fell and Pen-y-ghent in the distance.

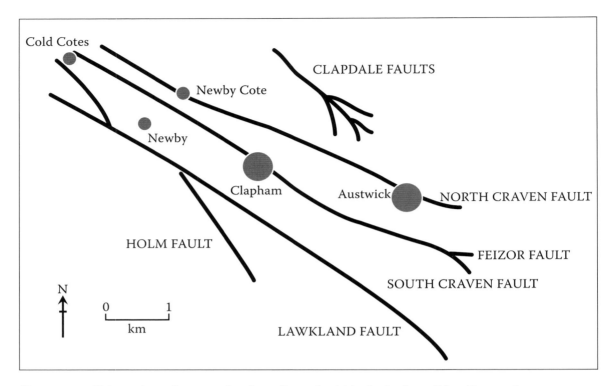

Cold Cotes

Newby Cote

Newby

CLAPDALE FAULTS

Clapham

Austwick

NORTH CRAVEN FAULT

HOLM FAULT

N

0   1

km

FEIZOR FAULT

SOUTH CRAVEN FAULT

LAWKLAND FAULT

Chapter 4 will investigate features that have formed within both the solid and drift geology around Ingleborough: here we are concerned with the drift material itself, using the term in its broadest sense.

Till deposits – those materials laid down under ice – extend almost up to the 500m contour and there is a broad if discontinuous sweep of such materials from Crina Bottom in the south-west of the Ingleborough massif to The Allotment in the east. Why there should be substantial areas free of till cover, such as Grey Scars, is difficult to explain but it must be due to localised factors of ice flow dynamics and glacial-period topography. The material here differs in one significant respect from that around Ribblehead in that it had a more local origin. Examination of clasts (cobbles and boulders) within till exposures on the southern side of the mountain shows a dominance of Basement and Wensleydale rock, probably derived from the mountain itself. In places, such as The Allotment and Hurnel Moss, a layer of upland peat 3m thick has developed on deposits of glacial till or head.

There is also a patchy and rather thin cover of till on Long Scar and Thwaite, on Moughton and at the head of Crummack Dale in localities that are otherwise composed of expanses of limestone pavement. The geological boundary between till and exposed Great Scar Limestone is vividly seen on the ground by sudden changes in vegetation, the former being generally a dull brown rather than bright green and markedly damper underfoot. In places pockets of till remain trapped within hollows such as shakeholes.

Figure 3.8
Tectonic Faults in the Clapham Area.
Source: British Geological Survey 1:50,000 Series, Sheet 60, Settle Solid Geology

Till (or boulder clay) consists of rock particles from small pebble to huge boulder in size within a matrix of clays, sands and rock flour which is the residue from rock that has been ground down to a fine powder by the attritional action of a moving ice mass. The clays vary in colour depending on what types of rocks had been ground down, and the boulders often bear scratch marks from constant abrasion as the rocks were being churned around within or beneath the ice. This unsorted mass can be clearly seen in cuttings on the outside banks of meanders on the Ribble as well as on smaller feeder streams and none of the material is layered; none was laid down in any measured way (Plate 3.10). It was simply dumped as an unstratified and unsorted amalgam. In thickness the boulder clay veneer can exceed 20m in this area, and more than 40m south of Settle, as proven by borehole tests.[10]

Till forms ground moraine which was laid down, in varying thicknesses, on the pre-glacial rock surface: in many situations ground moraine forms the veneer described above but in Ribblesdale ground moraine is the material which makes up the drumlin field of low streamlined hillocks extending down the eastern side of the valley from Ribblehead to Horton in Ribblesdale. Many of the depressions that pepper the landscape, as on Blea Moor, have also been partially infilled with boulder clay that became trapped within, or collapsed into, them.

South of the Craven faults there is a very different picture. The Wenning valley provided an easy north-west to south-east line of flow for ice issuing from Chapel le Dale and the Lune valley, and there are widespread deposits of till right across the valley which contains a drumlin swarm as impressive as that in Upper Ribblesdale (see the next chapter for a detailed examination of drumlins). Viewed from the southern slopes of Ingleborough, the swarm extends almost as far as the eye can see within the valley and towards the lower slopes of the Bowland Fells.

The Wenning valley also has evidence of fluvio-glacial deposition. In kettleholes between many of the drumlins sands, gravels and silts can be seen, especially where erosional processes have created small meander scars on current streams. The difference between glacial and fluvio-glacial deposits in such situations is immediately apparent: the former are unsorted with angular clasts in a clay matrix, the latter are graded and sorted in laminated (layered) bands. Newby Moor provides further evidence of immediate post-glacial water flow in the form of features called kames, which are flattened but conical mounds of sorted material. There are three between Green Hill and Upper Hardacre farms south-west of Newby village, centred on SD706 687 and SD710 685.

Our temperate glaciers experienced localised, and possibly seasonal, melting of ice at the glacier base, helping to lubricate it and causing water flow. These sub-glacial streams carried along material entrapped within the ice, much as any surface river does, material which was eventually deposited downstream. This process can be recognised, with detailed field surveying, where there are deposits of gravels, sands and silts within the boulder clay mass. These deposits are sorted and layered – or laminated.

Lacustrine Deposits

Lakes often grew beyond the snout of a glacier where subglacial streams emerged from beneath the ice only to be blocked by moraine dumps down valley. They would also have formed as glaciers were in their final melting phase, again assuming there was a natural dam across the valley. As in mature rivers, deposits within lakes are laid down in fine layers with well sorted silty material: the material is laminated. The most extensive lacustrine deposits in the western Dales can be found between Horton in Ribblesdale and Helwith Bridge, and there are as yet unproven deposits in Kingsdale beyond the huge terminal moraine adjacent to the gorge at Raven Ray (centred on SD694 756). In both cases the land is absolutely flat, except for recent down-cutting by the modern rivers, and river bank sections expose the parallel layers of dark silt, a good example of which can be viewed from the road at Keld Head (SD696 766). It has to be stressed, though, that detailed analysis of these sediments is still to be carried out and there is, as yet, no conclusive scientific proof that a lake did once exist here.

Between Helwith Bridge and Horton in Ribblesdale the valley is completely level: at Helwith Bridge the ground surface height is 220m OD, at Crooks Barn more than 1600m further north it is still 220m. Just south of Helwith

Plate 3.10
Boulder Clay Exposure, showing angular rock fragments, gravel and grey leached clay.

Bridge there is a severe constriction in the valley, forcing the Ribble into fast-flowing and turbulent mode as it flows through the minor gorge between here and the confluence with Stainforth Beck. It is probable that this gorge was cut in the immediate post-glacial phase and that, prior to this event, water was dammed up behind the constriction in a shallow lake that extended as far north as Horton. The floor of the valley here is made up of sorted and river-worn sands and gravels and in periods of heavy rain it readily floods.

Loess

Loess is fine wind-blown silt derived from outwash plains on glacial margins. In the immediate post-glacial period, before vegetation became established and surfaces stabilised, strong prevailing winds whipped up the silt and carried it over long distances. Until recently loess was not differentiated from boulder clay on geological maps though even a casual comparison emphasises how different they are. Loess does not have the pebble and boulder element and is much finer and more sorted than boulder clay. It has also been confused with brown earth, one of the most common soil types in the Dales but, again, they are very different in detail. Loess is yellowish to pale brown in colour and can often be seen in the back sections of small scrapes, such as where sheep have sought shelter from wind and rain, whereas brown earths are mid-brown.

You will not find loess deposits in the Dales on any published map; you will struggle to find a reference to it in any book. There is nothing new about our knowledge of loess in Britain but investigation of it in the Dales is recent.[11] It occurs in a broad band across southern England with the source of the loess having been the then dry southern basin of the North Sea. In the Dales it is found in much smaller quantities as isolated pockets, no more than 2m thick, on the moors and flatter fells with concentrations in depressions where it was either trapped or washed in by surface water flow. The depth of loess in the Dales now is without doubt much less than when first deposited.

It is not yet known where loess deposits in our area came from but detailed field investigations of particle size may enable identification of the direction they were blown in from. In theory particle size should decrease as distance increases so plotting particle size gradients could be used to chart its path. The problem, though, is that over subsequent millennia so much has been blown away again, or washed into cave systems, or generally disturbed from the Mesolithic period onwards, that an analysis like this may prove less than fruitful. Whether or not these loess deposits date from the Loch Lomond cold phase (or stadial) between 11,000 and 10,000 years ago is currently subject to detailed research and a number of dates have already been obtained from within the Mesolithic, between 9300 and 8200 years ago. Thus far, there has been a lack of hard scientific evidence to back up tentative conclusions.

Apart from colour and fineness, there are other clues to help locate a loess deposit in the Ribblehead area. It tends to support a more varied range of plant species than brown earths or boulder clay, especially where it has been washed into the cracks within limestone pavement or provides prime habitat for bracken. Because of its fine composition it often has extensive rabbit warrens because rabbits find it easy to burrow into. Ant nests are a further indicator as is bracken infestation because its rhizomes require the high levels of soil oxygen found in loess. Loess is only slightly acidic, is well drained and more nutrient-rich than brown earths or boulder clay, qualities recognised by early migrants to our area as being suitable locations to found an agriculture-based homestead. Much work remains to be carried out on the limestone plateau between Ribblehead and Selside to identify if there is indeed a positive correlation between loess deposits and settlement sites.

Alluvium

Rivers erode where their velocity is high and deposit where it is impeded, for example on the inside of a meander or where the gradient levels out on to a plain, and there is insufficient energy and volume of water to overcome friction, so the river begins to dump its load. The deposits are known as alluvium and they are sorted and often laminated either as fine silts or small particles of gravel. There is a narrow and discontinuous strip of alluvium alongside the Ribble from Ribblehead southwards beyond Horton, as well as on tributary streams. These are not the vast floodplains associated with the lower course of a major river but isolated sections of plain of limited spatial extent.

Peat

The Drift edition geology map shows large swathes of the area as peat. It forms a thick blanket, several metres deep, across many moors and flatter fells and is unmistakable by its dark brown to black colour, its frustrating labyrinth of groughs (mini–valleys) and haggs (upstanding sections), and the mass of partly decayed organic matter that it so clearly consists of (Plate 3.11). The most common organic constituents of peat are *Sphagnum* mosses but it also includes a range of flowering species, sedges and cottongrass. Where it has formed in depressions water collects and the peat takes on the form of a bog replete with sphagnum moss, cotton grass and sedges. Elsewhere, extensive peat bogs occur in flatter parts of the uplands where surface water is trapped and unable to drain away overland and where underlying rocks are impermeable. Such peat expanses can be seen on Swineley Cowm and Arten Gill Moss (centred on SD795 858) or Greensett Moss below Whernside (centred on SD745 820), or on the saddle between Ingleborough and Simon Fell.

Swarth Moor and Studfold Moss at Helwith Bridge is another area of interest in having seen the development of a layer of peat, several metres thick, which has developed on top of lacustrine sand and gravel deposits.

Peat is extremely slow to develop. Rates are not consistent and vary with nuances of climate, altitude and surface relief, but vertical accumulation takes place at between 200mm and 1000mm per year on average.[12] Some blanket peat deposits in the upland Dales developed more than 3000 years ago during a period of severe climatic deterioration.[13] This led to a withdrawal of people from the uplands and to a dramatic transformation of the natural order of things on our fells and moors. In warmer periods, such as the early medieval, peat growth would have ceased, but the prevailing cold and damp conditions of the Little Ice Age (c AD 1550–1850) saw renewed growth and accumulation. These issues will be explored more fully in chapters 5 and 6.

*   *   *

Having set out the geological background to Ingleborough, the following chapter concerns itself with how natural processes have shaped and modified the landscape. After all, what we see today is as much the result of ongoing landscapes processes as rock forming or tectonic forces.

·FOUR·
Landform Processes

Geological processes have to be considered across seemingly endless periods of time – hundreds of millions of years – and it is important to bear in mind that such processes have not stopped. They have always happened and always will, and landform processes are no different. As soon as any given strata were exposed on the surface, the various agents of weathering and erosion got to work to wear them down, to remove material from here and deposit it there, to modify the landscape. Some of these landform processes operate at an imperceptible rate. We obviously cannot see limestone being dissolved by rain, for example and the effect on the landscape of weathering only becomes apparent over thousands of years. Other landform processes, however, have had more dramatic effects and the action of ice must surely be uppermost here.

Ice and Ice Flow

The Ingleborough area is a glaciated landscape but not one that displays the classic features normally associated with upland glaciation in the Lake District or the Scottish mountains. There are none of the dramatic ice-carved features like corries, hanging valleys, arêtes, or truncated spurs. The hills here were not high enough, and thus not cold enough, to generate the quantities of corrie ice necessary to create such features. Corrie ice feeds by gravity into valley glacier systems: this did not really happen here. In addition, the valley glaciers that did flow down through Chapel le Dale and Ribblesdale deposited so much material to such a depth that many smaller erosional features may well have been masked.

One glacial episode cannot possibly have carved out all the landscape features seen today. Repeated glaciations have added their contribution to the mix. (Rock strata elsewhere contain convincing evidence that glaciations occurred throughout geological history, at least within the Precambrian, Ordovician and Carboniferous.) It might seem impossible that there are surviving surface remains from these archaic events but there is evidence of early Carboniferous surfaces in some stream beds and on limestone pavements. Within recent geological time, that is within the Pleistocene (see Figure 2.1) there have been periods of glacial advance and periods of glacial retreat stretching over two million years. Within the last 500,000 years alone three advances (called glacials) and retreats (called interglacials) have been recognised in Britain from analysis in the field, and these have been widely published, but there was also a slightly earlier – and still lesser known – glacial.

Around 650,000 years ago much of the British Isles was ice-bound in the grip of the Happisburgh Glacial.[1] A long interglacial after this was followed by the Anglian Glacial which was at its height between 455,000 and 300,000 years ago. A further period of retreat was again superseded by the Wolstonian Glacial between 200,000 and 130,000 years ago; with further retreat being replaced by glacial advance in the Devensian Glacial which began around 110,000 years ago and only receded 14,000 or so years ago.

Within a glacial period there may have been times of temporary retreat as temperatures increased above the critical limit for ice formation, and these warmer periods are known as interstadials. There were also colder spells between glacial periods, known as stadials, when ice advanced. One such stadial has been determined in northern Britain for the years from 12,500 to 11,500 years ago, the so-called Loch Lomond (or Younger Dryas) Stadial.[2] Since then, of course, in what geologists call the Holocene, Britain has been ice-free but … the very fact that glaciologists term those thousand years a stadial suggests we are now within an interstadial, and that the ice sheets will one day return. Herein lies a dilemma and a source of academic argument. Some maintain that the current global warming trend will prevent – or delay – a further glacial advance, particularly as polar ice caps inexorably melt away, but others take the opposite view. It may happen that global warming will upset oceanic circulation in the north Atlantic by feeding many more icebergs into it, thereby switching off the conveyor – or oceanic circulation – that moderates our temperatures. In turn this will lead to significantly colder conditions which will bring forward the next ice advance.[3] Icebergs contain fresh water which is less dense than salt water, thereby upsetting the saline balance of the North Atlantic which could lead to the shutdown of oceanic circulation, according to this school of thought. On the other hand, however, opponents of this way of thinking argue that ocean currents naturally oscillate from time to time, or change their latitudinal position.

Climate scientists call this possible shutdown phenomenon Abrupt Climate Change.[4] Time will tell, but clues from the past could provide the answer. It is generally accepted that the Loch Lomond stadial had a very rapid inception – decades maybe rather than centuries – and that the dramatic change in climate *may* have been brought about by the Atlantic conveyor switching off.[5] Evidence suggests that average British sea surface temperatures could drop to −6 degrees Celsius within thirty years of shutdown, an alarming prospect if the hypothesis is valid.

For the Ingleborough area whatever is to be identified in today's landscape as the result of glacial action probably dates from the Late Devensian Glacial. Most signs from earlier glacials were wiped out by Devensian ice. Earlier deposits can survive though as, for example, in some of the larger caves within the Dales. Victoria Cave near Settle has yielded material from the Ipswichian Interglacial of 114,000 to 135,000 years ago which contained valuable archaeological deposits. The Devensian is known to have peaked between 20,000 and 18,000 years ago which means the Late Devensian covers the years after that, *ie* from 18,000 to 14,000 years ago.

The general direction of ice flow in the area was from north to south: the full detailed lines of flow have only recently been identified.[6] The whole of the Dales would have been ice-covered during the Devensian with the highest parts – Ingleborough, Whernside and Cam Fell – having been localised ice growth poles in themselves. However, the main glacial movement through the area was from elsewhere. Ice flowed from the main growth pole in the uplands of Mallerstang (Wild Boar Fell and Swarth Fell) and the Howgill Fells to merge with ice coming off Cam Fell and Whernside to Ribblehead before diverging to flow through Chapel le Dale and down Ribblesdale.

As the dominant Scottish ice sheet receded, smaller growth poles like the one in the western Dales became more important as agents of landscape change. For example, whereas Scottish-derived ice had once flowed south *up* the Eden valley and Mallerstang into the heart of the Dales, the position was later reversed, with ice flowing north down the valley. Towards the end of the Devensian, as the ice sheet thinned, it degraded into individual valley glaciers and small corrie glaciers; and the latter also reappeared, briefly in terms of geological time, during the later Loch Lomond advance.[7]

Some ice probably overflowed from Langstrothdale through Greenfield into Ribblesdale; while Kingsdale was infilled with ice flowing off Whernside and Great Coum as well as from over the watershed from Dentdale where there is a distinct col at White Shaw Moss. Cols often result, in part at least, from a process known as glacial diffluence whereby ice overflows a watershed, either because its preferred direction of flow has been cut off by larger volumes of ice or because there is a major constriction in the valley. Ice flowing over the watershed erodes a passage between the mountains forming the col, in this case between Whernside and Gragareth. It is also possible that ice overflowed from Ribblesdale at Selside via Sulber into Crummack Dale to merge with ice flowing off the localised Ingleborough growth pole. The fact that ice flowed over watersheds indicates that the ice sheet surface exceeded 800m OD. Within the western Dales as a whole there was a series of dynamic radiating ice flows, and this must mean they were warm-based glaciers.

Research into the dynamics of glaciers in northern Britain is slowly unravelling the hitherto little known details of ice flow growth and direction, but there remain huge gaps in our appreciation of what was happening within and beneath glaciers, to what glaciology terms the basal thermal regime of a given ice stream.[8] It would seem to make sense to think in terms of cold-

Plate 4.1
Glacially deepened
Valley in Kingsdale,
looking north-east from
the terminal moraine.
The river channel was
straightened about 100
years ago.

based glaciers in the highest parts with warm-based ones in valleys and lowland plains. In a cold-based glacier, or ice sheet, the core temperature within the ice mass is always well below freezing point and thus well below the pressure melting point of ice. This prevents ice from melting at the base of the glacier which precludes the presence of sub-glacial meltwater and, in turn, means there is no lubrication layer beneath the ice: the glacier does not flow. In a warm-based glacier the mean core temperature hovers around freezing point which results in the pressure melting point being exceeded, maybe just seasonally, leading to melting beneath the ice. This gives the glacier a lubrication layer which allows it to flow and pick up momentum.

This has direct relevance to Ingleborough. Drumlins (see below) in our area are not generally found above 600m OD: this height level may well mirror the boundary between warm-based and cold-based ice in the western Dales. Only the warm-based ice had the potential energy and therefore the capability to transport material, later to dump it as moraine where energy levels dropped below the critical point.

The actual maximum thickness of Devensian ice here may have approached 200m which is more than sufficient for the development of moraine features. There are no classical moraine forms on the south side of the mountain but there are minor landforms. Near Trow Gill Clapdale turns sharply to the north-west where there are deposits composed of till. Much of Newby Moss and Hurnel Moss is boggy ground because of its till cover. Whether this was left behind by ice flowing down off the higher reaches of the mountain or cast aside from the Wenning valley ice flow is unknown. Detailed field examination of till exposures may answer this question by plotting the long-axis orientation of individual cobbles and rocks within the till which might indicate the direction of ice flow. The material which makes up the till is totally unsorted or at best very poorly sorted and it would be easy to jump to a false conclusion unless a very large sample size of individual stones was worked through.

There are also isolated pockets of till below Moughton Scars and on Thieves Moss beyond the head of Crummack Dale, in hollows on Sulber, and across Harry Hallam's and Lead Mines Mosses north of the mountain, where sediment was trapped and abandoned. Then there is the drumlin field in the Wenning valley whose plan form indicates that the direction of ice flow was near enough from west to east. Observations in current glacial areas provide much food for thought concerning drumlin inception. Scientists working on the Rutford ice stream in western Antarctica over a number of years have watched the growth of one drumlin from nothing in the early 1990s to a monster 10m high and 100m wide at the maximum and several hundred metres long by 2008.[9]

The limits on the ground of end moraine deposits may not necessarily represent the furthest point reached by an ice stream. They may well be deposits from the most recent Devensian advance but may equally be the residue from an advance at a point earlier in the Devensian or even from a pre-Devensian glaciation. The latest advance, for some reason, may have left no mark of its passage on the ground, or had its scant deposits swept away by later erosional processes.

Plate 4.2
Terminal Moraine by Raven Ray, Kingsdale. Kingsdale Beck cut a gorge through limestone bedrock, left of centre.

Processes of glacial erosion

Kingsdale is a typical example of a glaciated valley (Plate 4.1), being loosely U-shaped with steep sides and a generally level base, though its current flatness results from immediate post-glacial deposition. Whether or not Kingsdale was an over-deepened glacial trough cannot be determined now as the depth of these sediments is unknown. No glacial valley has been created, in its present form, by one glacial advance: as we have seen, repeated glaciations have built on what their predecessors achieved. Ribblesdale and the valley above Chapel le Dale do not fit into the classic glacial trough form as they are such broad valleys, though the latter between the Hill Inn and White Scar Cave does conform to what one would expect. It is debateable whether the River Ribble can be seen as a misfit stream – one far too small to have carved out such a huge valley – but the streams flowing down Chapel le Dale certainly can. In comparison to the scale of the valley both Winterscales Beck and Chapel Beck are tiny and could never have carved out such a broad feature. Kingsdale Beck also fits into the misfit stream mould. As suggested earlier, though, neither valley has true truncated spurs. The dramatic Twistleton Scars and Raven Scar either side of Chapel le Dale have certainly been cut off in the vertical plane but more work is required to identify truncation of preglacial hill spurs. True hanging valleys are also absent though Spice Gill near Chapel le Dale (SD737 762) could be regarded as such. The lack of hanging valleys is due in part to the underlying limestone geology: significant streams did not develop here, pre-glaciation.

Apart from glacially widened and deepened valleys the main landscape feature resulting from glacial erosion in our area is the vast expanses of bare limestone pavement. Though restricted areas of pavement have been swept clear of soil and vegetation by past agriculture, some of the pavements were undoubtedly planed off by glacial scour: flowing ice and debris at its base easily removed unconsolidated material lying on top of exposed pre-glacial bedding plane surfaces. In other cases the ice plucked at the ground surface rather than scouring it. The pavements of Scales Moor and Southerscales Scars are among the most impressive in the entire country. In some cases the debris acted like sandpaper on the surface of the rock leaving parallel scratch marks or striations. It is notoriously difficult to positively identify striations, especially on limestone where other post-glacial erosional and weathering processes, such as dissolution, have left their mark on larger rocks contained within boulder clay deposits. Surviving striations can provide valuable clues to establishing ice flow direction. Glacial erosion along the valley sides was also responsible for creating the lines of scars that can be seen in Ingleborough's limestone landscapes.

Processes of Glacial Deposition

The whole area from Gearstones to Ribblehead and southwards down Ribblesdale is rich in glacial deposits. A considerable depth of glacial till covers much of the solid geology within the valley bottoms and on the flanks of the surrounding hills up to a height of 490m. Just as all the details of ice flow direction are not fully understood, so there are large gaps in our knowledge of glacial deposits here. Ribblesdale's well known drumlins were mapped by the pioneer geologist Arthur Raistrick but that was in 1930 and no subsequent mapping had taken place until a student from Durham University mapped the drumlin field in Ribblesdale in 2007. Approximately 90 per cent of British drumlins have now been mapped, totalling well over 30,000.[10] Possibly the best view of the layout of the drumlins and associated features is to be seen on satellite images rather than on maps.

Glaciers deposit material at different stages in their life, and from different sections of their bulk; they transport debris in different ways, too. The bulldozing effect of the glacier snout pushes material ahead of the ice mass but, inevitably, some of the rocks and clay work their way round the edges of the snout and underneath to be dragged along between the glacier base and the ground surface. Some debris is entrained within the glacier while more is carried on its top surface, having tumbled from surrounding valley slopes. Glacier flow dynamics are very complex and the relationships between debris accumulation, transportation and deposition are equally so. Some of the subglacial material will be 'left behind', dumped on the valley floor behind an obstruction perhaps, or abandoned on the outside of a curve in the valley. Whatever the detailed reason for dumping the material may have been, a loss of momentum leading to a reduction in energy was invariably a major factor.

The landscape features resulting from glacial deposition are variations on the moraine theme. Anyone who has studied glacial deposition processes will know that a terminal or end moraine will form across the valley or plain at the furthest point of a particular glacier's advance. This is where the glacier stopped, where rates of ablation (ice wasting) exceeded rates of accumulation: the 'bulldozer' came to a halt. There was no more energy to push it forwards. A textbook example of a terminal moraine dams Kingsdale and its scale is impressive in every dimension (Plate 4.2). We will return to this later. Debris left along the edges of the glacier, plastered against the valley sides where energy levels were lower, will form lateral moraines. Again, Kingsdale has an impressive example: drive along the road from the bottom end of the moraine by Raven Ray and you are on it. Look across to the south side of the valley and you will see lateral moraine there, too. Textbooks tell us that a medial moraine will form where two glaciers converge, where energy is swallowed up. This divergence happened at Ribblehead but there is no medial moraine. If there ever was one here, it must have been swept away by later ice or

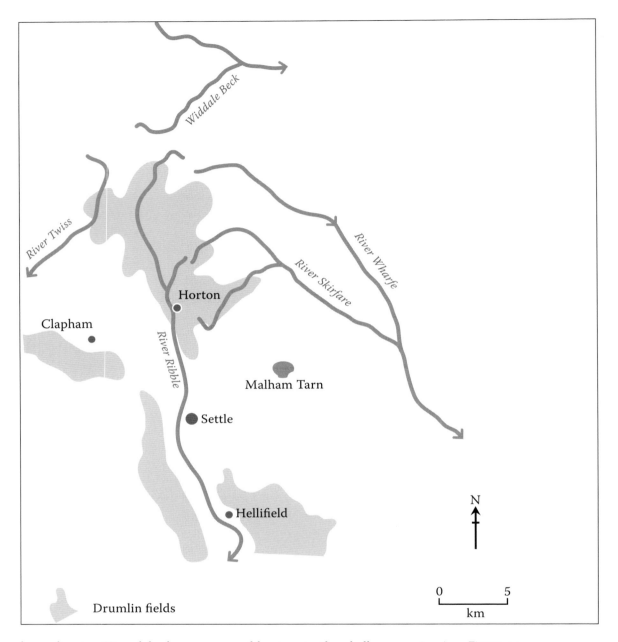

Figure 4.1
Drumlin Fields in North
Ribblesdale.

by meltwater. Kingsdale, however, possibly rises to the challenge again. A wall runs along the crest of the long slope dropping gradually down from Twistleton which may well be such a moraine formed from the merging of the Kingsdale and Chapel le Dale glaciers.

On the other hand it may be nothing of the kind. It could be a drift tail. These are very common in Wensleydale, Swaledale and Wharfedale but not so in the western Dales.[11] They almost always develop where two major valleys converge. Debris (the till material) is moved along the sides of each valley and then dragged out in an elongated fashion between the two glaciers. We should distinguish between the two in terms of total volume: a drift tail would cover a much greater area and would be thicker than a more linear and elongated medial moraine. Essentially, though, it is a question of emphasis and scale. If the moraine feature continues a large rock-based spur at the downflow end of a particular hill, it is probably a drift tail. In this case the Kingsdale example may not be a medial moraine after all.

Finally, ground moraine is what is left on the valley floor beneath the glacier. In more glaciated areas such as the Lake District or highland Scotland, ground moraine takes many forms from tiny hummocks to parallel ridges (fluted ground moraine), but it is the drumlins that dominate the post-glacial scene here.

Drumlins

A drumlin is a streamlined hillock, parallel to the direction of ice flow. Ribblesdale has more drumlins than can easily be counted (Fig. 4.1 and Plate 4.3). Study of a satellite image of north-western England, or of the *Glacial Map of Britain*, shows a spread of drumlins all the way down the Eden valley in Cumbria, across the Wenning valley and Aire gap between Lancaster and Skipton, and within upper Ribblesdale.[12] They come in all sizes: lengths range from 200m to 500m, widths from 50m to 150m, and heights from 20m to 30m or more. What most have in common, regardless of their size, is morphology, though there are always exceptions to the rule. In plan form they resemble an egg sliced longitudinally in half; in long profile they have a blunt end and a tapering end. The blunt end – the stoss – is invariably steep while the opposite end – the lee – is very gentle. In plan the stoss is rounded, the lee is more pointed (Fig. 4.2). The stoss was the up-ice end, the lee the down-ice end.

Nobody has come up with a convincing explanation for drumlins. Why are they, in general, so regular? Why do they occur in some localities and not in others that seem to share the same characteristics? Why are they so streamlined? Why do they occur in large numbers, in what are called drumlin fields or swarms? There are no answers to these questions here, though several hypotheses are proffered for consideration.

Work on drumlin fields in central Canada and New England has suggested that drumlins resulted from catastrophic flooding by subglacial meltwater and that their form is a direct result of shaping by this water.[13] Unfortunately the proponents of this idea have not explained what might have provided sufficient heat to melt vast volumes of ice beneath a glacier. Perhaps this one should be left on the shelf. It is generally accepted, though, that drumlins do develop under what is referred to as thermally-deforming ice, meaning warm-based and dynamic ice.

A possibly more convincing explanation begins with suggesting how an individual drumlin might have started its life.[14] This hypothesis suggests that ground moraine was trapped behind a rock barrier on the valley floor thereby building up a mound on the up-ice side of the obstruction. As more material was dragged along by the glacier it was carried up and over the mound and barrier to fall off and lie on the down-ice side as the glacier's competence was reduced, the deposits tailing off gradually. This explanation does sound more plausible than the meltwater idea but it still does not account for the plan form of drumlins.

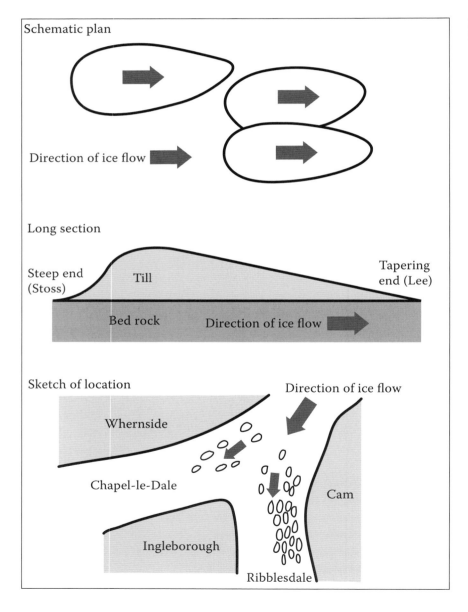

Schematic plan

Direction of ice flow

Long section

Steep end (Stoss)

Till

Tapering end (Lee)

Bed rock   Direction of ice flow

Sketch of location

Direction of ice flow

Whernside

Chapel-le-Dale

Cam

Ingleborough

Ribblesdale

Figure 4.2
Drumlin Morphology.

A third suggestion has been put forward: material was dumped by the glacier in a random hummocky fashion and this was later reworked and streamlined by meltwater. Yet again, though, this leaves much unexplained but the lack of any depth to till deposits between drumlins does suggest some kind of post-depositional scouring.

Until detailed field work is undertaken and published, drumlins will remain enigmatic. This would have to include coring to determine if drumlins have a solid rock core, and to see if sediment size in any way decreases from stoss to lee. Another issue is raised at Ribblehead. Ribblesdale has drumlins galore; the Chapel le Dale valley is devoid of them except around the viaduct area. Does this suggest that the dominant ice flow, and therefore the greatest amount of till, was down Ribblesdale? If so, why? Would it not seem more logical for the ice to have flowed in a straight line through Chapel le Dale rather than executing a major change in direction to flow south? Or, perhaps, was Chapel le Dale subjected to greater meltwater flow which cleared away glacial deposits?

Finally, we need to consider why there are so many drumlins here at all. Glaciers have the bulk and momentum necessary to shift staggering quantities of debris – in other words they have a high level of competence – but if their energy store is reduced they will no longer have the capacity to maintain this action. The direct result is deposition of the debris. As the main ice flow from Cam Fell and Mallerstang came down to Ribblehead the ice reached a point of divergence as some flowed down Ribblesdale and some through Chapel le Dale. It is easy to see how this would reduce the energy store within, and the competence of, the Ribblesdale glacier to the point where it began to progressively dump its load.

Most of the drumlins are aligned parallel to the sides of the Ribble valley, more or less north-south in orientation. Some, however, have a different alignment, especially around Birkwith and on Cam Fell where they trend more north-east to south-west. This supports the notion that some ice flowed over the watershed into Ribblesdale from Langstrothdale to the east.

The Ribblesdale drumlins are complex and some very large megadrumlins have smaller ones superimposed on them. This is evidence for changes in the direction of ice flow as the smaller ones usually have a different orientation from the ones that they were deposited on top of.

The Norber Erratic Field

Whereas drumlins continue to exercise the mind, erratics present no real difficulty. These are individual, perched blocks of rock brought in by a glacier and dumped. Some erratics are of the same type of rock as where they finished up; others are totally different. It depends how far they were dragged. In the Ribblehead area they are mainly of the same type telling us that they were only transported short distances. Even if they are of the same

Stage 1 Pre-glacial surface: no erratics deposited yet

Stage 2 Immediate post-glacial: erratics deposited

Stage 3 Current: limestone layers eroded back to leave some erratics on pedestals

Great Scar Limestone

Silurian Erratics

Figure 4.3   Helen Goldie's Model for the Development of the Norber Erratic Field. Source: Goldie (2005), pp.433–42

type, it is easy to recognise an erratic. They do not fit the general bedding and look out of place. The fact that these erratics had a local origin is firm evidence both that ice within this part of the Dales did not disperse very far and that the ice cover here (at least in the later glacial stages) also had a local origin.

Scales Moor has a smattering of erratics and they appear visibly out of place because they are mainly dark sandstone boulders perched on the light coloured and uniform limestone slabs.

Norber is one of those iconic localities that draws in geologists, glaciologists, karst specialists, university and school students, and tourists galore. Most people who know the Dales know of Norber, even if they have yet to experience it. The erratics here extend across a dozen fields and cover an area of about 1km², and there are thousands of them, large and small. The greatest density is on Norber itself but there is a liberal scatter below both Robin Proctor's Scar and Nappa Scar. They were all brought up here from within Crummack Dale, from Silurian outcrops mainly of the Austwick Formation, so the distance of travel must be perceived in terms of hundreds of metres rather than kilometres, with uplift little more than 100m.

No one has ever mapped the distribution of these erratics. Neither has anyone ever investigated whether individual blocks were carried here in one discrete movement or in stages, being moved and abandoned by successive ice flows. Yet again, there is so much still awaiting full explanation.

In 1924 two geologists, P. F. Kendall and H. E. Wroot, provided their interpretation of how these erratics came to be sitting on limestone pedestals, as if they had been lowered from above.[15] Their explanation became immortalised and has been repeated time and again since then without question. They assumed that since the last ice retreat 450mm of exposed limestone had been removed by sub-aerial processes, leaving the erratics sitting on pedestals that had been protected from weathering. A geological field guide to the Dales, published in 1994, did not quote rates of lowering but left the matter vague by saying the pedestals 'have been used to gauge the rate of limestone dissolution in post glacial times'.[16] Herein lies a problem.

If we assume the last ice receded around 14,000 years ago, it means the annual rate of lowering has averaged 31mm/Ka, according to general estimates. This is now recognised as being too generous and unrealistic through pioneering and detailed work carried out by Helen Goldie.[17] Her conclusion is that the maximum reduction in height of the limestone at Norber is 200mm, less than half than had previously been assumed. Solution rates are significantly less than hitherto thought, as proven at thirteen limestone pavement sites, not just in the Dales, where data have been derived from field measurements. This has relevance not just for interpreting these and similar pedestals but also karst features in general. If Goldie's estimate for lowering is tenable – and there is no reason to cast doubt – many karst features in the Dales and elsewhere in Britain need to be addressed in a much longer time frame.

Does this mean, then, that the Norber erratics were brought here before the final Devensian glacial advance and, if so, why were the smaller blocks not carried further south during that last ice push? Or, is there a quite different explanation for these pedestals? Certainly, at least three important variables were not taken into account by earlier writers – the role of other processes of weathering and erosion, the angle of slope of the main Norber erratic field, and details of the structure of the underlying Carboniferous limestone. Frost action, leading to the disintegration of blocks of rock, can be seen at work here and in similar situations elsewhere. There is, for example, a well-known perched block locally called Samson's Toe, at Winskill north of Settle, which has two smaller pieces of rock lying next to the main block. It is perfectly clear that these blocks were fractured off the main one, and further cracks indicate where the next piece will drop off. Water collects in the cracks and when it freezes it expands in volume, putting pressure on the rock until the point of equilibrium is broken. Biotic processes must also play a part in the process, adding acid to the equation. In wet or very windy conditions the more sensible sheep seek shelter behind and under these blocks and, sheep having minimal standards of personal hygiene, secrete acid in their waste where they lie. This potent acid has a greater dissolutional effect on the limestone than natural atmospheric carbonic acid.

As Goldie pointed out, the general angle of slope of the ground surface is between four and eight degrees from the horizontal, but not evenly so, whereas the actual topmost limestone bed dips at an angle far less than that. Aeons of weathering and erosion have left the ground surface as a series of very low steps and the limestone itself, being well jointed, has been considerably fractured vertically. The combination of fracturing and stepping can give a false impression, especially if a given erratic is approached from downslope. It may seem to be perched on a pedestal but some of them are sitting at the outer end of one of these steps (Fig. 4.3). Precision sighting and measuring of the height of a pedestal top in relation to the upslope ground surface do confirm this in many cases, even if one's eyes tend to suggest otherwise.

Very few of these erratics are on totally free-standing pedestals, though there are exceptions to the rule, notably the oft-photographed three-legged pedestal. It is these, however, that are more difficult to explain but the story is basically the same even here (Plate 4.4). Measure this tripartite pedestal height carefully and project it horizontally back to the ground surface, and it relates in the same way as do the others. It, too, will have been subjected to the same sub-aerial processes and it could be that the particular piece of limestone that became this pedestal was badly fractured even before the erratic was deposited here.

Some Norber erratics have pedestals greater in height than the average. There is an explanation for this phenomenon, too. Individual beds of limestone have different thicknesses and a very exposed section of slope may weather away more rapidly than a sheltered one so it is quite possible for two low limestone steps to have been worn back thereby giving the appearance of a large step or pedestal.

Acceptable rates for lowering of the limestone here are from 3mm to 13mm/Ka, not the previously accepted 31mm or more.

The erratic-solution rate issue is rendered more complicated when one takes into account blocks that have no pedestal at all. They sit directly on the bare rock surface, often limestone on limestone, and can be found in isolated positions dotted around Ingleborough.

Processes of Fluvioglacial Water Flow

Water is a potent agent of erosion, whether in a river or along the coast, and glacial meltwater was responsible for creating many of the landscape features to be seen in any glaciated upland area. Devensian glaciers and ice sheets did not melt overnight. As they slowly degraded water poured out owing to ablation at their front edges and to subglacial streams issuing from the front edge of warm-based glaciers carrying with them untold volumes of sediment of all sizes. Typical fluvial forces were magnified in meltwater flows and individual sediment particles were rapidly rounded off and reduced in size by the process of attrition. When this material was all finally deposited it was in clearly water-sorted layers: heavier rock particles settled out first, the finest silts last, giving a gradation from bottom to top and with increasing distance from the glacier. As with any form of water flow, meltwater eroded the ground surface, transported the eroded material and deposited it elsewhere.

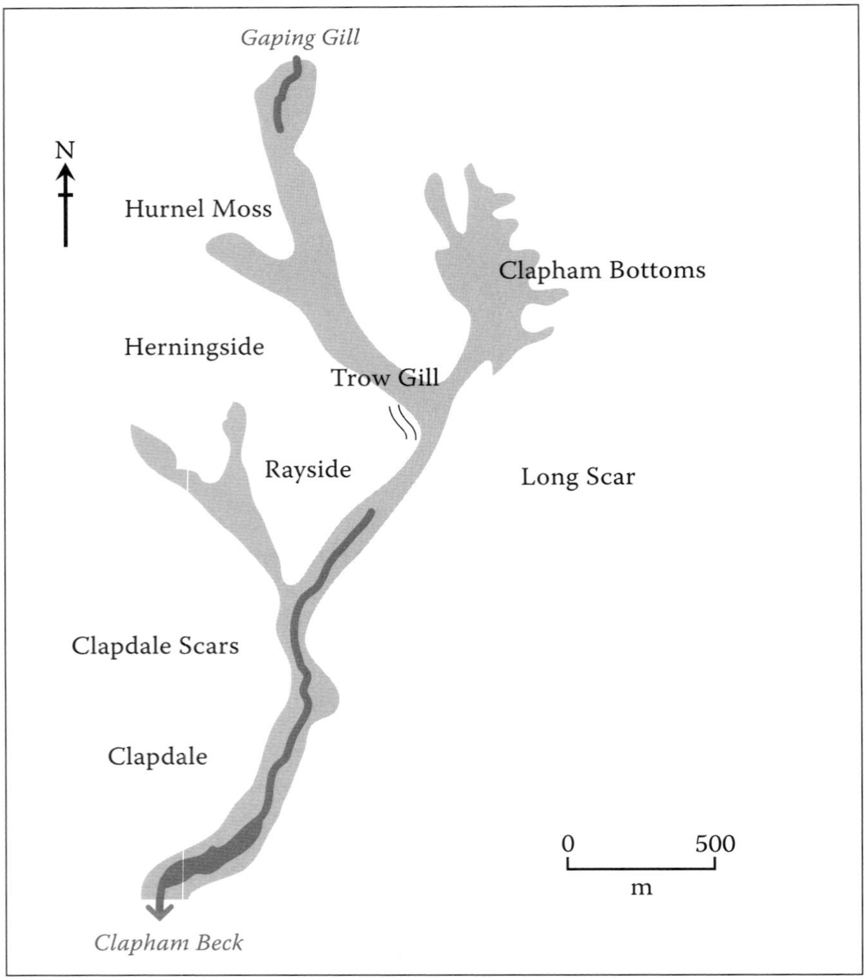

Figure 4.4
Meltwater Channels
around Clapdale.

The most common fluvioglacial erosional form in the Dales is the meltwater channel. Some take the form of gorges on a massive scale, cut through solid bedrock, such as Cowside above Arncliffe in Littondale, Gordale Scar near Malham, Watlowes above Malham Cove and Trow Gill above Clapham. In the Ribblehead area smaller and rather less impressive rock-cut meltwater channels can be seen at Ling Gill (centred on SD802 787) and Brow Gill Beck (centred on SD797 775) above Birkwith, at Thorns Gill (SD777 794) near Gearstones and at Force Gill (centred on SD758 820) below Whernside. Far more common than this type of channel, though, are the now grass covered and more gentle dry valleys no more than a few metres deep and little wider than an average upland river valley. They can be recognised by the absence of surface water, even on impermeable strata, or sign of a stream bed and by their seemingly not being connected to any current drainage system. In many cases these meltwater channels poured off the plateaus and cut nicks through steeper slopes below, as at Great Douk (centred on SD747 770) and Raven Scar (centred on SD728 752), Weathercote (centred on SD736 776) and Twistleton Scars (eg SD725 766), all in the valley of Chapel le Dale. In times of prolonged rainfall some of these normally dry nicks can carry turbulent runoff flows.

In the immediate post-glacial centuries all meltwater channels carried permanent water flow, even where the underlying bedrock is limestone, because the ground surface was frozen and any crevices would have been filled with glacial debris or persistent ice blocks, preventing water from percolating downwards. As the permafrost thawed out many of these surface flows were abandoned as the water found its way underground through Ingleborough's dozens of potholes and many kilometres of cave passage. It has often been said that the area's caves were carved after the ice age, but it is inconceivable for them to have been created in just 10,000 to 14,000 years. Rather, they have been growing organically for tens of thousands of years, increasing in length and depth as one drainage level was abandoned in favour of a new one lower down. Stalactite formations in Gaping Gill on Ingleborough (SD751 727) have been dated to more than 350,000 years ago and in Long Churn Cave near Selside (from SD772 755 to 773 757) to at least 120,000. One only has to look at this latter system to understand the point: the combined Upper and Lower Long Churn passages have current stream flow that follows a bedding plane not far below the surface but at the eastern end it plunges almost 110m down Diccan Pot (SD775 757) in a series of four pitches which in turn lead into Alum Pot (SD775 756), a massive pothole with a separate, single vertical drop of at least 130m. A pothole as deep as this cannot possibly have been formed just since the latest ice retreat.

In lower Kingsdale the glacier completely blocked the valley with an end moraine causing meltwater to back up and form a temporary, and probably quite shallow, lake. Eventually the sheer volume of impounded water broke through the dam to create the present stream course down the mini gorge at Raven Ray above Thornton Force (SD695 753). What is amazing is that the new river was prevented from adopting its pre-glacial course by the volume of material forming the dam: instead it cut a new channel (Raven Ray) through solid limestone bedrock at the eastern end of the moraine.

Trow Gill Meltwater Channel System

The Clapdale meltwater channel system is complex (Fig. 4.4). One branch started on Hurnel Moss and Herningside on the south-east edge of Newby Moss, and extended south-eastwards towards Clapdale farm. It shows up particularly well as a contour feature between Rayside Plantation and the farmstead. It takes the form of a broad but dry valley, aligned north-west to south-east, with a major tributary, aligned north-south, on the west side of the plantation. This system is impressive in its scale and serves to emphasise the unimaginable quantities of meltwater that poured off the mountain. The main channel exploited geological weaknesses along the line of a tectonic fault that runs from Herningside through the farm to Norber and beyond.

Another branch of the Clapdale system had its origins on Long Scar and in The Allotment, in each case starting as shallow dry valleys that become more pronounced as they converge from at least eight directions on the enclosed basin called Clapham Bottoms, centred on SD760 720. Palaeo mini-gorges and waterfalls mark some of these abandoned courses. All the water from the Bottoms exited through a very narrow, now completely dry, channel that joins Clapdale below Trow Gill.

The third, and most frequented, branch of the system includes Trow Gill itself but it is much greater than this. To find its source you need to look high on Clapham Bents in the valley of Fell Beck. In the pre-Devensian period, and during interstadials, runoff flow would have disappeared down the Gaping Gill system. When the cave system was choked, meltwater found its way over the surface carving the valley above and below Gaping Gill ever wider and deeper (Plate 4.5). A tributary flow from the north-west entered the main valley at a wall junction at SD751 720, adding to the combined water's erosive power, carving out the gorge that is Trow Gill (Plate 4.6). In the dry valley above Trow Gill there is a much greater covering of glacial till on the upper, eastern slopes of the valley than on the opposite side where the limestone beds can be seen dipping gently to the north-east. This could be taken to indicate that, on balance, water flow was directed more to the western side thereby removing more glacial sediments from there.

This dry valley from its north-west origin to the bottom of Trow Gill exactly parallels the fault running through Clapdale farm: perhaps the upper Trow Gill channel also exploited a similar line of tectonic weakness.

Clapham Bottoms has just one rather constricted exit channel, whereas Trow Gill and Clapdale are massive in comparison. The fact that Clapdale received waters from both directions helps to explain its size but we need to look for another cause, and it may be that Trow Gill, and thus Clapdale, were over-deepened by a massive and constant flow of water from the rapidly melting snout of the ice stream above Trow Gill. If this was the case, Trow Gill could have been cut very rapidly in geological terms, while the smaller channels may have been long-lasting, subglacial features.

There is the recurring theme in geomorphology of dynamism: nothing stands still; river channels, coasts, slopes, sand dunes are all constantly changing their form in response to changing energy levels or inputs. On a slower and less perceptible scale valleys are also modified and Clapdale contains a prime example of dynamism in meltwater channel development. Immediately south of the Trow Gill-Clapdale bend there is a prominent, but half-hidden, scar north of the track. Beneath this scar is Foxholes Cave. It is clearly an abandoned waterfall, and a big one. Above it, a short distance away, is a second smaller drop. Above that is a dry valley but it cannot be followed very far because it is truncated by the dry valley that becomes Trow Gill. The contours on the 1:25,000 map clearly depict the valley at its lower end but they very soon run out. The picture that builds up is of a meltwater channel from an earlier period being completely overwhelmed by a later – and presumably much greater – flow that began to carve out the Trow Gill line. As with other aspects of glaciation, we have to assume that one melt event could not have created something as grand as Trow Gill, which assumes repeated events, making the Foxholes channel definitely 'early'.

Clapdale does not enjoy a monopoly of meltwater channels on this side of Ingleborough. There is a very pronounced channel, in this instance aligned north-east to south-west, that drained melt from Moughton into Crummack Dale. It created a large open bowl on an extensive limestone terrace above the 350m contour before plunging over the imposing dry waterfall at Studrigg Scar and through the constricted valley to join Austwick Beck above the Wash Dub. The section of Austwick Beck between here and Wharfe also emphasises the scale of past concentrated water flow with its waterfalls, rapids and narrow, rocky gorge. As the present stream and valley approach Wharfe, though, all the drama is quite suddenly lost. Presumably, meltwater dissipated itself laterally across the more open ground south of here.

Study of a topographical map might identify a further meltwater channel in Cote Gill above Newby Cote. It is long, the contours give it a constrained appearance, it also has its source on Herningside, and it is a dry valley, but observation on the ground would very quickly lead to a very different conclusion. Cote Gill is broad and open and plastered on all parts with till – it cannot be considered a meltwater channel.

Periglacial Slope Processes

Periglacial conditions applied in the long run of centuries during and after the Loch Lomond Stadial when climatic and ground conditions would have been akin to those in northern Canada and Siberia today. Once the ice cover had melted away it took a lengthy period of time for vegetation to re-establish itself: pioneer plant species migrated slowly northwards as conditions ameliorated and these gradually gave way to more advanced plant communities higher up the succession. Before this inexorable process began, though, the ground surface in the Dales was essentially bare and therefore unprotected from slope and weathering processes. Some of the landforms within the Ingleborough and Ribblehead area can be ascribed to such periglacial processes.

Recent work into freshly exposed glaciated surfaces has produced surprising results of a biological nature.[18] The work was obviously not undertaken in this country but it does suggest possibilities for research here. The researchers found that, as soon as the ice had melted on given surfaces, microbial activity was apparent whereas it had previously been assumed that there was a

considerable time delay between initial exposure and the development of life forms. These microbes had managed to survive thousands of years under the ice feeding off pre-glacial carbon stores; this is a remarkable revelation with possible research implications in the Dales.

Glacial till deposits extend up to an altitude of about 490m in the area with head deposits above that, though not as a continuous blanket. Head here consists of fragments of sandstone and siltstone in a matrix of sandy or silty clay, rarely exceeding 1m in thickness, and much is now covered with peat. Head is the direct result of a process called solifluction, though the term gelifluction is more correctly applied to periglacial solifluction.

Gelifluction is the downslope creep of solid particles, under gravity, in summer when the top, or active, layer of permafrost thawed out. It can occur on slopes of only one or two degrees. This action was extremely slow and gelifluction rates are normally perceived in terms of millimetres per year. This form of creep should not be confused with what is called soil creep – this is an even slower process that occurs even now on slopes, again through gravitational pull. This process is responsible for the parallel terracettes seen on so many grassy slopes within the Dales.

As periglacial ground surfaces were not protected by vegetation they were subject to sudden slope failure, to the more dramatic forms of mass

Plate 4.5
Meltwater Channel above Trow Gill, with Little Ingleborough in the background.

movement or rock-slope failure. Rock falls, rotational slumps and landslides were frequent occurrences across the Dales during the periglacial period and some have left a major imprint on the landscape. Elsewhere within the Dales there are some truly impressive slope failures: Penhill Crags in Wensleydale, Fremington Edge in Arkengarthdale and Hooker Mill Scar on the western side of Kisdon in Swaledale are but three examples.

Several impressive fossilised, presumably periglacial, slips can be seen from the road through Chapel le Dale. One slip happened high up on Whernside at SD738 805, just south of Skelside, while a much bigger linear slip scar can be seen on the same mountain below Combe Scar around SD731 796. There is a huge one on the steep west facing slopes of Ingleborough between Black Shiver and Falls Foot at SD737 745 (Plate 4.7), and there is a series of slips on the northern slopes of Park Fell at SD764 773. The higher sections of slippage in each case result from rotational slumping and, in general, the material that slumped – or failed – was sandstone overlying weaker shales. These slumps may be no more recent than immediately after the ice retreated because there are no signs of subsequent disturbance of the slumped material by later slope failure, though it is also quite possible that the trigger for failure was earthquake activity.

Plate 4.6
Trow Gill, a meltwater channel.

It is virtually impossible to identify periglacial rock falls as rock failures do still occasionally happen. Ling Gill Gorge, just below Ling Gill Bridge, has a fine example of a massive rock fall which is little more than ten years old. It does not take much for the equilibrium of a slope or rock face to be upset: excessive saturation of slopes or freeze-thaw in rock faces can be the trigger for failure.

Raven Scar, the multi-tiered Twistleton Scars and the countless smaller scars in the area were also modified by periglacial processes, though weathering continues to modify their detailed form. The scar is the vertical free face on a given slope and the action of freeze-thaw and block disintegration causes fragments of rock to be dislodged from it. This happens now on a small-scale basis but the rates were considerably magnified during the periglacial as diurnal temperature differences were much greater. The sheer quantity of scree material below most scars precludes recent formation. The rock fragments collect at the foot of the free face building up what geomorphologists call the zone of accumulation or debris slope, what we might call scree. The material finds its own level of equilibrium, its own angle of repose, generally between 25 and 35 degrees, with larger fragments collecting at the scree base owing to the effects of gravitational pull. In some situations scree skirts the entire length of long scars; in others it tends to collect at the foot of chutes through a rock face in the form of a fan or talus cone.

Weathering processes like these, allied with rock slope failures, repeated many times help to explain how valleys become ever wider as the side slopes slowly and imperceptibly retreat through weathering or fail dramatically in landslides. The width of a valley like Chapel le Dale's is not just due to glacial action.

Weathering and Karst Landforms

The Yorkshire Dales are widely known for their limestone scenery and for the limestone pavements at Malham and around Ingleborough, as well as for their cave systems. The area is often portrayed as a karst landscape. Karst is a term derived from the Kras region of Slovenia which consists of classic limestone scenery. The German translation of Kras is Karst and we use that word in English-language geomorphology. Because our limestone pavements have been affected by glacial action they are often referred to as a glaciokarst landscape.

The traditional interpretation of limestone pavements is that they represent bedding planes scoured clean by the abrasive effects of glaciers. In other words the pavements were produced during the Devensian and superfi-cially modified through the Holocene mainly by dissolution or carbonation, with probable scouring in pre-Devensian glaciations. This long-held view is now being seriously challenged in the light of detailed geomorphological investigations around Ingleborough and in Cumbria. It is no longer accepted without question. Current understanding is that some limestone pavements were created during the Carboniferous.[19] Such landscapes should, therefore, be termed palaeokarst, the word palaeo meaning from the very distant past.

Within the early part of the Carboniferous there were repeated fluctuations in sea level. During each period of low sea level calcretes developed as a veneer on exposed limestone surfaces. These are calcium carbonate minerals weathered out of the rock and brought to the surface to form a hard protective crust. Calcrete surfaces resisted glacial scour, abrasion and plucking thus preserving the Carboniferous surfaces more or less intact.[20]

Four distinct types of limestone pavement are now recognised,[21] three of which have exemplars around Ingleborough's flanks. One type consists of pavement formed in the Carboniferous and this is a true palaeokarst feature. In simple terms exposed limestone surfaces were subjected to the processes of dissolution and carbonation during marine regressions within the Wensleydale Group sequence of repeatedly rising and falling sea levels. When sea level rose again, the surface was buried under fresh deposits: the next regression would expose the newest limestone surface in the sequence which would then be weathered in the same ways. Excellent examples of palaeokarst pavements can be seen on Scar Close north of Ingleborough, at Ribblehead Quarry, and on parts of Long Scar and Clapdale Scar. Such pavements have large blocks, or clints, with a low incidence of joints, or grykes (Plate 4.8). Despite the fact that these clints have high resistance to solution processes, their surfaces often have well developed networks of shallow channels called runnels and small saucer-shaped basins known as kamenitzas (Plate 4.9). Pavements such as these could be seen as relict features as the surface detail was initiated within the Dinantian and modified subsequently. Pavements such as these tend to have very deep grykes: not enough time has elapsed since the Devensian for these to have developed, thereby reinforcing their palaeo nature.

A second type of pavement was scoured by glacial abrasion during the Devensian. These, too, have large clints with few grykes but they differ from palaeokarst clints by having a much smoother surface and undeveloped or even absent runnels and basins.[22] Again, not enough time has passed since the Devensian for such systems to develop. Examples of these can also be seen on the mountain's northern plateaus, especially near Harry Hallam's Fold.

The third category was also eroded by ice but in a different way. Glaciers not only erode by abrasion but also by plucking, and this latter process has left a very different type of pavement, extensive stretches of which can be seen on Scales Moor between Chapel le Dale and Kingsdale. Here clints are small, grykes occur very frequently and clint surfaces are markedly shattered and broken up with a lot of loose clitter (shattered fragments of rock).

Very similar to this are the pavements on sections of Thwaite Scars and

Long Scar which are much more degraded and in large part vegetated over; and in the upper reaches of Crummack Dale and across large tracts of Moughton the pavement is so severely degraded and shattered that it is generally impossible to delineate let alone measure individual clints. Upper Crummack is a huge natural amphitheatre with hectares of continuous pavement (Plate 4.10) with very shallow grykes, totally shattered clints and heaps of clitter everywhere. In general, the most shattered sections occur in sheltered side valleys and around the perimeter of depression hollows. The question has to be raised if these were ever scoured by ice, and if it were physically possible for ice to have flowed across such a broken landscape. The answer is probably in the negative: these limestone surfaces were broken down by weathering processes; those in more open situations were more prone to scour.

There is also a direct correlation between the type of limestone pavement and the geological structure of the limestone rock.[23] The more solid and massive pavements are associated with more massive beds of limestone (such

Plate 4.7
Post-glacial Landslip at Falls Foot.

Plate 4.8
Palaeokarst Clints,
Sleights Pasture Rocks,
showing well-rounded
clints and deep grykes
(200mm scale).

as those lining Trow Gill) with a concentration of sparry calcite in excess of 80 per cent. These limestones are coarse-grained and crystalline and have few joints, characteristics which slow down weathering processes and thus limit the degree to which they decompose. Water cannot readily percolate through such limestone, with porosity being only 2–3 per cent, so freeze-thaw and frost shattering are much reduced. Shattered pavements – and some would argue that because of this attribute such areas should not be even designated as pavement – tend to consist of biomicrite limestone which has opposite characteristics, such as a porosity of 8 per cent, that make surface layers liable to rapid breakdown, particularly by ice plucking and frost shattering. Biomicrite means the limestone contains a relatively high proportion of mud. This concept is now recognised as being fundamental in helping to explain pavement formation.

Another variable affecting how pavements develop is tectonic faulting.[24] Faults by definition are lines of structural weakness across the landscape and rock stability is compromised. These are more prone to decomposition and tend to generate shattered pavements like those along the fault line on Thwaite Scars.

Many of the larger and smoother palaeokarst clints, and some large limestone erratics, are miniature landscapes in themselves. Grooves or shallow channels on the surface result from natural carbonic acid (water plus carbon dioxide) in rainwater settling and slowly reacting chemically

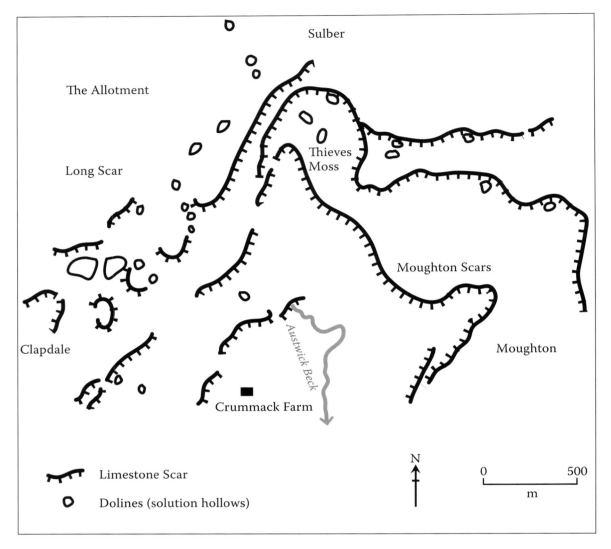

Sulber

The Allotment

Long Scar

Thieves
Moss

Moughton Scars

Clapdale

Austwick Beck

Moughton

Crummack Farm

N

0   500
m

Limestone Scar

Dolines (solution hollows)

with the calcium carbonate of the rock by the process of dissolution or, more precisely, carbonation. In brief, this reaction causes the calcium carbonate to be dissolved and to run off in solute form. Carbonation rates are magnified if the rock has a covering of acidic soil or vegetation owing to the addition of humic acid to the equation. Sometimes there are miniature networks of runnels feeding into the grykes. If an exposed limestone block or scar faces into the prevailing winds, that exposed surface will be battered by raindrops being hurled against it and, once again, the same chemical reaction will occur, this time leaving parallel horizontal grooves, or fluting, on the face.

Some stream beds on limestone bedrock are equally pockmarked with potholes which are also the result of dissolution, though cavitation (scouring by small swirling stones trapped in the hollow) has played a part in creating

Figure 4.5
Distribution of
Solutional Hollows
North of Crummack
Dale.
Source: Goldie and
Marker (2001), pp. 53–8

their rounded and smoothed form. Particularly fine examples can be seen at Ling Gill and Thorns Gill bridges. Such potholes in the Dales and similar areas are also being reassessed: they, too, are felt to be part of a now exposed relict palaeokarst land surface. There is no way these very large holes could have been produced in the 14,000 or so years since the retreat of the Devensian ice as dissolution does not work so rapidly, except in moist tropical climates. They have been forming for probably tens of thousands of years. In support of the palaeokarst hypothesis is the absence of evidence on the pothole faces of current wear by cavitation or of pockmarking by recent dissolution. Upstream of Ling Gill bridge there are several potholes that are partly hidden under the present river banks: if these potholes were still active features, it would be impossible to have part under the river bank.

Dolines

There are a few large solutional depressions, or dolines, on the northern side of the massif but recent research has suggested an estimated number of over 450 dolines in the block bounded by Kingsdale in the west and Wharfedale in the east and the South Craven Fault and Wharfedale to north and south (Fig. 4.5). Crummack Dale and Clapham Bottoms have some particularly fine examples. One prominent doline at the head of the former valley, centred on SD776 730, is not especially deep but is broadly circular with a diameter of about 50m. There is a much more impressive example among the limestone pavement of Long Scar, at SD769 727, adjacent to Hinkinshaw Peat Road. Its depth is 8m to 10m and diameter about 60m but it is a textbook example of a doline with its open funnel shape and totally enclosed form. Even better is the small solution crater more or less in the centre because this shows that dissolution is an ongoing process and that dolines are not necessarily fossil palaeo features.

The Oscar for best doline, however, has to be awarded elsewhere. This accolade rightly belongs to a run of three huge depressions in Clapham Bottoms, centred on SD756 719. Laid out in a perfectly straight east-west formation, obviously along a line of weakness in the underlying rock, these are bigger than the Dales average. The western one can only be described as dramatic in scale and form and, unlike its two neighbours, this bottoms out on bedrock whereas they have a partial infill of sediments supporting bog. In scale this one is on a par with Braithwaite Wife Hole on the north side of the mountain.

It is important to distinguish between dolines and their diminutive cousin the shakehole. Both are formed by dissolution of the underlying limestone, a process which is timeless though it is not unknown for a shakehole to develop with astonishing rapidity. Great excitement and weeks of local newspaper correspondence were generated when one appeared overnight above Foxup at the head of Littondale in December 1993. Apart from scale, they differ

Plate 4.9
Well-developed
Kamenitza on Clapdale
Scars (200mm scale).

in age. Shakeholes are contained within post-Devensian glacial till deposits which means they have only been developing since the last ice retreat. This is not to rule out dissolution of the bedrock during warmer periods within the Devensian, with crevices being temporarily choked by stagnant ice or sediment, but the shakeholes themselves are post-glacial.

Dolines, on the other hand, are emphatically pre-glacial features. They are far too large to have developed in just 14,000 years, and they are not contained within till deposits.

Doline diameter varies, in our area from 20m to over 80m, and depth is equally variable. The size of the hole is an indication of how much limestone has been dissolved away; the bedrock is dissolved and surface deposits sink down into the void that has been created and, if there is a cave passage down there, they will be carried away by subterranean water flow. Some dolines occur within limestone pavement, others are set into bays at the foot of limestone scars, but the Clapham Bottoms trio fits into neither category. They are just there in the huge bowl that is the Bottoms, which may itself be partly a solutional landform.

Dolines acted as sediment traps in the immediate post-glacial phase and soil coring has shown that most have a layer of post-Loch Lomond peat that has developed on a thick layer of yellow material, almost certainly loess, which in turn overlies either drift deposits or bedrock.[25] Pollen samples were obtained from superficial peat deposits in one doline on Thieves Moss in Crummack Dale, carbon dated to 9000BP. Not only did this exercise produce useful dating evidence, it also gave a clear picture of the dominant vegetation growing there before climatic deterioration led to the development of peat. Half of the pollen sample was from trees, mainly resistant species like hazel and birch, 43 per cent from grasses, 2 per cent heather, and the remainder rushes, ferns and algae.

Caves, Potholes and Resurgences

There are hundreds of potholes and caves across Ingleborough, and some of the most impressive are strung out in a line between the 400m and 450m contours, at the junction of impermeable Yoredale strata and permeable Great Scar Limestone (Fig. 4.6). A series of short and mostly anonymous streams rise at various levels on the impermeable beds only to disappear

Plate 4.10
Limestone Pavements
above Crummack Dale.

down a run of deep shafts when they reach the limestone (Fig. 4.7). Grey Wife Sike is unique: it starts its surface life in a named resurgence called Knoutberry Hole yet just sinks down an insignificant hole lower downhill.

The cave systems on the south side of the mountain need to be considered separately from those on the south-east side. Those on Newby Moss are well developed in the vertical plane but have very little or no lateral development along bedding planes at depth. Among the more impressive are Boggarts Roaring Holes (SD728 738) with its multiple shafts which drop 50m, Long Kin West (SD731 724) which is the deepest of all at 168m, and Pillar Holes (SD733 724) which sinks 87m. The only logical explanation for the lack of cave passage development is the proximity of the step faulting along the North and South Craven Faults where strata were downthrown to the south of each fault, thereby cutting off any possible lateral development and encouraging downcutting.

The Allotment contains more than twenty shafts fed by short-lived, south-east flowing streams that rise high on Simon Fell and sink in a series of even more impressive potholes than those already mentioned.[26] At least two, Juniper Gulf and Rift Pot, have developed horizontal passages along fault lines. Little Juniper (SD766 733) looks fearsome but is only 8m deep and is classified Grade I, the lowest grade for caves and potholes. The Gulf (SD766 733), in contrast, is Grade IV. The surface stream drops 21m into a long and narrow rift passage, visible from above for about 50m before it plunges into the depths in a succession of vertical pitches and cave passages totalling 130m in depth.

Long Kin East starts off at SD762 731 as a relatively easy (Grade I) if wet walk along a 256m vadose canyon not far from the surface, passes beneath a subsidiary shaft with a protective dry stone wall that encircles its top, then continues as an underground passage before it plunges 113m in a series of pitches. This, too, is a Grade IV undertaking. The next major one to the south-west is Rift Pot (SD761 729), similarly graded, which connects with the Long Kin stream. It starts off as a long narrow fissure, this time dry, but its drop is more sudden than Long Kin's. Total depth is about the same as in Long Kin but it is not far short of 1km in total length.

The pothole with the most spectacular surface hole – a doline in fact – is the Grade III Marble Pot (SD759 730). Like its Grade V close neighbour Marble Sink (SD759 723), it is over 100m deep.

Between Newby Moss and The Allotment is Hurnel Moss where a further series of short streams sink within large, super-developed shakeholes. One in particular, at SD745 724, is almost choked with glacial debris consisting of sandstone boulders and clay through which the stream has forced its way into the depths. In this stretch is one of the largest and most well-known caves in the country, Gaping Gill, with its nearly 12km of passages that make up a system with subsidiary shafts, phreatic tubes, vadose canyons and smaller chambers (see Figure 4.7; Fig. 4.8).

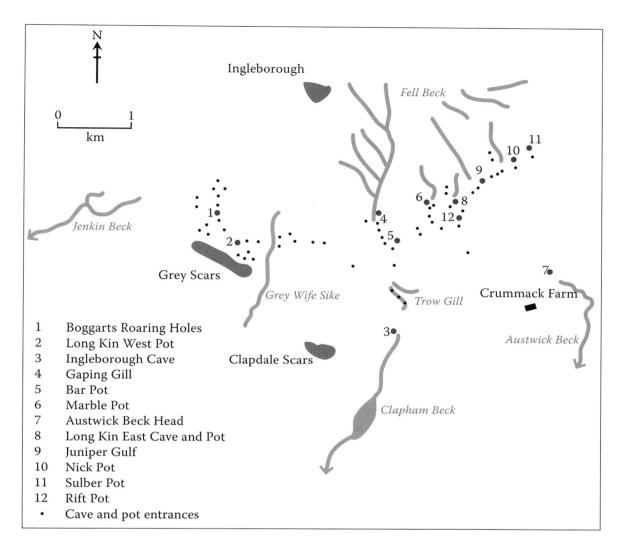

N

0 1
km

Ingleborough

Fell Beck

11
10
9
6   8
12
4
5
1
2

Jenkin Beck

Grey Scars

Grey Wife Sike

Clapdale Scars

Trow Gill

7

Crummack Farm

Austwick Beck

3

Clapham Beck

1   Boggarts Roaring Holes
2   Long Kin West Pot
3   Ingleborough Cave
4   Gaping Gill
5   Bar Pot
6   Marble Pot
7   Austwick Beck Head
8   Long Kin East Cave and Pot
9   Juniper Gulf
10   Nick Pot
11   Sulber Pot
12   Rift Pot
•   Cave and pot entrances

Figure 4.6
Distribution of Caves
and Potholes.
Source: Brook (1991);
O.S. Landranger, Sheet
98

It is believed that many of the potholes around Ingleborough's southern and eastern flanks must have developed under warm-based ice cover during repeated glacial periods as well as during warmer interglacials when unfathomable volumes of meltwater were pouring off the mountain, and sediments were washed into cave systems.[27] They may also have continued to grow under a cover of moraine deposits, even if the tops of the shafts were buried, as acidic water would have infiltrated through the till, dissolving limestone along the major joints. Abandoned high-level phreatic tubes are found in many cave systems, some of which contain deposits of pre-Devensian till up to 3m deep. The lack of direct surface flow into many of these shafts suggests that they are relict, or fossil, features developed long ago by now gone surface flow. Dates that have been obtained for cave deposits back up this pre-Devensian hypothesis.

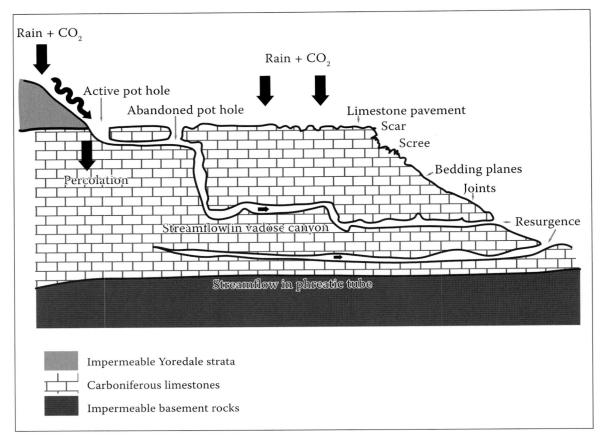

Figure 4.7
A Karst Hydrological
System.

Two much lower cave systems each has a very large resurgence starting out what is to become a river. Austwick Beck Head in Crummack Dale (SD776 718) is only 30m long as far as cave exploration is concerned, as the roof soon becomes too low to squeeze under, but most of the water flow from caves on The Allotment emerges here to form Austwick Beck. Far longer and of huge interest to cave explorers and tourists alike is Ingleborough Cave, the show cave near the head of Clapdale. First discovered as long ago as 1837, and opened to the public in the 1840s, even before the coming of the railway to Clapham, this 4.3km-long system has maintained its pull to the present day, though the show cave is only open for about 500m.[28]

The Alum Pot-Long Churn system, west of Selside, has all elements: vertical pot holes, Alum Pot and Diccan Pot; a flooded sump at the very bottom; Cross Passage, an abandoned and now dry passage linking Diccan Pot to Lower Long Churn Cave; passages carrying permanent but fluctuating streamflow, Main Passage in Upper and Lower Long Churn Caves.

The cross-profile of a cave passage differs depending on whether it is above or below the water table (see Figure 4.8). Those below the water table are permanently water-filled so the force of water is exerted equally on all

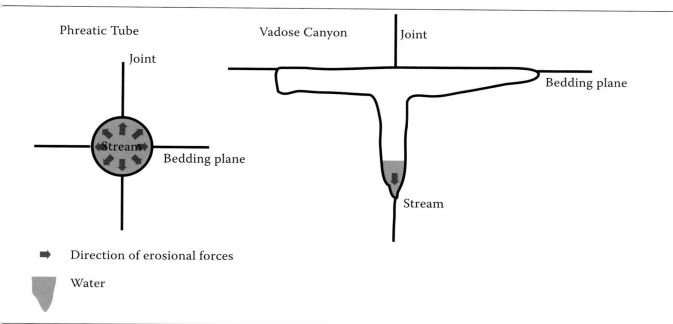

Phreatic Tube

Joint

Stream

Bedding plane

Vadose Canyon

Joint

Bedding plane

Stream

➡ Direction of erosional forces

▼ Water

Figure 4.8
A Model Cave Profile.

surfaces of the passage giving these phreatic tubes a cylindrical cross-profile. Those above have erosional forces concentrated at the base, with downcutting focussed on vertical joints, so they have more of a T-shaped cross-profile. It is within these vadose canyons that speleothem deposits develop as solute calcium carbonate is re-deposited as calcite on contact with air: the chemical reaction is effectively reversed. Common speleothem forms include the familiar stalactites and stalagmites (Fig. 4.9). When these merge they form a pillar. More delicate forms can be found, for example within White Scar show cave, such as helictites which adopt weird shapes that reflect air flow, and gour that grows outwards around the lip of tiny water-filled rock pools. Sheets of smooth flowstone sometimes cover sections of cave passage walls subjected to the constant dribbling of water from the cave roof.

Where a subterranean stream eventually emerges from the depths, where permeable limestone meets lower impermeable strata, there will be a cave entrance. Technically these are called resurgences or risings.

Tufa and Travertine

We must not leave the physical landscape without reference to deposits called tufa. This is a material, reddish- or dirty-yellow in colour, hard when wet but friable when dried out. It is often found on waterfalls, at springs and along stream banks. It is chemically the same material as in cave speleothems. In some localities it is actively growing, in others it is inactive and fossilised and owes its existence to life forms and to a chemical reaction.

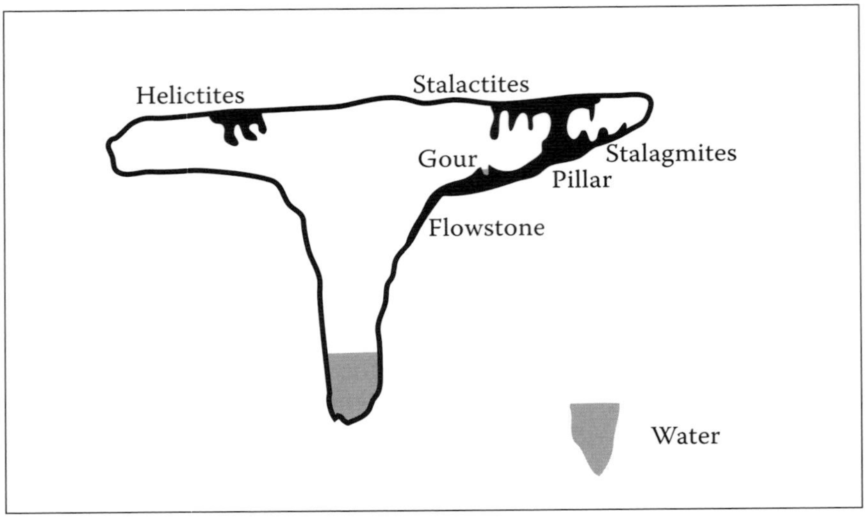

Figure 4.9
Speleothems.

Limestone consists of calcium carbonate and this is soluble in acid water, such as rain which contains weak carbonic acid. The dissolved calcium carbonate is carried along in cave streams in solute form but if this stream enters a large chamber or vadose canyon a reverse chemical reaction takes place as there has been a new input of oxygen. The dissolved material is precipitated out and re-deposited as speleothems. This same reaction can also happen when water percolating through joints in the rock drips into a cave passage, again forming speleothems. This precipitation also happens when an underground stream emerges on the surface at a cave entrance or spring. Here a tufa screen will form where the re-deposited calcium has spread over existing surfaces.

Tufa growth will be accelerated if certain conditions are met. Well-oxygenated, turbulent newly-emerged water encourages development especially as there is likely to be a covering of bryophytes (mosses and liverworts) and/or algae, and there is a direct chemical linkage between these life forms and the rate of chemical reaction. The surface of active tufa tends to be coated in dead diatoms which are minute algal forms naturally rich in silica that turns to quartz, thus explaining why tufa often has significant quartz content.

Travertine is a substance with contrasting definitions. Look in one geological dictionary and it will have you believe that travertine is re-deposited calcium carbonate associated only with hot springs; while another will suggest that it is a more solidified form of tufa. For example, the first entry to Ingleborough Cave in 1837 was achieved by literally blasting a way through a travertine dam, the remnants of which are still there.[29]

How rapidly does tufa grow? Some dating tests in the Dales have reported an annual growth of only 0.15mm but another test involving the creation, in 1979, of a deliberate stream diversion over a very small vertical drop where tufa was likely to be active, saw considerable growth by 2007.[30] Some fossilised tufas have been carbon dated to between 2000 and 4000 years BP. Streamside tufa deposits can readily be seen in feeder stream beds along the right bank of Clapham Beck downstream from the cave entrance to within the woods.[31]

*   *   *

Processes of erosion and deposition have made the landscape what it is now, or what it was at whatever time you care to think of the Dales, and people through time have selectively and cleverly responded to the opportunities offered by this environment, able to differentiate between the opportune and inopportune. It is to these human responses that we will now turn in Chapters 5 and 6.

PART 2

THE CULTURAL AND HISTORIC LANDSCAPE

Kingsdale Beck

Bruntscar

Apron Full Of Stones

SCALES MOOR

Thaw Head Cave

Broadwood

River Twiss

Southerscales

Raven Scar Cave

Ingleborough 'Hillfort'

Ellerbeck Pasture

Gauber

Sleights Cairn

Colt Park

Lodge Hall

Thorns

Nether Lodge

Birkwith

Gayle Beck

Cam Beck

River Ribble

N

0   1
km

Figure 5.1
Archaeological Sites
mentioned in the text.

· F I V E ·
Archaeology: Ingleborough North

Introduction

Certain parts of the country are recognised as having highly visible archaeology where signs of past activity appear as clear earthworks or stone footprints rather than as vague crop marks. This is certainly true for the Dales. Archaeology here can be identified on the ground: you do not need to be in a hot air balloon to see it nor an expert in interpreting aerial photographs, but sorting out the detail of the earthwork or stone remains can be challenging.

There are those who describe the Dales landscape as a historical palimpsest but this is not strictly correct because in a palimpsest one layer of archaeology (of past activity or occupation) replaces the previous one by almost wiping it out. This is not the case here so it may be more accurate to think in terms of a kaleidoscope where different elements from different time periods are superimposed, sometimes in a confusion of features. If we think like this, we will have gone part way to understanding the multi-period or multi-layered landscape that typifies the Dales and Ingleborough (Fig. 5.1).

To understand and interpret historic landscapes fully requires a plethora of skills. Some would argue that landscape historians have the most influential role as they compile and map highly detailed surveys of 'areas' rather than individual 'sites'. Their argument would be that you cannot begin to interpret a given archaeological feature without first putting it into a wider landscape context, with additional recourse to historic maps and documentary evidence; and that not to adopt this approach leads to errors of interpretation. On the other hand, the field archaeologist might contend that it is not possible to date or interpret a particular set of earthworks without 'taking the lid off' to see what is under the turf. How else can one obtain firm dating evidence, they might ask? Somewhere in between lies the landscape archaeologist who takes the wider view by looking at a set of individual sites within a broad area and then working out how they all fit together both in time and space. In reality there has to be room for all three approaches.

Overview

Many archaeology and history books and television programmes divide our past into distinct periods such as the Bronze Age and the 'Dark' Ages. Prehistory has been subdivided into three since the early nineteenth century: the Stone, Bronze and Iron Ages were recognised (in Denmark initially) based on what implements dominated a particular phase.[1] In 1865 this so-called Three Age System was modified by further dividing up the Stone Age into the Palaeolithic (Old Stone Age) and Neolithic (New Stone Age),[2] so nowadays we no longer talk of the Stone Age as such because it is such a vague concept spanning tens of thousands of years of human development. More recently still the Mesolithic (Middle Stone Age) was slotted in between the Old and New, recognising a cultural transition between the two. It is convenient to think in such terms but it should always be borne in mind that none of our distant ancestors ever saw themselves as being Neolithic or Romano-British or medieval. After all, how will people in the twenty-third century label us? There are strong arguments for getting away from an obsession with 'Ages' but it is something that most historically-minded people can relate to, so the system will be used in these chapters.

It should also be kept in mind that dates given to separate one period from another are not definite, and that change in one area may have happened much sooner than in another area, depending on accessibility and opportunity. It is often assumed that changes occurred in the south earlier than in the north, but coastal movements along the Atlantic periphery meant that the western fringe was often exposed to new external ideas and influences before they had chance to filter across the Pennine backbone to the east.[3] Change, such as from Bronze to Iron Age, did not occur overnight but was a very gradual and halting process that will have taken many generations. For example, flints are associated in most people's minds with the 'Stone' Age but flint tools were still in use in the Iron Age a full millennium later.

The time-line (Table 5.1) presents one interpretation of the subdivisions from the end of the most recent Ice Age to the dissolution of the monasteries in the reign of Henry VIII. It is but a suggestion and should be seen as such. Transition dates are not universally agreed and vary from country to country and even from region to region, but the table includes generally accepted dates.

Table 5.1 Archaeological Time-line

DATE	CLIMATE	EVENT
1536–40	generally wet and cool	Dissolution of the monasteries
1318–60	very wet and cool	Scottish raids, famine, plague
1066	improving after decline	Norman invasion
900	warm and dry	Scandinavian/Viking period begins
600–700	warming up	Anglo-Saxon migrations into the Dales
410	deteriorating: wetter	Roman withdrawal
70	cool and dry	Roman advance into the North; Romano-British period begins
AD		
BC		
800	cooling down	Iron Age begins
2500	generally warm and dry	Bronze Age begins
3500/4000	warming up	Neolithic begins
8000	warm summers, cold winters	English Channel forms
9500	Irish Sea opens up	
8000	very cold and dry	Mesolithic begins
	extremely cold, dry,	Upper Palaeolithic
	ice in retreat	

Patterns of Occupation

From Ribblehead southwards there are huge contrasts between one side of the valley and the other. On the western side the archaeological record is thick on the ground, and obvious, all the way from Ribblehead through Selside to Sulber; on the eastern side it is either absent or hidden from view, with a few exceptions. Between Ribblehead and Cam Fell, though, the differences are between north and south of the road. The fundamental reason for these contrasts lies in surface geology. Heavily settled areas are found where limestone outcrops: here the ground is well drained, the soils are generally alkaline and the pasture they support is considered to be 'sweet'. Past people avoided, wherever possible, those parts where bedrock is covered with deep glacial till. It is acidic and poorly drained, the rank grasses and

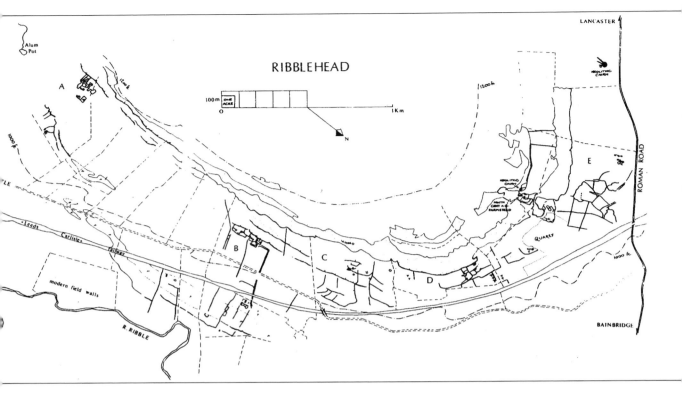

rushes it supports are not attractive to sheep or cattle, and soils are not conducive to the growing of subsistence crops. People from the very earliest settlement had the instinctive ability to distinguish between areas that could support their largely self-contained lifestyle and those where nature would inevitably conspire to undo their best efforts. Later attempts to tame those tracts were doomed to failure.

Modern 1:25,000 Ordnance Survey maps mark a string of early settlements from Ribblehead Quarry to the south of Selside (Fig. 5.2). They are all between the 300 and 350 metre contours and are associated with outcropping limestone pavements. To the east of the B6479 road there is just one on the map, by Lodge Hall, though there are a few other small sites on that side of the road on limestone as far south as Selside.

The valley of Chapel le Dale does not show the same contrast. Limestone outcrops much more extensively and areas of glacial till are largely limited to the lower slopes of Ingleborough and Park Fell. Opportunities for settlement were greater, and evidence for past activity is to be seen on both sides of the valley from the railway viaduct all the way to Ingleton.

Figure 5.2
Archaeological Sites at Ribblehead.
Source: King, A., 'Romano-British farms and farmers in Craven' in T.G. Manby and P. Turnbull, *Archaeology in the Pennines*, BAR British Series 158, p. 187 (1986)

Dating Sites

The matter of trying to date settlement sites is always contentious. It is perfectly understandable for the visitor to want to know how old this hut circle is, or for how long that site was occupied, or indeed which people lived there. Some guide books and television programmes aimed at the general audience tend to be too prescriptive by confidently ascribing this site to the Iron Age and that one to the Romano-British period, or whatever. A classic example of this is the excavated, and much visited, site at Gauber by Ribblehead Quarry which has often been described as a Viking site (Fig. 5.4), or Ingleborough's 'hillfort' as Iron Age.[4] Gauber might be Viking but the evidence to claim that with confidence was not found during the excavation (see later). It was definitely a 'Viking-type' site but no one can say it was built or occupied by Vikings. A site can only be dated if excavation reveals an assemblage of pottery or tools in sequence and in context (*ie* not just lying in the topsoil) that can be compared with dated finds from elsewhere, or if there are elements that can be dated scientifically; or, again, if documentary evidence of that site has survived, which in the Dales generally means from the medieval monastic period onwards though elsewhere, of course, there was documentation in the Roman period, often surviving as clay or stone tablets.

It follows, therefore, that this and the next chapter contain few firm dates. We are treading here strictly in the realm of hypothesis and conjecture. This lack of firmness must also apply to some of the narrative as there are so many aspects of prehistory that involve assumption and theory and many of the long-held ideas are being revisited and reassessed in the light of field- and laboratory-based archaeological research programmes currently underway in the Ingleborough area and elsewhere in North Craven.

Hunter-gatherers of the Mesolithic

The traditional view in this country is that the Mesolithic period was unexceptional in terms of culture and development, and it was seen as lacking the perceived glamour of the Palaeolithic and the order and progress of the Neolithic. Little work was done on it in the North so little was known. Dated sites within the Pennines were virtually non-existent until the last thirty years or so (with a few exceptions, such as the work of the pioneer Dales geologist and archaeologist Arthur Raistrick),[5] and unsafe conclusions have been drawn in the past concerning the extent of Mesolithic activity in the Dales. Evidence of Mesolithic activity in the western Pennines was limited until recently.[6] These attitudes, however, are beginning to change but our knowledge of that period remains extremely patchy.

The most recent glacial advance had finally given way to retreat, completed by 10,000 BC, and as climatic conditions slowly improved and vegetation communities became more complex after the ice had gone, small bands of nomadic hunter-gatherers began to exploit the resources of the Ingleborough-Whernside area on a seasonal basis. Precise dates cannot be applied to such distant times, and it sometimes seems there are as many suggestions as there are prehistorians, but the Mesolithic period is taken here to cover the years 8000 to 4000 BC. It is obvious that over so many millennia climate changed drastically bringing about a total transformation of natural vegetation and soil characteristics. Within the Mesolithic period people increasingly manipulated the landscape in which they lived rather than merely reacting to it as in the Upper Palaeolithic which preceded it.[7] It must equally be accepted that life at the end of the Mesolithic bore no relation to that at the start so when we talk of 'The Mesolithic' we are generalising in a major way. The earliest Mesolithic, for instance, is associated with tools forged from antler and to a lesser extent bone, whereas fine flint or chert microliths are typical of the later Mesolithic.[8]

The English Channel was formed within this period, changing for ever the relationships between peoples and cultures on either side, and the Irish Sea-Morecambe Bay coastline was very different then from now, but the valleys of the Ribble and Greta would have been much as they are today in terms of landscape generality though not of landform detail as thousands of years of weathering and erosion, of sediment removal and deposition, have drastically modified surface forms.

Recent seasons of excavation near Malham Tarn produced dated finds from an important Mesolithic site where major flint-knapping activities had been but part of a wider occupance,[9] while charcoal from a pit (SD712 799) excavated by the local archaeology group in Kingsdale in 2006 provided a radiocarbon date range from 6850 to 6640 BC (at 80.10 per cent probability).[10] On this basis the Malham and Kingsdale sites were broadly contemporary being firmly in the middle of the Mesolithic. Excavation in advance of the construction of a new major gas pipeline across the southern fringe of the Dales in 2006 and 2007 exposed a Mesolithic site near Wham south-west of Settle.[11] It was a flint scatter, a spot where people had knapped flint to make tools.

No one would have lived permanently in the Ingleborough area during the Mesolithic, unless at the Mesolithic-Neolithic transition when conditions were more conducive to year-round occupation. If we go along with currently accepted thinking, family or clan bands came up from their winter bases on the coast loosely following the major river valleys, slowly wending their way inland over a period of weeks to reach their favourite summer camping spots and hunting grounds.[12] Their camps were just that. They did not construct huts on these forays. Geophysical investigation at the Kingsdale site highlighted an arc of small circular anomalies around the pit and excavation of a sample of these may confirm them as the postholes of a shelter or tented structure rather than a formal hut.[13]

Mesolithic people were omnivorous, seeking a wide variety of foods in different ways. They hunted small and medium-sized game and birds; they fished in rivers and lakes (of which there would have been more then); they gathered fruits, nuts and fungi as available, and foraged for whatever nature provided. If the season was fruitful, they may well have remained in one tight area for the duration, with occasional hunting forays further afield. It is known that they used fire as a hunting tool, possibly to drive game towards a trap of some sort, natural or created, or to attract grazing animals to forest clearings where the hunting would have been easier.[14] Pollen analysis on the slopes of Ingleborough has confirmed woodland clearance, which was more likely to have been deliberate than accidental, during the late Mesolithic, knocking on the head the long-held view that it was the Neolithic farmers who first began to clear the wildwood.[15]

Of one matter, we can probably be sure: there must be much more evidence of Mesolithic activity under the surface in the Ingleborough area. If Kingsdale was deemed suitable, then so too must have been the area around Chapel le Dale and Ribblesdale, and there is archaeological evidence of Mesolithic activity buried under layers of peat that formed in later times, or lost as erosion removed soil layers from limestone surfaces over time. Flint scatters have been found in erosion scars within the Dales as well as early prehistoric hearths sealed by iron pans that developed later.

Neolithic and Bronze Age Farmers

It is not known for sure when farming first appeared in Britain but it was sometime around 4000 BC and it arrived by sea. Neither is it known for sure whether it was introduced by fresh incomers to these islands or by existing Mesolithic peoples who adopted new cultural and economic ideas, and new food sources, brought in from the continent. It is assumed that there was a period of transition between a culture based on hunter-gathering and one almost totally farm-based. Some say this transition was as much as 1000 years, though other estimates put it well below that.[16] It must be the case, however, that the new ideas made very slow progress through the country and that the early farmers initially stuck to the more fertile lowlands as long distance movement tended to focus on coastal waters rather than overland. Whether they reached the Ingleborough area later than further south in the Dales or not is yet another moot point, but ongoing work is pushing Neolithic provenance in the Dales further back in time than had hitherto been accepted.[17]

What can be said with confidence is that Neolithic people (4000 or 3500 to 2500 BC) did inhabit our area. Stone burial cairns, as well as circles and wall footings, can be seen on the northern flanks of Ingleborough around Harry Hallam's Moss and the cairns have been ascribed a probable Neolithic provenance. Douk Cave Pasture also contains a concentration of burial cairns. Raven Scar Cave (SD729 755)[18] and Thaw Head Cave (SD712 764) near Chapel le Dale have been excavated and artefactual finds (pottery fragments, worked bone and flints) recently revisited and interpreted as Neolithic and later. Both caves were used for burials, Thaw Head containing the remains of a late teenage female, for example. It is clear from other caves south-east of the mountain that these people were still hunting (but should this be surprising?) with red deer, wild horse, ox, wild boar, and wolf in their sights. Wolves, though, would not have been targeted as potential sources of protein but as competitors to be removed from the equation.

Scales Moor, bounding Chapel le Dale on its northern edge, has produced further archaeological evidence suggesting Neolithic activity as has Thaw Head Cave,[19] while Sleights Pasture contains a very prominent stone cairn, possibly a chambered cairn, of the same period.

Elsewhere in the country archaeologists have found remains of Neolithic houses. They were rectangular and made with wooden posts and thatch, and only appear in the archaeological record as postholes. None has been found in the Ingleborough area but, to use a hackneyed adage, absence of evidence is not evidence of absence. Did they build huts/houses here or rely on rock shelters and caves instead? We know from pollen analysis that they were felling trees, or killing them by ring barking, on a large scale and using fire as a clearance tool. There is also ample burial evidence, so they *were* in this landscape though as yet there is no pollen evidence of domesticated cereals. It has been found in the Craven lowlands, however.[20]

In an area such as Ribblehead it may well be that the people were herders rather than cultivators, trading animals and animal products for grain, hand axes and flint, and they may have practised transhumance, seasonally shifting from lower to higher pastures. It was during the Neolithic that the great henges were added to the landscape, though not locally, telling us a complex social – and possibly political – system was in place. It could be that a number of upland enclosures, built on a massive scale across the Dales, date from this period rather than from the Bronze Age as previously thought.

Bronze Age people (2500 to 800 BC) were also farmers and stock keepers and in many ways lived a life indistinguishable from their Neolithic predecessors. There is no firm agreement as to whether the Bronze Age represents an influx of new people or, more probably, of new ideas and ways infiltrating slowly across our landscape. What marks Bronze Age people out and gives them their own period in prehistory were major changes in material culture.

One such change was in textiles. Clothing in the Neolithic was plant-based, derived from bast (soft, inner tree bark), nettle fibres and probably flax, whereas Bronze Age folk wore rough woollen clothes. Perhaps the most obvious change was in tooling. Bronze Age sites can still reveal flint but metal technology had been introduced with hand axes and other artefacts now made from bronze. This suggests organised trade to obtain either raw materials or finished products. This provides a further discussion point: were these fine bronze objects intended for everyday use or as prestige objects?

Woodland clearance was much greater in extent during the Bronze Age and it has been estimated that tree cover in our region had been reduced to only 15 per cent of the total area by 1500 BC. There were a number of factors contributing to this clearance.[21] Greater population numbers put pressure on land for crop growing and grazing and timber was needed for building. A favoured source of fodder was elm leaves and it is likely that this, rather than disease, was the cause of a drastic decline in elm tree cover in the Bronze Age. Cattle, being browsers as well as grazers, can soon turn open woodland into a series of forest glades within which tree saplings would not have a hope of reaching maturity. Over time the wildwood disappeared to be replaced with open grassland. Clearings which had existed within the wildwood through the Mesolithic – possibly created by large native herbivores – would have readily coalesced into ever larger open areas.

Bronze Age settlement is usually associated with large round houses, stone-built at the base with a thatched roof laid on a lattice of poles. Various such huts have been excavated in the Dales and given Bronze Age provenance from artefacts,[22] and there is evidence in the Ribblehead area of deliberate attempts to improve land for agricultural use. This must have been associated with permanent settlements. On Scales Moor and in the fields immediately west of Ribblehead viaduct, especially in Ellerbeck Pasture, north of the road, are large spreads of small stone piles. They are called cairns which could be somewhat misleading because cairns are often piles of stones covering a burial structure but these are clearance cairns. Whoever was living in the area, probably during the Bronze Age, went to great efforts to clear away loose stones either to create space for growing crops or to make the pasture easier to manage. Excavation elsewhere in the Dales suggests that people of this period lived in single or multi-family farmsteads but it would be premature to conclude that social organisation was the same everywhere. As with so much, we simply do not know.

Round houses of possible Bronze Age date have been located all around Ingleborough, for example below Raven Scar Cave and on Scales Moor, and field walking is almost bound to identify further such sites. Bronze Age burial practices are well documented, with round barrows and small tumuli (*mounds*) being associated with this period, though it should be borne in mind that a barrow may be Neolithic. One Bronze Age barrow was fully excavated in the early 1970s. Called the Apron Full of Stones (SD708 787) in Kingsdale (Plate 5.1) and, though partly robbed in Victorian times and eroded by the river, this mound contained a cremation burial and a scatter of flint debris and was ascribed to the Early Bronze Age (2500–1600 BC).[23]

One archaeological feature closely associated with the Bronze Age is the burnt mound, and few features can have exercised the archaeological mind more than these. Many have been located in the North Pennines and in

Wensleydale and Swaledale, and one was excavated in 2005–06 at the head of Kingsdale.[24] Burnt mounds show on the ground as low mounds, often close to a stream or spring, and they extend about 5m to 15m in diameter. The Kingsdale mound had been exposed by stream erosion which provided the excavators with a ready-made section through it. Beneath a thin layer of topsoil was a deep layer of moderately compacted black material containing thousands of fire-reddened and shattered sandstone pieces among the matrix of ash, sooty material and charcoal. When this was trowelled away by the excavation team a shallow dish-like depression was exposed, again highly affected by fire. Adjacent to this was a sunken area, separated from the dish by standing orthostats (thin upright slabs of sandstone in this case) with a flagged floor beyond these, slightly less than 2m in each dimension.

Burnt mounds are a very common feature of the upland British Isles: over 2000 have been plotted in Ireland, over 850 in Scotland, with others found in the Lake District, Isle of Man, Wales and even the West Midlands. The Kingsdale mound was fixed by carbon dating to around 1500 BC. Their characteristics have been well documented but no one can agree on their usage.[25] It was formerly accepted that they were for cooking: the stones were burned on a fire and then placed in the tanks to heat the water and to maintain a high temperature. Later on a rather more arcane suggestion was put forward, suggesting that they were saunas, while others have nominated brewing, leather working and wool processing as possible explanations. The last of this list may turn out to be the most sensible and could be confirmed by laboratory analysis of sediment extracted from mound deposits. Wool can be separated from the hide by immersing it in a solution of lye (potassium hydroxide) which was produced by soaking burnt ash in water. On the other hand, however, burnt mounds may have been multi-functional. Recent excavations along the route of a new gas pipeline in South Wales found one with evidence of a 'definite industrial function' while others were associated with pottery and worked flint.[26]

Plate 5.1
Apron Full of Stones, Kingsdale. The stone revetment was built to prevent further structural damage from Kingsdale Beck.

Ingleborough Hillfort

The summit of Ingleborough is dominated by what has been termed a 'large univallate hillfort', meaning it is bounded by a single bank feature (Plate 5.2).[27] Tradition tells us it is of Iron Age date, but this is no longer universally accepted.[28] In fact, the very notion that it was ever a *fort*, a defensive structure, is now being seriously questioned. Other Pennine hillforts, such as Almondbury near Huddersfield and Harehaugh in Northumberland, have even been dated within the Neolithic (2680 BC and 3300–3000 BC respectively), and there are some archaeologists and prehistorians who believe Ingleborough has possibly Bronze Age origins. It is a fact that the late Bronze Age saw a severe climatic deterioration and received knowledge will have us believe there was widespread abandonment of upland settlements which would have put increased pressure on more favoured lowland areas. According to this argument this led to conflict between established folk and incomers and to a general breakdown of established social norms in the Late Bronze Age and Early Iron Age as people became increasingly confused and disorientated by the collapse of their ordered existence. The natural result, supposedly, was the creation of defensive hillforts into which bands of people could retreat when under threat from others.

This sounds plausible until the detail of Ingleborough is considered. For a start, if this was a time of such serious climatic decline, a locality as exposed and bereft of shelter as the top of this mountain would hardly seem an attractive option. Add to this the lack of water on the summit plateau and the development, even then, of peaty soils on the higher parts of the massif, and we have a problem in accepting the hypothesis. No other hillfort in England stands higher than this one.

But, the argument continues, there are twenty 'hut' circles on the summit so people must have lived there, even if only temporarily. However, six of them are only half-circles. The plateau has not been comprehensively surveyed using geophysical techniques but the absence of hearths within two circles that have been surveyed, added to the lack of midden (domestic waste) deposits and flint debris anywhere on the plateau, suggests this was not a settlement of any kind.

There is also the question of defence. By definition, a hillfort was a defensive structure so one would expect the ramparts to be effective in repelling invaders. Cursory examination of Ingleborough's ramparts emphasises a lack of effectiveness. Indeed, it is somewhat misleading to call it a rampart because this suggests a direct military function. Perhaps we should adopt the term perimeter embankment instead? The strongest embankment is at the extreme north-east corner where nature in the form of the almost precipitous Arks must surely have been sufficient without constructing a massive stone rampart, had its function been defensive. The embankment is weakest on the south side, facing Little Ingleborough. Anyone intending to attack the 'fort' would have had easy passage up that gentle slope. A defensive purpose for the site simply does not make sense.

An alternative hypothesis suggests that the twenty circles are not huts at all but ring cairns, that the 'fort' had symbolic and ritual significance rather than defensive, with the cairns having both a burial and ceremonial function.[29] There is much that is attractive in this idea. Viewed from afar, from whatever direction, but notably from east and west, Ingleborough stands out as a massive, brooding presence completely dominating the landscape. As weather and light conditions change, so does the mountain and it requires only a vaguely vivid imagination to impute a quasi-religious function to the site. It would have been a natural focus for a wide area for ceremonial occasions, the north-eastern embankment making a strong statement about the importance of this place, especially when approached from Ribblehead, and it would have been unforgettable in the minds of the people. If they are ring cairns, we can confidently push back the site's dating to the second millennium BC.

Defensive hillfort, sanctuary or ritual site? Iron Age or Bronze Age? Here we have a number of hypotheses to ponder over, but let us throw in another suggestion for good measure. Are the circles contemporary with the embankment? Did the summit plateau start off as a ceremonial site in happier and warmer times to be reworked later on as a place of temporary refuge? There is much work still to be done on Ingleborough. Of one concept, though, we can probably be definite: the summit has to be a multi-period site: Bronze Age and Iron Age almost certainly; Roman period possibly, given the fact that Roman pottery has been found on the summit plateau, though only one sherd was found; and maybe even Neolithic. Of another we can also be confident: it cannot have been a defensive fort. Indeed, it is doubted now if any of the northern so-called Iron Age hillforts were primarily forts. Current thinking tends away from perceiving these sites as defended hilltop settlements.

Iron Age and Romano-British Settlement

The Bronze Age, broadly speaking, gave way to the Iron Age in the Pennines around 800 BC. It used to be thought that the new technology came into the British Isles with waves of 'Celtic' migrants from the continent, but this has long since been rejected. As with earlier imports, the use of iron as a medium superior to bronze was introduced through a slow diffusion of new ideas along the coasts and up the river valleys into the interior. The new technology was not imposed by anyone; change did not suddenly happen: rather it was a matter of gradual absorption and assimilation as the late Bronze Age was imperceptibly transformed into the early Iron Age. It is always crucial to bear this in mind regardless of the period being considered.

Iron is much harder and longer-wearing than bronze so axes, spear heads, knives and hammers made of iron had clear advantages over bronze. Iron also meant that the Bronze Age/early Iron Age designs of wooden ards could be replaced by primitive iron-tipped ploughs making the farmer's task an easier one. The wooden tip of an ard was merely dragged along, pushing the soil aside so that seeds could be sown in the shallow trench, whereas a plough turns the soil over. New crops were introduced, including a variety of wheat called spelt which was hardy enough to withstand the wet climate and heavier, clayey soils of the Dales, particularly in the later Iron Age after 400 BC when annual rainfall totals increased.

There is evidence that Iron Age people learnt how to drain their land in a simple way, and pollen records tell us that there was accelerated woodland clearance, at least in the early Iron Age, as more land was opened up for crop growing and stock grazing. There is even evidence that hemp was being grown on the flanks of Ingleborough. Some known or assumed Iron Age settlement sites also have clear signs on the ground of stock droveways giving access from homestead to higher pastures through enclosed fields.

The traditional view was that the Iron Age in the Dales was an undeveloped society[30] with downtrodden peasants eking out a meagre living with beans as a major food staple. Archaeological work over recent decades has shown this to be an erroneous view. Certainly they were leading a subsistence lifestyle, the Ribblehead area was clearly marginal for crop growing and the remoter parts could well have been relatively backward, but we must not overdo the hardships they faced. Discoveries of pottery, coins, metalwork and different types of querns for grinding grain show they were not in the least materially destitute.

We have no real idea how to classify people earlier than the Iron Age in terms of ethnography or language, though Celtic or proto-Celtic languages may well have been spoken in the Bronze Age. For the Iron Age it is another matter. Roman writers provided us with some information. The Iron Age people in our area were called the Brigantes which probably means 'hill folk' and they spoke a Celtic language, a precursor of modern Welsh. They had a political and social structure but the Brigantes were a loose confederation of tribes rather than one unitary group. East of the Pennines they had large settlement centres but in our area they occupied small homesteads consisting of round huts, quite similar in essence to Bronze Age huts – if it works, why change it? Surrounding the huts were small paddocks and enclosures of varying size and examination of settlements on the ground indicates they expanded organically, new living or storage huts being built as family size increased, new paddocks being added on as increased wealth allowed more stock to be kept.

It has often been said that the Iron Age was brought to an abrupt end by the coming of the Romans with Iron Age Celts in our area taking on a new identity in AD 70 as the Romano-British. The Romans, we were once led to believe, brought the right-angle along with many other 'improvements'. The hostile, painted, long-haired and wild tribesmen were cruelly subdued by the invading Roman forces and they endured 340 years of colonial oppression until Rome withdrew its tutelage in AD 410, leaving the *Brittunculi* (the horrible 'little Brits')[31] to their own devices. The Brigantes, we are told, hid in places like Ingleborough hillfort constantly carrying out guerrilla raids on the Romans passing from fort to fort. Thankfully, this description bears little relationship to reality.

Yes, the Romans landed in AD 43 and they did carry out occasional military forays into the North during the AD 50s and 60s with the main push into the north of 'England' to occupy and fully pacify it between AD 71 and 74, but there the myth ends. Many tribes, though not the Brigantes, were already trading with the Romans long before the invasion and, as with earlier periods, new ideas and ways had long since infiltrated across the country. Some people, including some tribal elders, did oppose the Romans, and there were occasional rebellions and skirmishes, such as the Brigantian civil war in AD 69–70, with a possible full-scale revolt in AD 190. Many people, though, would have remained unaffected and for the greater mass life and work no doubt continued in its same old way.[32] The Roman historian Dio Cassius said of German tribes along the Rhine 'they became different without knowing it' and the same may well have applied in our area. On the other hand it could be argued that Roman occupation had only minimal impact on areas like the Dales: if so, maybe we could refer to this era as Britto-Roman rather than Romano-British. For some the Romans brought new opportunities for advancement socially and economically, and we have an excellent example of this near Ingleton.

In 2003 an enclosure of previously unknown date and function was excavated (Fig. 5.3).[33] The site was called Broadwood, just outside Ingleton, and it revealed an enormous amount of material for a settlement that crossed the divide between the Iron Age and the Romano-British period. It was a rectangular enclosure, surrounded by a low bank, supplemented by a ditch at least on the southern edge, with four sunken pounds within the enclosure and a more or less centrally placed oval hut. Carbon 14 dates and pottery evidence proved that the site was occupied from the late Iron Age to the very end of the Romano-British period. The fact that it is rectangular, but pre-Roman, might point to the diffusion of new ideas northwards that were discussed above. In the Iron Age and early Roman phases this site had an agricultural basis and it was ideally placed being sited on level, well-drained and south-facing ground. During the middle part of the Roman period the people who lived here branched out into secondary metal working, or blacksmithing. Broadwood lies very close to the Roman road down from Chapel le Dale and there was obviously a river crossing of some sort close by so it may be that these people were exploiting an economic opportunity. They were responding to a new market that had opened up with traffic – military or civilian – along the road. (For a discussion of Roman roads in the area, see Chapter 7.)

As we have seen, there are a number of settlements running along a broad limestone bench southwards from Ribblehead, all of which are associated with walled field systems, as shown on Figure 5.2. They have not been excavated so no firm dating evidence is available to differentiate between Iron Age, Romano-British or immediate post-Roman. Native life in each of these periods would have been broadly similar and continuity of settlement was an undoubted reality.

What happened in our area after the Roman withdrawal from Britain is unknown but there is no archaeological evidence from forts in the North that the end was dramatic or catastrophic, and the Broadwood site contained pottery evidence of occupation up to the late fourth century, not long before the Roman withdrawal. It is probably safe to assume that, just as at the Iron Age-Romano-British transition, life for the majority continued as before. They were still largely subsistence farmers whose lives were little affected by events in the wider world. Those who had geared their lives to the Roman economy, as at Broadwood, would have felt the impact of withdrawal as traffic and trade declined in the early years of the fifth century, if not several decades earlier. Certainly there is

Figure 5.3
Aerial View of the
Broadwood Enclosure.
Source: National
Monuments Record
2178/3033

a long gap in the pottery record at Broadwood between the late Roman and the medieval period. Perhaps we should think in terms of gradual decline, or slow adaptation and evolution to a less centralised and managed system, rather than a sudden collapse of all that had gone before.

Early Medieval Pastoralists

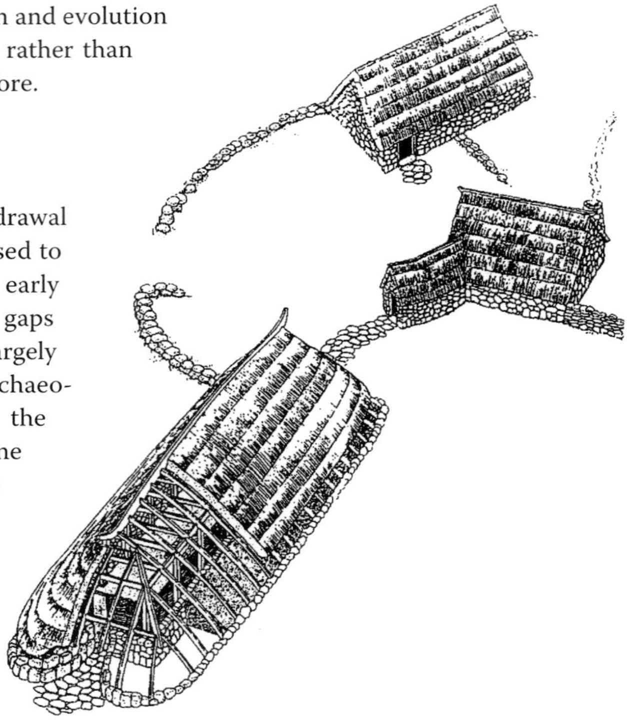

The centuries between the Roman withdrawal and the coming of the Normans in 1066 used to be known as the Dark Ages but the term early medieval is preferred now. There are large gaps in our knowledge of this period. This is largely because parts of the record are blank: archaeological visibility is lacking, especially for the fifth to eighth centuries. No coins came into Britain, or were minted here, after AD 402 and the production of pottery on a commercial scale seems to have ceased once the market system fell into decay – the Roman administration and military had been major consumers of pottery – and the Dales appear, from archaeological evidence, to be aceramic in the post-Roman period and coin-free from the early fifth to the eleventh centuries (with the notable exception of the Gauber site which will be discussed shortly).

Figure 5.4
Viking-type Site at Gauber, Ribblehead. Source: The Yorkshire Museum

It is widely assumed nowadays that Romano-British – *ie* native – political and social systems continued more or less intact into the seventh century and that the tribal elite that had prospered under the Romans retained their position as the elite in new 'kingdoms' that came into being. One such kingdom was Elmet to the east of Leeds, which survived as an independent entity until AD 616 or 617 and another was Craven, encompassing the area from Ingleborough through Malham Tarn to Grassington, the *Cravescire* (Cravenshire) of the eleventh century Domesday Book.[34] One theory suggests that Tor Dyke, a massive linear earthwork above Kettlewell, may have been the eastern boundary of this kingdom.

If we can backtrack a little, whether the end of Roman Britain was reflected in changed population totals in the Ingleborough area is a matter of debate. Two unrelated sets of circumstances indicate that much marginal land, and by association settlements connected with it, were abandoned in the fifth and sixth centuries. We have already noted that there had been a reduction in the market economy which can be directly translated into reduced demand for foodstuffs which, in turn, meant less farm land was needed. Areas of high potential would have continued in production, and settlement, but marginal areas such as around Ingleborough were no doubt abandoned. Adding to the inhabitants' woes was rapid and dramatic climatic deterioration in the late 530s, thought to be due either to a volcanic eruption emitting huge quantities of sun-blocking dust into the global atmosphere or to the impact of a meteor.[35] Certainly the 530s and 540s, at least, were significantly colder than hitherto and harvest failures inevitably resulted, followed by outbreaks of plague, with climatic deterioration reported not just in the north but in the Mediterranean and as far away as China around 540. There may even have been a global pandemic at this time.

At first sight, two facts are seemingly hard to reconcile: after this climatic cataclysm there was a general trend for warming that lasted into the late twelfth century, with average diurnal temperatures one or two degrees Celsius higher than now, yet the pollen record indicates a regeneration of the forest estate from around AD 750 to 850. One might have expected warmer conditions to stimulate settlement and agriculture, but there is a plausible explanation. Population levels take time to recover from a crash and, in the interim, less land is needed to provide food so 'natural' vegetation takes full advantage of more favourable climatic conditions. Only when optimum demographic levels have been achieved again is there renewed assault on woodland.

As the early medieval period progressed slow migrations brought incomers from the east and west coasts into the Dales. These were the Anglo-Saxons who arrived here probably during the seventh century. During the sixth century much of the country had come under English (Anglo-Saxon) control with kingdoms being established.[36] By the start of the seventh century most of the north was part of the Anglian kingdom of Northumbria but, to confuse the issue further, there were smaller administrative units within the kingdom known as *regione*. In the late seventh century Bishop Wilfrid was granted extensive estates in what are now Sedbergh, Garsdale and Dent by the kings of Northumbria and Deira and a contemporary source includes mention of lands in *regione Dunutinga* which is thought to have encompassed Dent. It has been suggested that the name *Dunutinga* means 'people of the Hill' and that the hill in question must have been dominant in the landscape – therefore it must be Ingleborough.[37] This argument has been taken further to speculate that the summit had been the central place for a Brigantian clan grouping and that its centrality persisted into the early medieval period.[38] Acceptance of this theory presupposes that the summit was an occupied place but, as we have already seen, that point is strongly contested.

No documentary evidence is available to shed light on how Dunutinga was administered or on the relationships between the native British inhabitants and the Anglian newcomers. We know the Anglo-Saxons were here partly because place-name evidence tells us so but, frustratingly, there is a lack of evidence on the ground of definite settlements from this period. It may be their remains lie under present-day villages, or may be some of the known earthwork settlements assumed to be Romano-British are in fact early Anglo-Saxon. Perhaps there was a continuum from one period to the other. In this sense the Dark Age in Craven is dark – we know so little about it.

Over the next three to four centuries other peoples appeared in the Dales. How did all these peoples get here and where did they come from? It is generally accepted that three distinct groups of people migrated into the Dales during the early medieval centuries: the Angles themselves, Vikings (or Danes) from the east and other Vikings (variously called Norsemen or Hiberno-Scandinavians or Hiberno-Norse) from the west. Viking is a word which has often been misused.[39] In the Icelandic *sagas* the word viking was used to refer to a warrior or a pirate or to someone undertaking a great expedition. It became generally used to indicate a raider, and it could be misleading to talk about Danes (the *Dani*) coming from modern Denmark to the east coast of England, with Vikings or Northmen (*Nordmanni*) or Norse coming from Norway round the west coast of Scotland. Both sets of people were Vikings. What we should perhaps talk about are Viking-age movements.

Plate 5.3
Viking-type (top right)
Farmstead at Gauber.

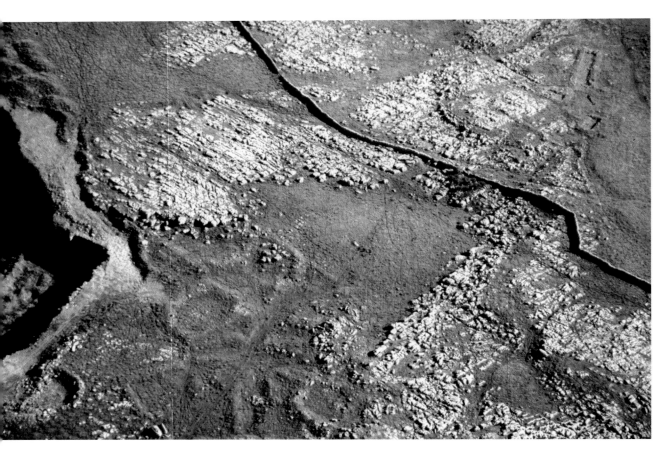

Place-names containing the Anglo-Saxon element 'ley',[40] which means a forest or woodland clearing, are very common across West Yorkshire though rare in Craven. Following the Aire valley from Leeds you would pass through a string of 'ley' settlements: Armley, Bramley, Shipley, Bingley, Keighley, Cononley and Bradley; or the Wharfe through Weardley, Otley, Ilkley and Beamsley. These are all in West Yorkshire. Higher up both valleys there are no more 'ley' settlements and the element 'ton' (farmstead or village) becomes dominant. Moving north-westwards from Bradley you pass through Skipton, Coniston, Long Preston and Horton; from Beamsley through Bolton, Linton and Grassington. If you were to come from the south-west there is an absence of 'ley' settlements but a corresponding profusion of 'ton' sites following the Lune valley: Caton, Claughton, Farleton, Wrayton, Burton, Thornton, Ingleton and Twistleton, though this may reflect an absence of woodland in the areas with no or few 'ley' place-names.

If you were to follow the Ribble valley northwards you would find 'leys' and 'tons' in close proximity, which might indicate that 'ley' settlements were created within woodland clearings as opposed to 'ton' farmsteads which had already expanded across more open and productive ground.

Using place-names in a definitive fashion has its pitfalls.[41] For a start we have names which can be either Anglo-Saxon or Scandinavian, as some word elements are found in both, but there is the deeper issue of what place-names reflect. Whether a given name is Anglo-Saxon or Scandinavian or British (Celtic) could reflect who originally founded that settlement or who lived there when the place-name was finally fixed – there could be many years between those two events. Who would have given a name to a farmstead or village? The people who lived there and thereabouts knew where they lived so we have to ask if they would have needed a name for it, but the authorities (notably the tax collectors in the medieval period) would need a name to record payment, and increased population mobility required people to have some means of identifying to others where they came from. On the other hand a place-name could equally well represent influences from afar. It is worth bearing in mind also that Scandinavian personal names did not go out of use (out of fashion, perhaps?) until the mid-thirteenth century. Furthermore, at least in the Eden valley, to the north of the Yorkshire Dales, the Scandinavian place-name element 'by' was still being applied to new settlements in the twelfth century.[42]

And why did the Anglo-Saxons not rename Pen-y-ghent whose name is at least partly, and probably totally, British? Why did the Scandinavian settlers not rename Ingleborough and Whernside, both of which are, in whole or in part, Anglo-Saxon names? The same applies to the main rivers, in the Dales and much more widely: the Lune still has a British name while Ribble is Anglo-Saxon. Does this imply that the Scandinavians had no interest in mountains or rivers? Surely they must have, given their ancestral heritage. Place-names should be treated with circumspection.

Many place-names in the area have Scandinavian (or Norse) origins, in fact between Settle and Sedbergh approximately 60 per cent of all names do. Some of the common words still in daily local use are Scandinavian: rigg, fell, dale*, beck, gill, syke*, ling, keld, birk, holme, force, foss and pike (* these can also be Anglo-Saxon words). Settlements around the mountain contain a variety of place-name elements: the reader is referred to the Place-name glossary at the end of the book. Of the ten farmsteads between Ribblehead and Chapel le Dale, all but one has Scandinavian elements in the name.

The Scandinavians we are talking about were the Vikings and they came from the west, from Ireland, which explains why some place-names in our area are Hiberno (Irish)-Norse rather than true Scandinavian. They tended to seek out upland pastures so there was no conflict between them and the lowland Anglo-Saxons or Anglo-Danes. We can only assume, from place-name evidence, that Viking settlement around Ribblehead and Chapel le Dale was widespread. We cannot say with certainty, though, whether they lived here all year round or just practised transhumance, herding their cattle and sheep up into fresh pastures for the summer to give lowland grassland a rest.

It would be logical to expect to find Viking settlements in the landscape and there is a clear danger of misinterpreting any rectangular earthwork structure as Viking. Shape does not tell the whole story. Gauber, a site excavated in the 1970s, has been frequently quoted as a definite Viking settlement. Unfortunately, this cannot be taken for granted, as we shall now see.

The earthwork remains in Gauber High Pasture (SD784 768) consist of three buildings (Fig. 5.4).[43] The main building, probably a house, is 19m by 4m internally so was on the large side, and there are two smaller buildings interpreted by the excavators as a kitchen and a workshop (Plate 5.3). The walls were stone-based, up to 1.80m thick along the sides but broader at the gable ends, with a presumably thatched roof rising from them. Figure 5.3 is very much an impression rather than reality and it displays a good deal of artistic licence. The roof structure, for example, is highly complex and such a design would have required a significant quantity of sound timber. Even though there were local pockets of wooded ground, timber of the size needed to construct something so complex as this could not have been obtained locally and to purchase it all, to fell it, to haul it up here and to shape it all, would have cost a small fortune. To return to reality, the buildings were contained within a group of small enclosures with a wider area of fields stretching over 1.20ha in extent. Excavation unearthed a variety of artefacts including two knife blades, a spearhead, a bronze-plated iron bell and a spindle whorl, with evidence of hearths and an oven or corn drying kiln. A scatter of bones hints at their diet: cattle, sheep and/or goat, red deer, pigs and birds were all represented.

Any or all of these finds could have been either Anglo-Saxon or Viking.

The shape and form of the main building suggest Viking tradition, so why can we not conclusively agree that the site was Viking? The difficulty arises from the discovery of four coins in or around the main building. One was too severely corroded to reveal its identity but the other three were all firmly dated as Anglo-Saxon from the ninth century at the time the Vikings were making their first incursions into eastern Yorkshire and well before they could have been living up in the Dales. Have we been deflected in our conclusions by assuming the rectangular form of the building has to be Viking, or should we not forget that Romano-British structures were often the same shape? Did the building tradition survive the so-called Dark Ages? Did Anglo-Saxon settlers here adopt the local native building methods, or did they build the house to their own rectangular design? Gauber is but one set of buildings and we have nothing locally to compare it with so we must be content to think of it as a 'Viking-type', but Anglo-Saxon or Anglo-Danish, settlement. A discarded sherd of pottery or two, in context, would have made all the difference to understanding this settlement.

One thing was clear from the excavation: there was no evidence of different phases of building, nor of repair work, so Gauber cannot have been occupied for long. The reason for this may lie in the field system which is now just bare limestone pavement. The occupants may have found that taking the grass cover off the soil, whether through animal stocking or garden cultivation, exposed it to wind and rain very quickly leaving them with no alternative other than to move out.

Monastic influences

Whichever peoples settled in the various nooks and crannies of the Ribblehead area may never be firmly identified but they would all have followed a similar existence largely based on pastoral farming. Their basic subsistence diet of grains and pulses, with dairy products and meat, would have been supplemented by game shot or trapped and by nature's seasonal offerings, and it would have been difficult to distinguish the houses and farmsteads of one people from those of another. It is quite probable that some of the farms we see in the area today had their origins in the early medieval period, with signs of early habitation hidden by later structures. Different languages merged into one common dialect, heavily influenced by words with both Scandinavian and Anglo-Saxon roots, as original ethnic differences and nuances were subsumed within a new and slowly emerging common identity.

Much of the north suffered from William the Conqueror's Harrying of the North in 1069–70 during which Norman-led forces exacted retribution for native risings against the new political and military order. The Ingleborough area may have escaped relatively unscathed as its scattered peasant population could not have posed much of a threat, though the vengeance wreaked across the north did not seek to differentiate between innocent and guilty. Large tracts of the western Dales were set aside as baronial hunting grounds partly because the new elite could see only limited income deriving from this marginal land if it were all tenanted by the peasantry.

In the later twelfth century and the first half of the thirteenth it became increasingly common for the ruling classes to grant extensive stretches of their estates to newly founded monasteries, though the practice tailed off after 1250. In their view they were not giving away something for nothing. Rather they were guaranteeing their position in the afterlife. It was their way of ensuring that their generosity would be rewarded for ever by intercessional prayers said by the monks. In this way landowners would be fast-tracked to heaven instead of having to hang about in the half-way house of purgatory, never mind being consigned to hell or the everlasting state of limbo from which there was no escape. It was perceived as an astute move on their part to gift land.

Three monastic houses, all Cistercian and all founded between 1123 and 1156, came to exercise control over much of our area, though Kingsdale remained in baronial hands throughout. Fountains Abbey held a large area east of the Ribble including the slopes of Pen-y-ghent. They also held Langstrothdale until 1294 when they exchanged it for Littondale with the powerful Percy family, with whom the abbey had endured a long-standing dispute. Jervaulx Abbey enjoyed large estates around Horton, Birkwith and Studfold; while Furness Abbey held lands encircling Ingleborough including all the way from Selside through Ribblehead and Chapel le Dale as well as in the Gearstones and Newby Head area.

Initially monastic estates were held as demesne land by the abbeys and managed by lay brothers, or *conversi*. These men were an integral part of the monastery but did not hold holy orders. It would not have made sense for an abbey to have large numbers of lay brothers because they would prove to be a burden on the abbey's resources once they grew too old or infirm to perform manual labour. Like monks, they literally had a job for life, so to speak. Hired labourers did not have to be looked after in the same way so varying numbers of grange servants were taken on as and when needed. They still had to be paid and fed while working so it was far preferable for an abbey to have had peasants gifted to them as part and parcel of a gift of land. Monastic charters record names of peasants handed over in this way. The poor peasant had no say in the matter: he was a bondman with no freedom of choice. His family, of course, was part of the package.

It would have been impossible to manage their remote estates directly from the abbey so the Cistercians (and other orders) introduced a system of granges. In each area they chose somewhere to develop a local headquarters which consisted of domestic quarters for lay brothers and the grange manager, barns, cowhouses and stores as necessary, and most probably a 'spital' where travellers and visitors could rest over and where the infirm

Plate 5.4
Southerscales Deserted
Medieval Village with
the clear footprint
of two rectangular
buildings in the
foreground.

could receive support. From this description it will be apparent that granges were few and far between in the Ingleborough area. It is not correct to call any monastic farm a grange. Furness, for example, exerted control over the whole of its Ingleborough properties from a grange at Newby south of the mountain, established by 1170.[44] Jervaulx's grange for the area was at High Birkwith (SD800 768).

Each grange headed a scattering of farms known as lodges, many of which had been pre-monastic farm holdings. Sometimes below, and sometimes at this level in the hierarchy, were cattle farms (*vaccarie*) and even more remote sheep houses (*bercarie*). None of these has been positively identified in our area. Jervaulx maintained lodges at Horton and Studfold (SD813 703); Furness at Lodge Hall (SD780 779), Nether Lodge (SD793 777), Colt Park (SD772 779) and Bruntscar (SD737 789). Two of those names give a reasonably convincing clue about their purpose in the monastic scheme: *Colt* Park and *Stud*fold hint at the breeding of horses. Park Fell at Colt Park is partly bounded by a curving ditch and bank feature: current archaeological investigations hope to test the hypothesis that this is contemporary with monastic management here.

We need to envisage in the centuries of monastic overlordship a managed pastoral landscape producing large quantities of wool, cheese, butter and breeding stock, with a network of tracks linking outlying farms and lodges to the grange, and grange to abbey. For the ordinary peasant it can have made little difference to his daily struggle whether he was at the disposal of an absentee lord's steward or a grange manager. The latter, though, given their monastic position would hopefully have looked after him better when he was down to his last bean.

For much more than one hundred years of monastic control life was relatively tolerable for the peasantry. Climate gradually warmed through the twelfth century, though it seems to have become increasingly wet and stormy in the following century, and sound land management by the abbeys saw a flourishing of the rural economy. Indeed, the mid- to late thirteenth century is regarded as a time of 'high farming' with regular food surpluses and peaceful conditions hand in hand. The next century could not have been more different and the Ribblehead area without doubt was devastated time and again. Circumstances conspired to make life an often fruitless battle for survival.

Climatic deterioration led directly to repeated harvest failures and food shortages which in turn both caused frequent outbreaks of various diseases sometimes referred to as the plague, but actually cholera, typhus or dysentery. The Black Death of 1348 was true plague, of the most horrific proportions, but there is doubt as to how prevalent it was in the rural uplands of the North. If the situation across northern England was dire, it was far worse in Scotland. Food there was in very short supply in a succession of years and one common outcome of famine and hardship is a breakdown in law and order and in social organisation. The end result, as far as Dales folk were concerned, was a series of raids from Scotland which were well documented in the monastic record, partly due to deteriorating environmental conditions in Scotland and partly to political turmoil between the two kingdoms.[45] Famine, disease and ravages from the north kept the Grim Reaper busy here from about 1318 to 1360. Decimation of the population brought about a severe labour shortage for baronial and monastic landlords with many bondmen and tenants being able to break free and set their own terms. Cistercian houses had no choice other than to accelerate a process which had begun in the late thirteenth century of leasing parts of demesne land to free tenants in return for an annual farm rent. In 1363 Fountains obtained permission from the main Cistercian abbey at Cîteaux in France to convert nine of its granges in the Dales into vills because of their 'reduced state'; and Jervaulx converted its grange at Birkwith into sixteen messuages (houses and associated buildings) around 1342.[46] From now on the monastic houses were increasingly landlords of tenanted estates rather than direct managers of the land; detailed examination on the ground reveals quite a number of possibly medieval house sites, especially in Chapel le Dale and quite possibly in Kingsdale.[47]

There is no documentary or, as yet, archaeological, evidence of the impact of fourteenth century travails on individual settlements in our area: we can but assume they were affected and wonder how they coped with all that was thrown at them. We can ponder how the inhabitants of Southerscales village (SD742 768) above Chapel le Dale fared (Plate 5.4). Southerscales is a deserted medieval village, once part of an extensive monastic estate, and earthworks clearly show the footprint of six houses and associated barns and stores with streetways running between them. It is well documented in the records of Furness Abbey, especially in perambulations of the boundaries of their property in 1220 and 1251, where it is recorded as *Souterscales*.

At the Dissolution of the Monasteries, when a full inventory was drawn up to enable Henry VIII's officials to squeeze out the maximum amount to add to state coffers, six tenants were listed at Southerscales which correlates with the ground evidence. Five of these tenants were described as 'widow'. This is odd. Life expectancy was known to have been low, life was indisputably hard and it may be that men died at an earlier age than women, then as now, but for five out of six to have died from natural causes defies belief. There has been a suggestion that these women were widowed at the battle of Flodden in 1513 where many local men helped crush Scottish forces. It seems unlikely, though, that the widows could still have held tenancies here well over twenty years later.

There is a possibly more plausible if sinister explanation. In 1536 a rebellion against the king, known as the Pilgrimage of Grace, spread rapidly across the north of England and attracted many followers in the Dales due in large part to one of its leaders, Robert Aske, being a Yorkshireman. Several of the newly dissolved abbeys became embroiled in the uprising, including Furness which owned Southerscales and, when it was put down the following year, royal revenge was swift and brutal. Abbots and priors, monks, lay brothers and tenants were despatched to the gallows as a visible way of getting the message across to the rest of the population that dissent would not be tolerated. Were the five men of Southerscales caught up in this?

The monastic ideal, if it had still persisted, came to an end in the late 1530s when Henry VIII ordered the dissolution of all monastic foundations, seizing their lands and wealth and selling it all on as a means of raising finance. In effect the free tenants who had worked individual farms under monastic tenancies simply exchanged one landlord for another ... and life went on much as before.

· S I X ·

Archaeology: Ingleborough South

hapter 5 provided an overview of life in the Ribblehead area since the latest retreat of glaciers and ice sheets, showing that people not only responded to the opportunities offered by the environment but also began to manipulate it to their own ends. This chapter builds on that broad brush approach by focussing on specific archaeological sites across the southern part of the Ingleborough massif and in Crummack Dale, using them as exemplars. As in the previous chapter, few firm dates will be proffered simply because there is insufficient archaeological or archival dating evidence. Some of the sites to be discussed cannot even be ascribed to a particular 'Age', hence my – possibly frustrating – use of the term prehistoric rather than Bronze Age, Iron Age or Romano-British. If there is the possibility that a given site can be assigned to a particular period, it will be indicated in the text. We must first retrace our steps from where we left off in the previous chapter, and return to prehistory.

Cave Archaeology

The first site to come in for scrutiny in the area was dated by archaeological excavation in the 1920s.[1] At the head of Clapdale there is a fossil waterfall in a glacial meltwater channel. Tucked beneath the overhang is the excavated drop to the now-guarded entrance of Foxholes Cave (Plate 6.1). Outside the overhang is a large spoilheap, some of it thrown up by cave explorers, some by archaeologists whose primary concern was under the overhang and not the inner cave.

The site was firmly ascribed to the Neolithic by a range of artefacts. This included over a hundred pottery sherds of typical Neolithic form, and four flint arrowheads. Two of these were leaf-shaped and the others barbed and tanged (Fig. 6.1). Human bone fragments were also unearthed, including two skulls, but they were disarticulated rather than being in skeletal form and showed signs of having been burnt. Two skewers made from animal bone also formed part of the total assemblage.

You only have to stand beneath the overhang to begin to understand why this site was chosen for occupation in the Neolithic, if indeed it was actually occupied. It faces south and thus catches the morning and early afternoon sun and is very sheltered from wind and rain. Being partly hidden, it would also have provided a useful lookout point if the valley had been used for hunting or trapping game. Remnants of a low walled enclosure around the overhang space are probably contemporary with its occupation. It would be premature, though, to think of this site, or similar ones, as being places of settlement on a permanent or semi-permanent basis. It could have served as a favoured temporary summer camp, but one interpretation favours its use as a sepulchre, a special place of ritual significance within those people's lives, rather than as a camp in which case facing south and catching the sun would obviously not have been significant.

Researchers in the Giggleswick Scar Project have investigated a number of caves west of Settle and have reassessed human and animal bones from much earlier excavations. Four caves on the Scar have yielded seventeen carbon 14 dates from within the Neolithic. A further cave above Arcow Quarry at Helwith Bridge was the focus of a recent rescue excavation by archaeologists from the University of Bradford and this, too, produced bone from the early Neolithic. What is particularly interesting about these dates is that they are broadly contemporary with dates obtained from sites in southern England: the new, Neolithic culture based on farming came to the Dales no later than in the south. The long-held concept that new ideas slowly spread north through the country is now seriously called into question and the corollary is that diffusion must have come from the Irish Sea.

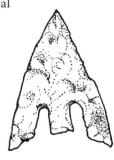

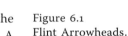

Figure 6.1
Flint Arrowheads.

Cup Marks

There has been an increasing interest within the Pennines in recent decades in what is termed rock art.[2] Some might dispute the suitability of the word 'art' but the justification is that rock art adds an extra dimension, on the micro-scale, to the landscape, and that the forms may not have been carved to serve any practical function but for aesthetic or cultural reasons which we can only guess at. On the other hand, though, some see rock art as territorial boundary markers. Rock art has been located – and accurately surveyed – in areas where evidence of both prehistoric hunter-gatherer and pastoral farmers has been confirmed. Typically it has been found on sandstone boulders with at least one regular, workable surface, usually on ground which commands a view across a valley or lowland expanse.

It is hard to see how rock art could ever be dated because it takes the form of carvings rather than paintings,[3] but tentative estimates can be made if the art is found in an archaeological context, in other words if it is found as an integral part of a landscape with identifiable features. Thus, the tradition may have originated in the Mesolithic-Neolithic transition and evidence from careful field scrutiny suggests usage over at least a millennium.

Rock art takes several forms. Some carvings are ornate and intricate, and have been interpreted as (to us) primitive maps; others have a cup form; yet others are cup and ring forms, with a carved ring or concentric rings surrounding the central cup hollow. Many sites have been found in the northern Pennines and on the moors either side of Swaledale but very little work has been carried out in the western Dales.[4] It is not easy deciding if cup marks are in fact prehistoric art rather than natural solution hollows, especially if the cups are on the top surface of a rock. If they are seen on a vertical side face it is a different matter, as naturally-formed, cone-shaped solution hollows would not develop on such faces.

Simple cup forms – as yet unprovenanced – can be seen on Ingleborough, on several flat sandstone rocks overlooking the broad valley of Cote Gill where there is a settlement site, and sitting within an area of what can only be prehistoric 'field' enclosures. A second site can be seen below Herningside where a large sandstone block has fairly convincing cup marks adjacent to the footprint of a rectangular stone structure. Ingleborough still awaits systematic field surveying of rock art.

Early Prehistoric Settlement Sites

Cote Gill Head seems the most unprepossessing place imaginable for a settlement yet, hidden among the rushes in what is now a very damp valley head, there are the remains of a prehistoric site. Try and define its detail in summer and vegetation growth will make it impossible; even in winter it is not an easy matter. There is, nonetheless, a much degraded perimeter wall, clearer and more intact on the eastern side than elsewhere but it exists at best as little more than the foundation courses. Hidden away within the central rushes are signs of hut circles, again very degraded. As mentioned earlier, traces of enclosure walls rise westwards out of the valley towards the line of Grey Wife Sike, and there seems to be a coaxial boundary roughly parallel to the sike. This means it is a major wall line with other similar lines running off it at right-angles down into the valley. Without detailed field investigation it is not possible to determine whether these lines are contemporary with the settlement in Cote Gill or with the nearby cup marks or with a possible burial cairn on Seat Haw. Indeed, coaxial boundaries in general may not be prehistoric: some could be early medieval or medieval. This may seem to be

hedging bets but it needs to be constantly kept in mind that surface features cannot be dated simply by looking at them. In archaeology dating needs firm and irrefutable evidence.

There is an equally enigmatic site between Thwaite Lane and Robin Proctor's Scar on the Clapham-Austwick parish boundary. It is cut by the parish boundary wall and lies on a low bluff immediately west of the drained Thwaite tarn; the plan form of the site can be readily made out from on top of the scar in terms of grassed-over banks marking out small enclosures. Assuming the tarn had existed in prehistoric times, it would have been an ideal place to settle with waterfowl on the doorstep and, no doubt, visiting mammal species, adding to the diet of whatever people would have grown whenever they had lived here. As part of the current and ground-breaking Craven's Ancient Landscape project, a series of soil samples is being obtained by coring so that pollen analysis can be carried out.[5] One such sample was cored in 2007 in the former tarn. Scientifically-derived dates are still awaited but preliminary conclusions seem to suggest that woodland species on this site were replaced by grasses around the Neolithic-Bronze Age transition. The implication of this is to confirm that people at the time were manipulating the natural order of things by clearing woodland for farming purposes. Recent pollen samples from elsewhere in North Craven have shown that the

Plate 6.1
Foxholes Cave, Clapdale. The banks either side of the entrance are excavation debris.

natural woodland estate was expanding and retracting periodically during the Neolithic, again pointing to land management. The intention of the project is to obtain further samples from across the district to enable a more detailed picture of the prehistoric landscape, and of people's role within it, to be constructed.

In that huge expanse of limestone pavement between Long Scar and the wall at Sulber Gate, formerly known as Ingleborough Pasture, there is a further settlement site which is more defined in plan and easier by far to understand. It cannot really be seen either from the next limestone level to the west or from the open grassy ground to the east. It is a site you tend to fall into. The site sits within a large shallow bowl, or embayment, naturally cut into the limestone and bounded by the remnants of a discontinuous and crudely built wall, in places set on pavement, encircling the bowl. The bowl is very shallow yet is remarkably sheltered from north and north-west winds. Within the enclosure are four hut circles, all of which are very well preserved and have very different constructional forms. By any standards, it is a fascinating site and one that is little known. It would repay careful examination and surveying.

One of the hut circles, arguably the most impressive, lies at the lower end of a narrow passage that slices through the limestone pavement from the nearby low scar. This bears all the hallmarks of an artificial cut. The hut circle has an internal diameter of 6m or 7m with a possible doorway facing south or south-east. The walls are very clear, if partly vegetated over, and in places still stand to a height of 1.50m. They were built as a rubble-filled, double-skin wall with a few large orthostats (upstanding slabs) forming the inner skin apparently still *in situ*.

A second hut circle is slightly smaller, at 5m to 6m internal diameter, lying a short distance to the north-east of its neighbour, on the other side of the linear cut. Vegetation growth hinders full examination of this structure but it does seem to be slightly more oval than the other one. One standing orthostat has survived here and the wall also seems to have been constructed with a double skin. A possible doorway faces towards the south. Internally this hut poses a problem as the floor area is very uneven and it appears to have rough slabs of limestone within it. Only vegetation and turf clearance would determine if these are displaced wall stones or the remains of crude flooring.

The third structure is of a similar size to the previous one but has been completely grassed over masking its internal and wall detail. There is, it should be said, no evidence to prove that these three structures formed part of the same discrete farmstead or whether all had a domestic function.

This same area contains other archaeological features worthy of mention. It is impossible to say if they are contemporary with the hut circles. There is a series of very small heaps of stone set prominently on a limestone bench, running in a line from north-east to south-west parallel to Clapham Road green lane, with the typical characteristics of Bronze Age burial mounds. In each case the stone cairn is set on a circular base with a diameter greater than the cairn's, and every one has distinctive moss growth around the base. They also share a long-range view across Crummack and Moughton, important to their occupants if one accepts the concept that they required a vantage point to oversee their domain in the afterlife.

One, much larger, stone-built feature stands out as a prominent mound adjacent to Hinkinshaw Peat Road where it cuts through a low limestone scar. It is sub-rounded in plan and very solidly built with massive walls. There is no trace of a doorway and the internal floor space is so restricted in size that it cannot possibly have been a building. Externally it extends for 7m by 6m. It was not a building, and the only explanation that seems at all plausible is that it is a very large robbed-out burial mound.

Later Prehistoric Settlement Sites

The inclusion of sites to be discussed here has been very selective, based on subjective observation and, emphatically, not from any dating or excavation evidence. Each is very well-preserved, complex in form and of considerable interest. Just east of Jenkin Beck outside Ingleton is a site marked on the 1:25,000 Ordnance Survey maps as Settlement. It is locally known as Yarlsber. Oval or sub-rectangular in plan it has a strong earthen perimeter bank and no obvious internal features. To the west of the beck there is another site, also indicated on the maps, which has banks broadly similar to Yarlsber's – which is not to say they are contemporary. Yarlsber has defied interpretation though some people believe its earthwork was thrown up with defence in mind, and that it had some connection with the supposed hillfort on Ingleborough's summit plateau. This is pure speculation. The bank may simply have served to demarcate a domestic site/farmstead (if that is what it was) from where stock would have grazed. A lot of effort clearly went into its construction. It could be Iron Age, or Romano-British, or even medieval.

Further east, between Clapham and Austwick, there is a much larger and more complex settlement site, again marked on modern maps. It consists of one or two circular structures, possibly huts, with surrounding paddocks or small enclosures that seem to have grown organically with small enclosures having been added on to others. No excavation has been carried out here but, some years ago, a metal detectorist comprehensively searched along the public right of way close to the site, turning up artefacts that spanned two millennia.[6] Among the finds were eight Romano-British brooches, a Roman ring, a spear butt, an enamelled button and a Roman-period key, all of which could suggest late Iron Age/Romano-British occupation of the site. It must be borne in mind, however, that the person concerned maintained that all these objects came out of the ground along the footpath and not from within the settlement. If that is the case, the objects may originally have just been

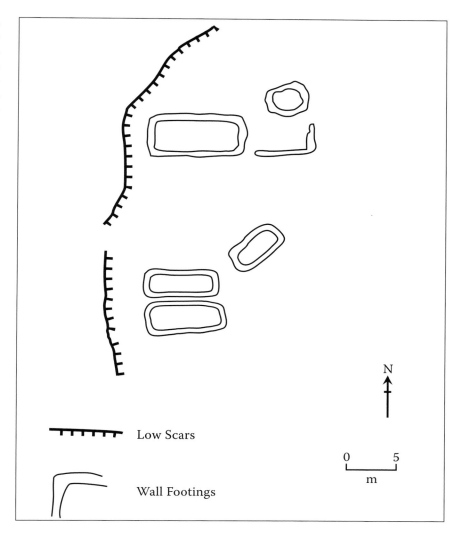

Figure 6.2
Probable Romano-
British Settlement in
Crummack Dale.
Source: With
acknowledgements to a
survey by Michael and
Jill Sykes in 1988

Low Scars

Wall Footings

N

0   5
m

dropped in passing, but one would have to wonder why so many valuable objects had been so carelessly discarded or lost.

Within a rough and steeply sloping field adjacent to White Stone Lane, where it leaves the hamlet of Wharfe, there is a settlement site far more complex than that just discussed. It consists of a series of building platforms cut into the natural slope, giving the site a terraced appearance. There is more than a hint of rectangularity to the platforms which has led to the suggestion that it has a Romano-British date, but there is nothing to say it is not early medieval or even medieval. As so often happens, this site keeps its secrets well hidden.

Away to the north of Wharfe, nestling below Beggar's Stile, is yet another site. Standing on the stile and looking south, especially in winter and spring when grass and bracken are flattened, one large walled D-shaped enclosure immediately below the slope up to the stile is obvious. Sub-divided into two this is just one element of a wider complex. Further degraded wall lines enclose the cul-de-sac side valley west of the stile, and a long straight wall line runs south-eastwards from the footpath. These are all enclosures designed for stock management, arranged around what must be two separate farmsteads. The eastern complex has two rectangular buildings parallel to each other and very close together with a smaller sub-rectangular structure offset at the east end. Each survives as stone-built wall footings largely grassed over. Associated with these are small and irregular enclosures and a further pair of structures, consisting of the footings of a building, which has a rounded and sunken form, with an adjacent rectangular building and attached walled paddock or pound (Fig. 6.2). All these structures are in the lee of a low limestone bluff which offers a surprising degree of shelter from westerly winds. Also in this sheltered position is a grassed area between the two sets of buildings, about 18m by 18m, completely cleared of stones. The apparent link between early settlement sites and loess soil has been recognised in the very recent past and it is probably no coincidence that this clearing contains loess. Well-drained and naturally fertile, it would have been an obvious place for a garden.

The other farmstead lies 40m away on the same limestone bench that shelters the first site. It consists of two stone-built rectangular buildings, set in an L-shape, with the largest one on a north-south axis and a smaller aligned east-west; a small enclosed area at the right-angle of the two buildings; and a curved wall connecting the gables of the buildings to enclose a small paddock or garden. A short distance downslope from this complex is a permanent water source. Whether or not the two sites are contemporary is not known, nor are their dates. As with the Wharfe site, they could be Romano-British and Arthur Raistrick carried out limited excavations here in the 1930s, and considered them to be late prehistoric.

Excavation archaeology is, by definition, invasive and destructive. It is impossible to dig a site without disturbing it and removing parts to reach lower, thus older, layers. Nevertheless, it can often be the sole way of working out what is under the soil, of dating it, and of identifying form and function. There is a need for a balanced approach though. To simply go around digging artefacts out of the ground, just to see what is there, is no more defensible than renegade metal detecting. Digging objects out of the ground in these ways takes them out of their archaeological context thereby reducing their value in interpreting the site, and certainly removing any chance of their being used as dating evidence. Excavation should be seen as part of a process and the starting point should be a ground, or topographical, survey because no site existed in isolation from its surroundings. Raistrick did not do this, but he should not be blamed because he was a man of his time, and landscape surveys were not normally carried out then. A holistic approach is the preferred option nowadays.

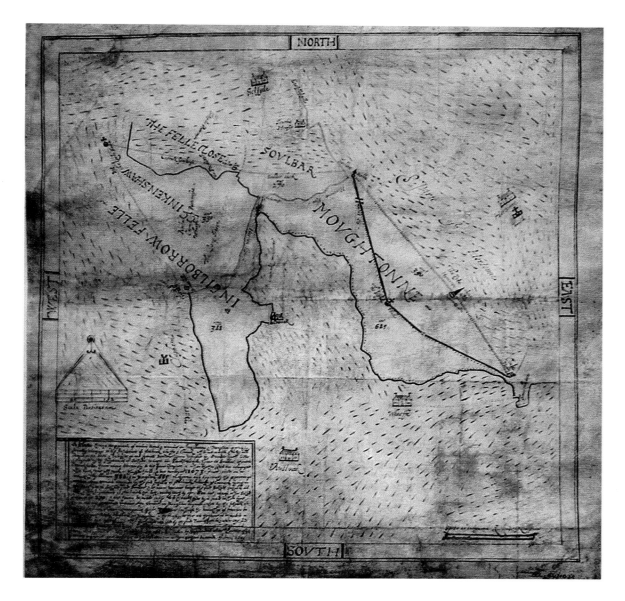

Figure 6.3
Plan of Disputed Lands
in Crummack Dale, 1619
Source: National
Archives MPC1/235

A Probable Medieval Site in Clapham Bottoms

Certain sites above Clapham and in Crummack Dale have features that are characteristic of medieval buildings though, in the absence of dating evidence, they remain unproven. In each case the buildings are rectangular and larger than those described in the previous section. Each is associated with paddock and field enclosures, which are generally quite impossible to date unless good fortune happens to provide something identifiable beneath a wall line and therefore earlier than it. Hopefully, detailed ground surveying might shed some light on the matter.

Clapham Bottoms is a natural bowl-shaped valley at the head of Clapdale with wall lines, especially on the northern side, enclosing an area in excess of 200m by 250m. Though totally ruinous now, the wall lines are still quite clear and contain many sandstone orthostats. The enclosures seem to be centred on a longhouse-type building, aligned north-west to south-east and set above a low limestone bluff. Internally the building measures 14m by 4m, with double-skin walls. Offset at the south-east end of the building is a much smaller structure measuring 2.50m by 3m, with another rectangular structure adjacent to the main building. A curving 20m wall connects the small structure to the northern gable wall of the house, and there is a second, rectangular, enclosure on the opposite side of this long building joining its north gable to the edge of the bluff. The wall bounding this paddock is of much poorer quality than the others suggesting, perhaps, that it was a later addition. There is enough archaeological evidence here, even without excavation, to claim that this particular site is undoubtedly a distinct medieval farmstead.

In the same general area there are several other small discrete enclosures which may well be contemporary with occupation of the farmstead. Also, on the eastern side of the Bottoms, in a very narrow field, there is a further enclosure, associated with loess deposits, and a well-built, squared stone feature. This has dry stone walls still standing to full height but the rear of the feature is bounded by a vertical limestone scar rather than by walls. The site was deliberately selected: it made use of natural attributes and is such a sheltered spot. It is too small internally to have just been a sheep fold, and to have a fold here anyway would not make much sense. It could have been what was historically called a hull.

A plan of the Crummack area,[7] drawn up in 1619 in connection with disputed boundaries, marks two hulls (Fig. 6.3) – 'The highe Hull' on Moughton, which I have tentatively located on the ground (at SD7843 7123) west of the triangulation pillar (Plate 6.2), and 'Duttons Hull' which was plotted on the map just beyond the north end of the westernmost wall that then ended where Clapham Road crossed its line. Duttons Hull can be tentatively located because its position on the map ties in with the stone-built feature mentioned in the previous paragraph.

The word hull (or helm) derives from an Old English term meaning shelter, but for whom? Were they built as an emergency shelter for shepherds caught out in foul weather, or for stock? Folds were generally built to gather sheep together for a specific management purpose such as clipping or washing, whereas hulls were provided so that sheep and shepherds could seek shelter. The problem is that we do not know what these hulls looked like when in use.

The concept of building shelters for stock is not as far-fetched as it might seem and any upland area, at least in the north of England, has shelters peppered across the open fells. They are generally depicted on 1:25,000 maps, sometimes as short sections of isolated straight wall, sometimes as L-shaped sections of wall, and infrequently as short walls built in the form of a cross. The Ordnance Survey occasionally labels them as 'bield' which simply translates as shelter.

A Probable Medieval Site in Crummack Dale

A short distance south of the probable late prehistoric settlement below Beggar's Stile there is a farmstead that can tentatively be placed somewhere within the medieval period. It comprises three discrete buildings, all rectangular, and all with double-skin dry stone walls. It is bounded on the south side by the footings of a boundary wall, with parallel orthostats precisely where the footpath cuts through it. Within this enclosure is a water hole that was formerly protected on the southern side from unwanted stock incursion by a stone wall. Fifty metres north of this is the farmstead (Fig.

Figure 6.4
Probable Medieval
Settlement in
Crummack Dale.

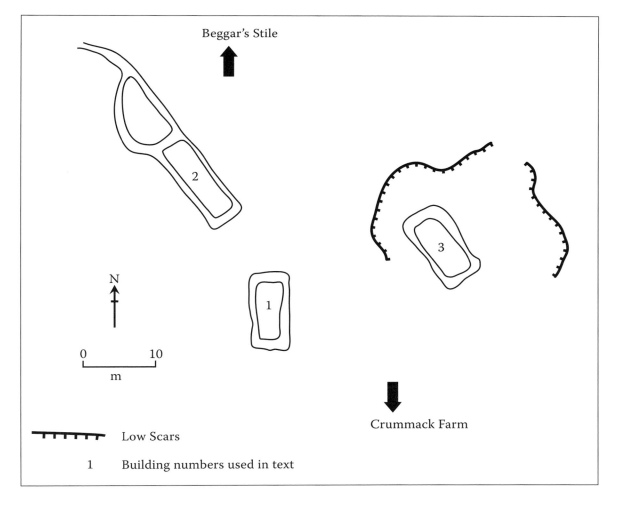

Beggar's Stile

N

0   10
m

Crummack Farm

⊤⊤⊤⊤⊤⊤   Low Scars

1   Building numbers used in text

6.4). The southernmost building measures 10m by 3m internally, has very clear wall lines, and is aligned north to south. There may be a doorway in the north gable.

The second building, 10m north of the first, is larger and is comparable in size to the Clapham Bottoms building, being 13m by 3.50m internally. This one is aligned north-east to south-west and has a possible entry in the south gable, and a contiguous D-shaped enclosure at its northern end. The third building, 30m to the east below a low bluff, is roughly the same size as the first one, being 9.50m by 3.50m internally, constructed on the same alignment as the second, but there is no obvious doorway.

This complex can be seen as a self-contained pastoral-based farmstead consisting of a domestic building (building number two) with attached paddock and two further buildings which may have served other functions. Without excavation no firm conclusions can be drawn and we can only speculate but, assuming they are indeed contemporary, they could have served as store, kitchen or workshop.

Plate 6.2
Possible 'highe Hull' on Moughton, shown on Richard Newby's map of 1619.

There are further, probably medieval, structures above Crummack Dale, tucked beneath a limestone scar and half-hidden among limestone outcrops. Two are long and very narrow with one lying north of the other on a north-west to south-east alignment. Their plan was determined by the lie of the land as there was no room between the outcrops for a wider structure. Both structures are unusual in design. One side and both gables of each were built as normal dry stone walls with the western side of one structure utilising natural upstanding clints with no surviving traces of built structure. This design, together with the southern structure's shape and 14m by 3.20m to 4.20m internal dimensions, are difficult to interpret. It could have supported a roof, assuming a certain amount of timber was employed, so was it a building? There seems to be a doorway in the north gable, but it is rather narrow which would tend to militate against the structure's having been a fold which, in turn, adds weight to the building theory but it does not look as though it was a domestic building? The adjacent structure is equally puzzling, given its shape and size. This one is built into clints on its eastern long side and internal width is variable, dependent on the lie of the clint edges. The northern end is indeterminate so it has not been possible to measure internal length. A short distance away, and on the next bench up, is a third structure of similar size to the previous one. This complex may have been simple buildings designed to house sheep. In the medieval period monastic foundations and baronial estates had sheephouses, or *bercarie*, where breeding ewes were over-wintered and sheep brought to be milked and clipped.[8] A sheephouse (bercaria) was not just one building but an entire farm complex, complete with paddocks and large enclosures, as can be seen on Prior Rakes south of Malham Tarn or at Coniston Pie in Upper Wharfedale.[9] If the Crummack site was a sheephouse, though, it was on the small size.

A Post-medieval Miscellany

The previous chapter started with the dual premise that the Dales are full of visible archaeology and that it is multi-layered and kaleidoscopic. Let us continue by briefly examining a selection of visible archaeological features which have one characteristic in common, namely they are all linear in form.

In monastic times Newby was the administrative and business centre of a vast estate held by Furness Abbey. None of the current buildings can be directly traced back to a monastic origin but Laithbutts Lane was almost certainly one link in a major east-west routeway at that period. Most of Ingleborough Fell was monastic demesne land, mainly put down to extensive, shepherded stock rearing, and the improved land below the head wall on Hagg and Wetherpot Heath would have been a mix of hay meadow, winter grazing and cropland. Lay brothers and farm labourers, and later abbey tenants, carried on a way of working the land that had endured for centuries before the monks ever entered the scene.

The evidence for cultivation is there in the modern landscape in the form of terraces, or strip lynchets. There is a wonderful array of these cultivation platforms at Clapham, between Limekiln Plantation and the village (Plate 6.3) and a less visible field system in the fields below Old Road between Newby and Newby Cote. Lynchet systems were aggregations of individual strips worked in an open-field manner. Exactly when open-fields came into being, and when lynchets first appeared in the landscape, is subject to a certain degree of dispute. Some would maintain that they came in with early waves of Anglo-Saxon settlement whereas another school favours development during the later Anglo-Saxon period. Equally vague and contentious is for how many centuries they were in use, and when they were converted from arable to pasture.

It does not need much imagination to appreciate the amount of labour that went into creating these staircase landscapes. I use the word 'created' advisedly: they did not come about by accident, most did not slowly evolve but were deliberately made in a programme of communal effort that surely required a high level of local social and political control. Some lynchets, like those at Clapham, have very low 'risers' (the slopes separating one strip from its neighbours) while others have risers more than 2m in height, so were lynchets created over a long period of time by repeated ploughings, or were they built before being put into use? These questions have exercised many minds. Medieval ploughs were cumbersome ox-drawn implements and the coulter mechanism was designed to turn the soil to one side only. When the ox team reached the end of a strip it had to be turned round and walked back to the starting point before ploughing could resume. This constant action had the effect of turning soil one way, downslope. If any stones were turned up, the ploughman would have removed them to the side of his strip, and it would seem to make sense to carry them to the downslope edge where they could also act as a revetment to help prevent soil erosion. This explanation seems to make perfect sense if the risers are very low, say no more than half a metre high, but some of the Clapham risers are far too high to have evolved in this way. These can only have been constructed by digging out soil along the uphill edge of a strip and depositing along the lower edge. In optimum light conditions, when the grass is neither too long nor too short and when it is still growing, it is possible to identify where soil was deposited and where not by looking along the length of a strip. The downslope section will almost invariably be a darker green and growth will be more lush. In drought conditions the darker side will still be green, the other will take on a yellowish hue. This is because the deposited soil is deeper, has more nutrients, more bacterial and worm activity, and retains moisture longer.

Individual lynchets can be anything from 50m to 200m in length and in practice topographical detail dictated how long they would be. Each strip was allocated to a different household within the manor and, in some parts of the country, allocation within the open-field was based on the geographical relationship between different households within the village.

Not all open fields had lynchets. This system developed where land was too steep to plough without terracing it but, if the land was reasonably level, the cultivated area was divided up into individual strips with no wall or fence boundaries. Medieval open fields in such situations can often be recognised by parallel low and broad ridges separated by shallow furrows – the classic ridge and furrow landscape. Faint traces of ridge and furrow can be seen in the walled fields below Hagg. These walls are of no great age but just inside the headwall there is an earthen bank close to and parallel to the wall: this is the original, probably medieval, boundary to this set of fields, separating improved land from common fell.

It may be useful to explore this oft-used word 'field'. We of today all know what we mean by a field. It is enclosed by a wall, fence or hedge, has at least one entry gate, and is used for one crop at one time, be it grass or cereals or whatever, and it belongs to one person or farm unit. Our medieval forebears would not have recognised this use of the word. To them a field was a large open area of land divided into strips, either ridge and furrow or lynchets. Thus, all the modern fields between Hagg and Newby Cote were one field in the time when the bank was the only external, stock-proof boundary. Within a (medieval) field there were blocks of parallel strips, perhaps determined by topography or by manorial dictat. Each block formed a furlong; each furlong was split up into individual strips which were known as selions. This pattern can be seen in the Clapham lynchet system. Here, some selions run downslope while others run along the contours, making it quite feasible to map the furlongs.

Each open-field had other essential features which are less easy to identify on the ground in this particular system. Balks were narrow uncultivated strips between selions that acted as walkways through the field; butts were also uncultivated patches where, for example, one furlong butted against another at an awkward angle; and headlands were uncropped sections at the ends of a selion where the ox-team was turned round.

Some medieval field systems tended to be dynamic in the sense that, for reasons we can only guess at, furlongs were re-aligned on a different axis. In places there are landscape signs that lynchets were done away altogether and replaced with a totally different field pattern. The lynchets west of Newby, for example, were at some point replaced with ridge and furrow, a transformation that can still be seen in the fieldscape. Elsewhere, on the other hand, medieval arable strips have been preserved with post-medieval or early modern dry stone walls respecting the gently curving edges of the now grassed strips.

*   *   *

High on Clapham Bents there is an odd stream pattern. The 1:25,000 map shows a stream contouring across Thack Pot and Seat Haw, passing through a tributary of Fell Beck. Nature does not allow this to happen so it has to have been manmade. Follow its line on the map and it becomes Know Gap Sike and herein lies the key to understanding it: it is labelled as a drain. It can be traced across Herningside, round the western and southern edges of Clapdale Scars, to Clapdale farm. According to the map it terminates at Clapdale Barn but, in fact, it runs all the way to the farmstead. It is an artificial feature but the Ordnance Survey is not correct in calling it a drain. The word drain suggests that it was cut to de-water a wet area, to take away excess water, but the sike is doing the exact opposite.[10] It was collecting water from high up and feeding it to Clapdale farm, the now vanished Know Gap farm whose three original buildings survive as one isolated barn, and even to Flatts farm to the south. Know Gap, incidentally, was still occupied in 1885.[11]

For much of its course, above Herningside, it looks like any other small stream and gutter; through the Know Gap and Clapdale enclosures it has the form of an unlined ditch; but in between water was channelled through sections of open earthenware pipe. Where the sike crosses walls, which it

Plate 6.3
Lynchets at Clapham showing two discrete furlongs.

does three times, the wall was constructed on a bridged lintel. See the sike on the ground at any given locality and it seems mundane, nothing to get excited about, but consider it in its entirety and it mutates into a feat of engineering. In total length it is 4km and the total height drop is 200m, giving an average gradient of 1:20. Like many averages, though, this is a meaningless statistic. The last 2km or so see a drop of only 70m giving a gradient here of just 1:30, and for the final 1000m it is barely 1:50. The original surveyor was meticulous with his calculations. He had to achieve a balance between ensuring that the water found its way purely by gravity to the farms in a consistent flow but not at too high a velocity.

There is no record of when the channel was built but it was depicted on an 1814 estate plan[12] and on a plan of 1829 which shows it running beyond Clapdale farm down to Clapham Beck.[13] It is also marked on the 1847 Tithe map. It continued in use, providing Clapdale and Flatts with water for all their domestic and farm needs, until the decision was taken by the Ingleborough Estate in 1929 to replace it with a hydraulic ram from Clapham Beck.[14] This was not the still-operational ram just below Ingleborough Cave which was installed later on.

*   *   *

Richard Newby's map of 1619 (see Figure 6.3) shows the walls that existed at the start of the seventeenth century.[15] The wall that encircles Crummack Dale and Thieves Moss is shown, as is the wall forming the parish boundary between Clapham and Austwick above Thwaite Scars as far north as the former Clapham Road. No walls are shown within the valleys either side of Thwaite because enclosure here came much later, though the map does label "ancient inclosures" within Crummack. An earlier map, dated 1603, drawn up by the well-known cartographer Christopher Saxton,[16] only shows the walls on the eastern side of Crummack Dale from Lord's Seat on Simon Fell to Moughton, and the other boundaries are shown as pecked lines indicating they were in dispute. Saxton's map also has a label 'The Broken Wall' above Crummack Dale. It is not clear from the map exactly in which direction this ran, but there are two possibilities, and today both are emphatically 'broken'. One follows the limestone rim round the top of Thieves Moss then cuts south-eastwards across the limestone pavements from below Sulber Gate. This is a very fragmentary and crude wall, most of which has long since gone. The other possibility runs south-westwards from just south of Sulber Gate, initially parallel to but on a level higher than Clapham Road. In places this wall still stands to its full height but elsewhere it has completely collapsed. Careful examination of the method of construction of this wall and comparison with the nearby wall, shown on the 1619 map, suggest that the latter is less old.

It is often repeated that dry stone walls out of the valley bottoms were put up as part of the parliamentary enclosure process, roughly from 1750 to 1850, especially the ruler-straight walls, but this is far from the case. True, many of the walls climbing up and over the high fells, clinging to ridiculous gradients, do date from that period, but we have proof here in Crummack Dale that walls still sound today were there before 1619 and 1603, and that the 'Broken Wall' was already in a ruinous condition by 1603.

Before we set aside the archaeology of Crummack Dale, let us briefly visit two more 'heaps of stones' in the vicinity of Long Scar. Both were houses; one is shown on Newby's map.[17] There is a pile of stones – a cairn – on top of the prominent knoll on Long Scar, formerly called Dudderhouse Hill, between the two arms of Clapham Road. Close by is a long ruin, a collapsed building, which looks to have had three internal bays, or rooms (SD7654 7189). It is totally ruinous now but its shape is recognisable enough. It is approximately 18m by 5m internally. It could be the same building that, in 1682, was mentioned as the place on Dudderhouse Hill where woollen cloth was woven and sold.

Not far away to the south-east are more ruins, this time of a two-bay structure. This enjoys a sheltered position, unlike the other one which is very exposed to every wind direction, and it faces the morning sun. Externally it is only 9m by 6m, on the small side for a building, but it has some very fine surviving stonework, particularly corner quoins. I cannot supply a name for it but it was there in 1619, and it was a house. Newby's map uses pictorial symbols for settlements: villages like Horton or Austwick, and hamlets like Wharfe or Selside, are shown as a three-bay building with two end wings and a central door. Farmsteads like Crummack or South House are depicted as two bays. This ruin was shown as a one-bay building with a central doorway, and a roof that is given exactly the same form as the larger settlements. We can safely conclude that this was a small house, still extant in Newby's day.

*   *   *

Scattered across the limestone pavements of Long Scar and Moughton are slabs of pavement that have been set in an upright position within grykes, sometimes near a drop but more often not. Some are small enough for one person to have moved but others would have required a communal effort. They are a total mystery – when it was done, by whom and why are unknown quantities. If they are early modern features, we can perhaps explain them away as the work of creative shepherd boys with time on their hands wishing to add their little signature to the landscape. If, as some believe, they are prehistoric the rationale for doing it will no doubt elude us for ever. We can theorise, and try to draw parallels with 'traditional' societies and behaviour patterns across today's world, but we would merely be indulging in guesswork.

There is a view that their rough dating – prehistoric or modern – could be ascertained from a study of lichen cover on the stones. If they were set upright in ancient times, one might expect to find extensive lichen cover on upstanding faces above the clint tops with none within the grykes; conversely, if they were set in early modern times, lichen cover would extend across all surfaces that had lain uppermost before the slabs were ripped off the pavement. However, my cursory examination of selected uprights can add nothing of value: I have found some with deep-set lichen and others with minimal cover.

*　　*　　*

So far in this part of the book we have seen how people have made use of the landscape over 8000 or more years, where they settled or dallied awhile, and how they impacted upon the landscape that each set of folk inherited. None of this could have happened without some form of movement, whether into our area from elsewhere or within it, so it is pertinent to examine lines of travel within the Ingleborough area, which is the subject of the next chapter.

SEVEN

Routes through the landscape

Old Roads and Travellers

Modern maps show only two roads through Ribblehead: the Ingleton to Hawes road (B6255), with a branch road north into Dentdale, and the Ribblehead to Settle road (B6479). To the south of Ingleborough the modern A65 broadly follows the line of much earlier routeways, with the first representation of a road here having been on a map of key routes drawn up in the early years of the reign of Edward III. Ordnance Survey maps also show a network of footpaths, most of which run broadly from north to south with the notable exception of the path from Horton in Ribblesdale to Ingleborough summit. In past centuries many of these footpaths were themselves roads and a close study of the Ingleborough area reveals a dense network of 'lost' roads (Fig. 7.1).

These former roads, though, were not roads in the modern sense. They were not regularly maintained and could be impassable in winter or wet weather; they were the cause of constant complaint from hapless travellers; and they were not necessarily confined within stone walls. To visualise a road from the past we need to think more of routes rather than roads. We need to imagine a general, and often vague, line across the landscape, sometimes paved with hard-packed stone cobbles but more often unpaved, potholed, rutted and alternately dusty and muddy. Then we need to think of this line as a broad swathe rather than as a modern road, because past travellers chose the best option for getting across a particular section of ground. If the obvious track was too rutted or muddy or covered in water, the sensible traveller would pass alongside on drier or smoother ground, extending the width of the track, changing its course, time and again.

We should not think of old roads as roads in the modern sense but as rough tracks or simply as route lines.

Nowadays people who pass through Ribblehead or between Ingleton and Settle may be tourists or visitors – walkers, nature lovers, those interested in railway history and architecture – or farmers going from farm to field or market; they may be wagon drivers delivering stone from local quarries; or they may simply be passing through on a longer journey across the Dales.

Why, though, did we need so many routes in the past, and who was using them? Where were these people going, what were they taking with them, why did they come through the area, how did they travel, and where did they stay on their journey? This chapter will explore these issues at different time periods in Ingleborough's history.

Figure 7.1
Road Network in the
Ribblehead Area.

Prehistoric Lines of Travel

It is impossible today to point to a given route and say that it was an Iron Age or Bronze Age route. To make such claims would be to ignore the realities of the prehistoric Dales. Population totals were small, certainly before the coming of the Romans, and people were widely scattered across the landscape. The vast majority of people moved on foot so there was no need to create roads as such. They went from here to there using the easiest line, depending on the season and the purpose of their journey, and the density of movement was too low for actual permanent defined tracks to evolve on the ground. Our distant ancestors knew the details of their landscape far better than we do and they did not need signposts or satellite navigation systems to complete their travels.

Travel in the Mesolithic

The earliest travellers in the area came here from their coastal retreats on summer forays searching for game, foraging for fruits and nuts, and generally building up a stock of provisions for the winter season (Fig. 7.2).[1] No such coastal lowland sites spring to the average mind for the west coast – though flint knapping sites have been found on the southern coast of South Lakeland – but Starr Carr, inland from Scarborough on a former extensive lake, is a major site that has undergone intensive archaeological exploration for more than fifty years.[2] Our Mesolithic forebears did not permanently live in the Ingleborough area so there would only have been temporary camps: temporary camps did not need roads or even defined tracks. What we need to think of, in the Mesolithic and Neolithic periods, are invasion routes but not invasion routes in the military sense. These people were here for food.

In those times the climate was very different from today and there was much more woodland and forest. Apart from during a part of the Mesolithic it was significantly warmer than now and there would have been different habitats for the people to explore and exploit so they would have had a whole network of lines of travel, possibly determined in part by vegetation density, by water courses, by animal migration routes, or even by a personal preference for returning to last summer's campsite in a particular location dear to the hunter's and forager's heart.

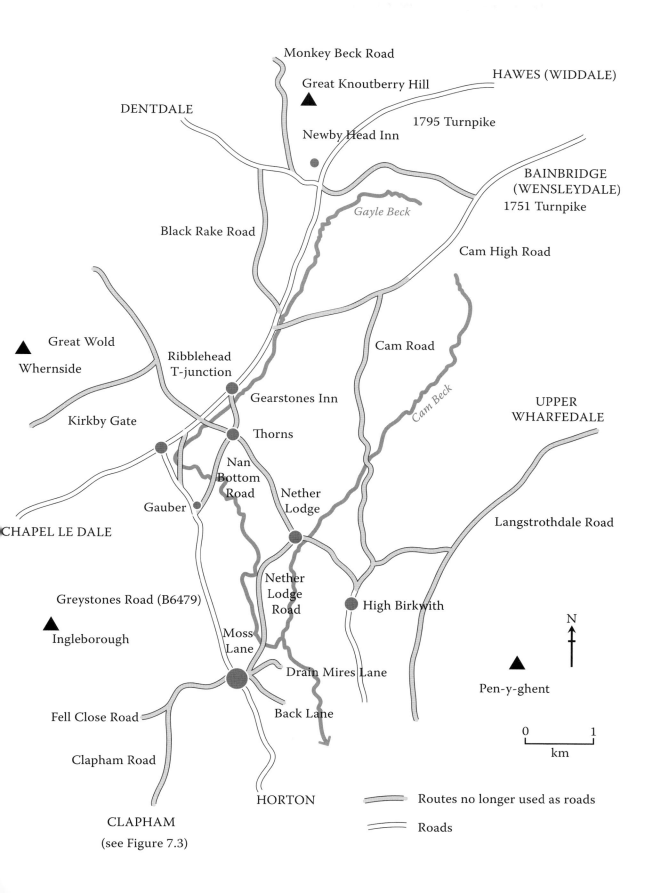

Added to these vague lines of travel were the more regular trading routes that began to develop in the Mesolithic. Worked flint from this period has been found across the region, including in Kingsdale, but no flint occurs naturally within the Dales. It was all brought in, probably from eastern Yorkshire and traded with, or by, our summer migrants. Still, though, the volume of movement was too small to lead to the creation of clearly defined trackways.

What we can say with some certainty is that their seasonal routes would have been more or less fixed. Mesolithic peoples returned to their coastal base before the onset of winter and one obvious way to get from the coast to the Ingleborough area was along the major river valleys rather than over the watersheds, so we can imagine roaming bands of people slowly making their way up the Lune valley from Morecambe Bay and up the Ribble valley from what we now know as the Fylde, and back again in autumn, taking many weeks to complete each journey. Contrary to this hypothesis, though, is the probability that river valleys would have been much more densely vegetated making progress here more problematical than on higher ground.

Viewed from the air, had that been possible, Mesolithic lines of travel within the Dales would have appeared more like meandering animal trails across the landscape rather than as roads.

Routeways of the first Neolithic Farmers

People were able to settle down for the first time in small village settlements or scattered farmsteads once farming had found its way into the Dales and surrounding areas. As we have seen, these Neolithic inhabitants grew crops and maintained flocks of livestock. They traded more widely and more often; they regularly used droveways for transferring stock from farmstead to fell pastures; and they had more social contact with other family or clan groups. Viewing the scene from the air in the Neolithic, our time traveller would certainly see a denser network of tracks, especially given the widespread woodland clearance that had taken place, but it is doubtful if any of these would have been recognised as an actual roadway. The volume and frequency of travel were still too low for this. Continuing archaeological investigations may shed light on Neolithic lines of movement because scatters of flint tools that are being found may mark stopping off points on their travels.

In the Later Prehistoric Period: the Bronze and Iron Ages

During the Early Bronze Age the climate was still much warmer than today and the region was able to support a growing population.[3] As there is more evidence of settlement and burial, it can be assumed that there was more trading and thus more travel. Most years would have seen food sufficiency, or maybe even surplus, giving people more time to socialise and enjoy themselves instead of having to spend all their time in the business of merely existing and subsisting. Different clan groupings would have come together at

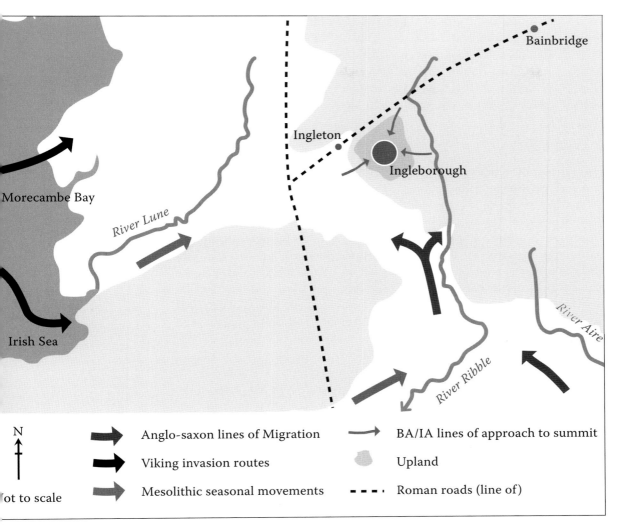

Figure 7.2
Invasion Routes and
Lines of Travel.

key times of the year for social and economic intercourse, or for reasons of religion or ritual. All this would have generated more movement and a more clearly defined set of routeways, local and long-distance. However, it is still unsafe to point to a given track as having Bronze Age origins. Later on in the Bronze Age there was severe climatic deterioration and depopulation of the higher parts.[4] Woodland regenerated, pastures were reclaimed by nature, and much of the complex system of tracks would have been lost.

The population resurgence during the Iron Age and the consequent spread of settlement in the area were intertwined with further forest clearance and renewed economic activity, including trade and social interaction. Use of the enclosure on the summit of Ingleborough – for whatever purpose – without doubt led to the growth of linear lines of approach from dale bottoms to the summit. There are few sensible options to get from the valleys to the summit enclosure and the present paths used by hillwalkers may well be on the same lines as Iron Age tracks, such as from Philpin Sleights (SD744 777) through Humphrey Bottom, from Colt Park (SD772 779) up Park Fell, from Ingleton past Crina Bottom (SD723 735), and from Horton through Sulber Nick. Walking these paths today may well be following in the footsteps of our late prehistoric ancestors, even if only symbolically.

Roman Roads

The process of subduing the native Iron Age tribesmen was not an easy one and the Roman occupiers were subjected to years of guerrilla warfare before they were able to claim full control over various parts of the country. The catalyst for Roman military activity in the Dales had been civil war among the Brigantes, and the Romans moved in to support the pro-Roman queen, Cartimandua. The legionary fortress for the north was based in York and the conquest was set in motion in AD 70.[5] To enable it to happen the Romans built a series of forts at strategic locations. They also built smaller marching camps set at a day's marching distance apart, that is at intervals of about 20km, but whether these were integral to and contemporary with the fort network, rather than having been built during the initial military pacification campaigns, and therefore earlier than the forts, is a matter of conjecture. Whichever was the case, all forts and camps were linked into a network of engineered roads, not always arrow-straight in the Dales as the hilly topography made this impracticable. The early roads were probably just waymarked trackways and it is thought they were only paved in the early to middle second century AD.

There was a major fort at Bainbridge (*Virosidum*) in Wensleydale, built between AD 90 and 105, and one at Overborough (*Calacum* or *Alauna*)) in the Lune valley controlling the major north-south artery. A Roman road connected Bainbridge with that road and it passed through Ribblehead. The exact line of the road is confirmed from Bainbridge to Gearstones where it is now known as Cam High Road for much of its length, though it would be stretching the truth to say that the present surface of the road is Roman. It is a Roman road without doubt but it has been altered and repaired many times through the centuries. The road has recently been upgraded as part of the Pennine Bridleway scheme and archaeological trial trenches were laid out on the assumed line of the Roman road on Cam End, but the results were not conclusive: earthwork traces that may have been Roman were found. The road forded Gayle Beck somewhere near the modern ford and footbridge crossing and there must have been many occasions when troops and auxiliaries were held up waiting for a flood surge to subside (Plate 7.1). From Gearstones to the known line of the north-south road the exact route of the Roman road is not certain. Pointing to the straightness of Oddies Lane, some claim that is the line of the Roman road and, indeed, the Ordnance

Survey maps mark it as such, and there are clear signs of an old approach down the steep drop just above the church at Chapel le Dale which could be Roman. However, this has not been excavated so it remains mere theory.

The total distance from the fort at Bainbridge to the north-south road is about 38km, too far for one day's march, so they must have had a preferred place to camp somewhere in between. The half way point is on Cam End where the Pennine Way and Dales Way now diverge. This spot is just over 400m above sea level which might seem too high for a tented camp but the known marching camp near Malham Tarn lies at 380m. The Roman strategists would have sought a generally flat piece of ground up to 10ha in size, clear of trees with unbroken lines of sight in all directions. Cam End would have been ideal and, if the troops had marched further west they would have had to camp at Gearstones in the valley bottom with restricted lines of sight, or at windswept Ribblehead. There is, however, absolutely no evidence on the ground of a camp at Cam End. Cam End would also have been an ideal spot for a signal station but, again, no evidence has been found on the ground.

There was also a Roman route from the north-south road to the fort at Ilkley (*Olicana*). The precise line of this east-west road is recognisable on the ground from the fort to Skipton but not so further west though various suggestions have been made. None is any more or less acceptable than the rest. One slight hint of its line was provided by the chance finding in very recent times of a Roman *hippo sandal* (a temporary iron shoe worn by pack animals) in a field close to the A65 between Ingleton and Whinney Mire.[6]

When the Roman occupation came to an end many of their roads soon fell into disuse as troop movements ceased. The end of a centralised system meant taxes were no longer collected; intensive farming that had generated cash to pay those taxes was no longer viable; collapse of the market system led directly to collapse of local manufacturing; and the end result was decline and probable slow abandonment of settlements associated with Roman forts which, in turn, soon led to a decrease in trade and regular traffic, making roads redundant. The Roman road from Bainbridge to Gearstones, however, survived because the engineers had chosen the only sensible route over the watershed, leaving this road in use until the present road up Widdale was constructed at the end of the eighteenth century.

'Dark Age' Invasion Routes

There is a long gap in our knowledge of the Dales between the Roman departure and the Norman Conquest and it used to be believed that this area, like much of the country, sank into a chaotic abyss with economic collapse and political and social turmoil. Archaeological excavation here and elsewhere is showing that this traditional view needs to be reassessed, and the term early medieval is preferable to talking of the Dark Ages.

The political vacuum left by the Roman withdrawal was inevitably filled by native warlords or chieftains who established control over a series of separate, and probably warring, lordships (some writers call them kingdoms). Much of the Lake District became Rheged, the north-eastern fringes of the Dales became Catraeth, and the south-eastern Elmet.[7] Sandwiched in between was Craven, the *Cravescire* of Domesday Book.[8]

The first Anglo-Saxon settlement in Yorkshire occurred in the early fifth century on the banks of the Humber and a westward spread really only began towards the end of that century as swelling family or kinship bands slowly moved up the major river valleys towards the Pennine heartland.[9] In the Dales, though, nothing would have changed until the seventh century as the region was too remote and climatically marginal for these early farming settlers to bother about. In addition, the Angles could not penetrate the Dales until the defeat of the native chiefdom of Elmet in 616 or 617.[10] Even so, their new ideas would have invaded the Dales long before the people themselves started to put down roots here.

Movement into the Dales was a slow process spread over several generations. A growing population put pressure on land causing some to seek fresh ground to set up their family or clan home. Over time this led to a gradual spread of new farmsteads and hamlets further and further up the main valleys and into the side valleys. The main lines of Anglian migration in our area were probably north-westwards through the Aire Gap, northwards up the Ribble valley and north-eastwards up the valley of the River Greta beyond Ingleton. All of these movements would have led to the evolution of a system of routeways, or could have built on surviving Roman period tracks.

The first Danish raids in England happened in 789 and it was not long before these Vikings brought over their families to start a new life in 'Yorkshire'.[11] Like the Angles, they too spread slowly up the rivers like the Wharfe, Aire and Ribble, sometimes settling in existing villages and sometimes creating new ones, again with routeways becoming more ingrained on the landscape. Because it took many years – even a few generations – to reach the upper Dales, it is more useful to refer to these incomers as Anglo-Danish rather than Danish or Viking. Whether they still spoke their ancestral language is not known, and the Danes are generally indistinguishable from the Angles by DNA analysis, making informed study of settlement patterns and ancestry problematic.

Another wave of migrants came from the west. They were originally Northmen and Danes who had come round the north of Scotland and settled in Ireland, only to be evicted from there after defeat in battle in 902.[12] Many settled in the Isle of Man, others sailed across to settle after 915 in Cumbria, while large numbers sailed up river estuaries like the Ribble, Douglas and Lune, with the Ribble valley having been their main artery with its easy links through the Aire Gap to the Viking town at York. These people were more used to a pastoral lifestyle than a crop farming life so they tended to look for more open places to settle. By the time these folk reached the Ingleborough area they had lost many of their ancestral ways and their language had already been much altered from the original Old Norse or Old Danish. These movements from the west would have added to the overall route network around Ingleborough.

Packhorse Routes

During the Middle Ages much of the Dales was managed either as monastic estates, manorial demesne or hunting forests. By this time the various waves of migrants had become fused into a rural population whose livelihoods were partly based on subsistence farming though trade and regular movement out of the area was common. Butter and cheese, wool, building materials and general provisions needed to be transferred from isolated farm to and from monastery or manor house, as well as to markets such as Settle, Skipton and Kirkby Lonsdale. Minerals such as lead, and vital products such as coal, lime and salt (the latter from Morecambe Bay until the 1670s) needed moving from source to consumer. There was, in fact, more travel than we may have imagined. Most of this was done on foot with goods being transported by packhorse trains and a whole network of packhorse routes developed, criss-crossing the Dales. Many of these became later Enclosure or coach roads where suitable, as in Clapdale and Crummack Dale (Fig. 7.3), as we shall see later.

Packhorse routes were in use for many centuries, especially in the Dales as the terrain and climate made the use of lumbering carts and wagons impracticable for long-distance movement, though not so in lowland regions.[13] Wheeled vehicles were slow and this mode of transport was just too expensive to be of more than limited use. The coming of the railways in the middle of the nineteenth century killed off the packhorse though a few operators did struggle on till the end of that century in remote areas.

Packhorses were not horses but ponies and a number of breeds were in common use. The Scottish Galloway pony was hardy enough to cope with the climatic conditions on the fells and some packhorse routes became known as the Galloway. Locally these ponies were called gals and those that carried burnt lime were limegals.[14] Others used local Dales ponies which were tough and able to carry over 100kg as long as the goods had been properly and expertly loaded, well balanced on both sides of the pony's back. How the goods were carried depended on what they consisted of: sometimes baskets or panniers were used, sometimes sacks or barrels, and some loads were just laid across their back (Fig.7.4). Whatever system was used, however, the key was to strap the burden down carefully and firmly but without cutting into the pony's flesh.

In some areas a group of packhorses was known as a *jag* and the drivers as

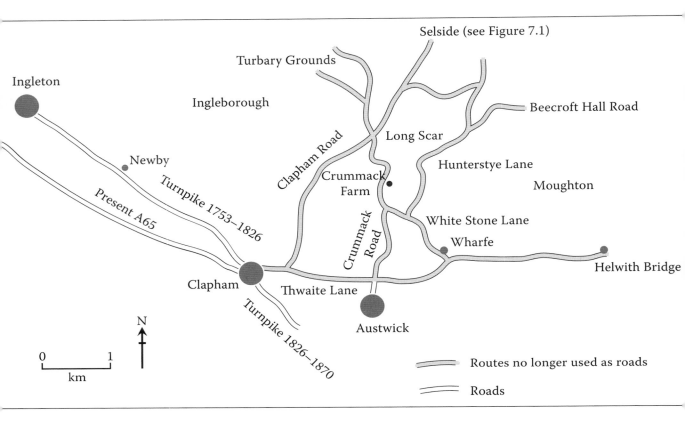

Selside (see Figure 7.1)

Turbary Grounds

Ingleton

Ingleborough

Beecroft Hall Road

Clapham Road

Long Scar

Newby

Turnpike 1753–1826

Hunterstye Lane

Crummack Farm

Moughton

Present A65

Crummack Road

White Stone Lane

Wharfe

Helwith Bridge

Clapham

Thwaite Lane

Turnpike 1826–1870

Austwick

N

0   1
km

Routes no longer used as roads

Roads

Figure 7.3
Road Network in
Crummack Dale and
Clapdale.

jaggers or *jaggermen*, either because a German breed of pony called a Jaeger had been used in medieval times or because of the Old English word 'jag' meaning a load. In the Dales packhorse trains were often called gangs.

A gang covered 50km on a good day though progress would be affected if conditions were wet and the tracks muddy. The ponies were able to cope with most conditions and George Walker wrote, in 1814, that the ponies had 'a manner of going peculiarly their own'.[15] Drivers and assistants ate a rather monotonous and basic diet, consisting of oat-cakes, bacon and dried meat, washed down with weak ale, and life was hard, especially in winter conditions. The ponies were sometimes allowed to graze as they went unless the drivers wanted to get a move on, in which case they were muzzled. Ideally nights were spent at inns that specialised in catering for gangs, having small paddocks to turn the ponies loose in and undercover storage for precious goods. Such inns were often called *The Packhorse*. For example, the present *Craven Heifer* in Stainforth in Ribblesdale was originally *The Packhorse*. Some longer and more remote packhorse routes had hedge alehouses, small and basic inns where food and ale could be had, a bed for the night could be found often on straw and, again, the ponies could be turned loose in surrounding paddocks.

One early nineteenth-century account, written by a coachman staying the night at a packhorse inn, gives us a graphic insight into the trade.[16] He wrote

> Ah, sir, them was jolly times. The packmen used to travel in a lot together, and when they put up at an inn for the night, there was fun – but what they was a bit rough like. Packmen at times carried a lot o' money about with them …

They did indeed often carry large amounts of money, either to pay for goods they were on their way to collect or from goods they had just sold.

Apart from these long-distance packhorse movements, there was more local traffic. Broggers went from farm to farm buying up wool and taking it to weavers to be processed; badgers went from farm to market buying and selling grain; and chapmen were pedlars who made regular rounds of farms and outlying cottages carrying basic household goods as well as trinkets (the *hustlements* of seventeenth-century probate inventories) and the occasional luxury for special occasions (Fig. 7.5). Householders always looked forward to their coming because they also brought news from the outside world and, perhaps more importantly, gossip from elsewhere!

Several of these packhorse routes passed through the Ingleborough area (see Figure 7.1). Great Wold or Craven Way was a major north-south packhorse route that came from Dentdale over to Ribblehead, now followed by a public right of way. Hare Holes (SD739 849) was a managed watering hole maintained for ponies to slake their thirst on the long climb out of Dentdale, though little sign of it has survived on the ground. This route originally headed south-east from Little Dale to Ribble Head House but this has now been completely lost. From there it crossed over the beautiful packhorse bridge at Thorns Gill (SD777 794), to reach the now deserted hamlet of Thorns (Fig. 7.6 and Plate 7.2). This, incidentally, is a classic packhorse bridge. We often read that packhorse bridges, being very narrow, had V-shaped refuges for people to get out of the way of the ponies. The problem with this notion is that the bridge parapets would have blocked the ponies' progress because their panniers or whatever hung out at each side. A genuine packhorse bridge did not have parapets. From Thorns the route headed south through Nether Lodge to High Birkwith, Horton in Ribblesdale and southwards.

Figure 7.4
Contemporary Views of
Packhorse Drivers.
Source: W. H. Pyne,
J. Hill and C. Gray
(1808) 'Pictureesque
Groups for the
Embellishment of
Landscape', London:
W. Miller

Plate 7.1
Line of the Roman
Road at Gayle Beck,
Far Gearstones. The
exact fording point is
unknown.

In addition to general goods, this road was important in its latter days for transporting crafted pieces of Dent marble (actually polished, fossil-rich black limestone) from Stone House in Dentdale to the Leeds and Liverpool Canal at Gargrave, and butter from the same dale to market in Settle and Skipton.

Cam High Road (the old Roman road) from Bainbridge through Gearstones to Ingleton was the main east-west route north of the mountain. Again, apart from general goods, this route carried large quantities of quicklime produced in a string of lime kilns along the road to the east of Cam End. It also fed into the Wednesday markets held at Gearstones from the medieval period until 1892. Strings of ponies would have been seen loaded up with sacks of corn – mainly oats – and oatmeal brought over from farms in Wensleydale to be sold to traders who came here from all over to attend these highly important economic and social occasions.

The Driving Road, also known as Monkey Beck Road, was another north-south artery. It climbed up from Garsdale as Galloway Gate, contoured round Great Knoutberry Hill, dropped directly down to Newby Head farm and then headed south-east through Gavel Gap to Cam Houses and Wharfedale. Much of this route was restored in 2006 as part of the new Pennine Bridleway, though the original section down to Newby Head is now just a linear depression through the enclosed fields. Locally-sourced products frequently seen on this road were coal from pits and lime from kilns on Wold Fell and Cross Pits.

A branch from this road was Black Rake Road that cut across Stoops Moss to Gearstones to link with the Great Wold road; Cam Road branched off Cam High Road at Cam End (SD801 804) and headed south over Ling Gill to High Birkwith; and Kirkby Gate (gate is from an old Norse word meaning road) branched off Great Wold road and connected a string of farmsteads below Whernside to Ingleton and westwards.

On the southern edge of the Ingleborough massif there was another very important east-west packhorse route linking Fountains Abbey and its estates in Wharfedale with the port of Lancaster and its Borrowdale estates. Well known as Mastiles Lane between Kilnsey and Malham Tarn, this route continued along Henside and Moor Head Lane, or through Rainscar and down Long Lane, fording the Ribble at Helwith Bridge. Quarrying at Dry Rigg has destroyed part of the onward route but it can be picked out on the slopes below Moughton Scar contouring above Newfield House, passing through the now ruined original Far End and then White House to enter the hamlet of Wharfe (see Figure 7.3). This long-distance road now joined with other routes traversing Crummack Dale from the north before heading west through Clapham (possibly roughly along the line of Thwaite Lane) and up Laithbutts Lane to the Furness Abbey grange at Newby, then ever westwards along lines now lost.

Packhorse roads tended to follow direct lines wherever they could but not so if they encountered a steep incline. Loaded pack animals struggle on steep slopes, whether ascending or descending, so routes here tend to take a longer but more gradual line, sometimes zigzagging. In times of wet weather, and for much of winter, these trackways became muddy and slippery water channels. Progress at times was made impossible and it is for this reason that packhorse drivers picked out a new line to avoid time wasting and possible accidents. All this has become fossilised in the landscape as a series of holloways, sunken and now grassed over channels that interconnect as they seek the line of least resistance. Particularly good examples can be seen alongside the modern road climbing out of Kingsdale at its southern end (Plate 7.3), where local researchers are currently engaged in detailed archaeological examination of the exact line of the medieval route up Kingsdale; and on the approach to Crummack Dale from Austwick where the holloways pass from one side of the tarred road to the other. Here the holloway seems to stop at the top field wall whereas it continues beyond parallel to the present road. Whenever that wall was built the old road line had already gone out of use, or else was diverted at that time.

Plate 7.2
Thorns Gill Bridge a
packhorse bridge in its
original state.

Drove Roads

If the inhabitants of lonely farmhouses welcomed the infrequent coming of the chapman or badger, they would certainly have gone overboard with joy when the drovers appeared over the horizon (Fig. 7.7). There is documentary evidence that cattle droving was part of the rural economy from 1323,[17] but the trade was prohibited by decree in 1598. It was resumed in 1611 following on from the union of the English and Scottish crowns in 1603 after which the troublesome border region settled down into a state of parlous peace. The border reivers who for generations had occupied themselves with the dubious pursuits of cattle raiding and plundering were compelled by circumstances to find a new role for themselves, and many turned to cattle droving – a case of poacher turned gamekeeper if ever there was one. The trade really began to take off when prohibitive tolls imposed in 1611 were abolished in 1672.

Figure 7.5
Contemporary View of a Chapman.
Source: as Figure 7.4

There was a less obvious result of pacification. It stimulated selective breeding programmes in cattle resulting in the development of the Galloway breed. They were small in stature, black, long-haired and extremely hardy and they quickly began to replace local native breeds like the Craven Longhorns.

From the reign of Queen Elizabeth drovers could only operate if they obtained an annual licence which required them to be married and a householder aged over 30.[18] To be a drover was to be a respected member of the community, even though many months each summer were spent on the road. The western Dales were one of the country's most favoured areas for fattening drove cattle before they were sold on to dealers and butchers from the nation's growing urban centres. It was reported late in the eighteenth century that the grasslands of Craven fed the textile workers of the West Riding and Lancashire primarily because the area was almost exclusively pasture land, recognised as of a very superior kind possessing the feeding qualities required to rapidly fatten up cattle to achieve optimum prices at the market. Licensed drovers – or topsmen – sometimes became very wealthy men as the profits from a successful drove were impressive. One of the leading drove masters of the mid-eighteenth century, John Birtwhistle, came from Skipton.[19] He and his sons owned a lot of pasture land around Long Preston and Coniston for fattening the cattle they had brought down from the great trysts at Falkirk before selling them on at the cattle fairs of Malham Moor and Boss Moor near Bordley. The topsmen headed north in April or May each year and popular stories of the day claimed Birtwhistle had up to 10,000 head on the road at any one time. It was big business indeed. One businessman, John Brearley, noted in his diary in 1761 that from Settle and Skipton there were '1000 and ten thousands of Scoth (*sic*) cattle driven into the south of England … each year,'[20] all of them having been driven through Leeds and Wakefield on their way south.

If, however, a drove was struck by cattle plague, or raided by opportunists,

or if the selling grounds in Craven were overstocked, the drove owners saw their potential profit turned into a loss. After all, they had to pay upfront for the beasts in Scotland so the loss was their's. The topsmen and their assistants were waged so had less to lose.

Whereas a packhorse gang could manage 50km in a good day, cattle moved much more slowly, constantly pausing to graze, and covered barely 20km on a good day. The cattle were shod, with three separate shoes per hoof, for the long journey but still the topsmen tried to keep off paved roads and stuck wherever possible to higher ground where roads were unmade. Each individual drove contained on average 200 to 300 head split into groups of 50 or 60, each with its own man or boy to make stock management less of a problem. When checking the herd the drovers counted in units of 20 and scored a mark on a stick which explains why we still refer to 20 as a score.[21] Drovers also avoided toll roads wherever possible: in 1753, for example, tolls on the Skipton to Kendal road were set at 2s per score of cattle, raised to 3s.4d in 1790, but reduced to 10d in 1855.[22] They also kept clear of enclosed farm land and villages, preferring to stick to routes where grazing would be readily available.

The Honourable John Byng travelled through the Ribblehead area at the beginning of the 1790s and he published a detailed diary with some graphic descriptions interspersed among more mundane observations. He recounted that:[23]

Figure 7.6
Thorns Gill Bridge,
Etching by Godfrey
Wilson, 1939.

The Scotch are always wrap'd up in their plaids – as defence against heat, cold and wet; but they are preventions of speed or activity; so whenever any cattle stray'd, they instantly threw down the plaid, that they might overtake them.

At the end of one long and hard day crossing over the tops from Bainbridge he was dropping down towards Gearstones at whose inn he planned to spend the night. It was not to be a comfortable stay, as he wrote that:

at length we procured some boil'd slices of stale pork, and some fry'd eggs, with some wretched beer and brandy:- to which my hunger was not equal; and from which my delicacy revolted.[24]

His journal records that he saw 'vast droves of Scottish cattle passing to the south[25] and that he:

... was much fatigued by the tediousness of

the road whereon we met two farming men, with whom we conversed about the grouse, and their abundance. Crossing a ford, Mr Blakey led me to a public house – called Grierstones the seat of misery, in a desert; and tho' filled with company, yet the Scotch fair held upon the heath added to the horror of the curious scenery: the ground in front crowded by Scotch cattle and the drovers; and the house cramm'd by the buyers and sellers most of whom were in plaids, fillibegs etc ... The only custom of this hotel or rather hovel, is derived from the grouse shooters, or from two Scotch fairs; when at the conclusion of the day's squabble the two Nations agree in mutual drunkenness ...[26]

What the aristocratic Byng had stumbled on was one of Gearstone's twice yearly cattle fairs when cattle were sold before being driven on down Chapel le Dale into Lancashire or down Ribblesdale to Leeds, Bradford and Wakefield. The last cattle fair here was held in 1872, the trade having been killed off by the new railways, while the inn closed its doors for good in 1911 after a bout of serious trouble there.[27] It needs a vivid imagination to conjure up the scene during a cattle fair. For a start the soft green pastures we see today were churned up by countless hoofs. Add the mooing and bellowing, the constant commotion, the men's shouting, the boys' shrieking, the disagreeable odours, the smoke of numerous campfires, the hairy, unwashed and blanketed drovers ... and you will have some idea of what Gearstones was like twice a year.

Apparently many butchers who came to the fairs disdained Gearstones and preferred to put up at another inn, now Newby Head farm, north-east of Gearstones.

To help keep the cattle in some sort of order drovers had their dogs, often of a now extinct breed called the Talbot. Some drove inns, like the one that still exists in Settle town centre, were called *The Talbot* for this reason, though droves would have kept well clear of the town bounds. These dogs seem to have been highly intelligent and there are, possibly apocryphal, stories of droves reaching their end and the men and boys heading back north by coach, or even by boat along the coast, with the dogs being sent off to find their own way home. Innkeepers en route would feed them and collect payment next time the drovers passed that way.

Much of the time, though, drovers slept under the stars, with someone – no doubt a boy! – staying awake to keep an eye open for any cows with the mood for straying. Wherever possible overnight stops were made at what they called stances on open pastures to avoid having to pay for grazing but there is no doubt this was an important source of income for those farmers on drove routes who had pasture to let. As many of the drovers were Scots, some farmers are said to have planted clumps of Scots pines as a way of advertising a welcome. Not all farmers welcomed the drovers, though, and in some instances within the Dales the extent and impact of this free grazing was cited as a reason for enclosing common land within stone walls. Certainly, the enclosure process was a significant factor in killing off the drove trade.

Food, as for the packmen, was simple and designed not to go off. Oatmeal was again the basic fare washed down with whisky (no ale for these men), copious onions were chewed, and black puddings were a welcome and nutritional addition to their foodstock. To make a black pudding they needed three main ingredients: meal (which they carried), fat (they would kill a pig bought at a farm on the way) and blood (which was supplied, no doubt grudgingly, by the cattle chosen to be bled but it did them no lasting harm).[28]

Gearstones was the focus of droving in this part of the Dales and some of the packhorse routes also served as drove roads. Galloway Gate and Great Wold were the main approaches from the north, with the old Roman road the main one from Wensleydale and on into Lancashire. Thorns Gill bridge was obviously too narrow for cattle to cross so there was another road loop from Gearstones Inn fording the stream to skirt round Thorns hamlet from the north-east. Other drove roads headed past Chapel le Dale through Ingleton to Lancaster, and from Ingleton, joining with beasts driven down the Lune

Plate 7.4 Clapham Road at Sulber Gate, looking north, with cosh in the middle distance.

Valley from Westmorland, to follow eastwards the rough line of the modern A65. The modern Ordnance Survey 1:25,000 map picks out a further drove route running southwards from Clapham to Clapham Moor from where it headed due south along Keasden Road. The road surface is standard width for a minor road but there is a broad swathe on each side, shown on the maps as Open Access land. This width is a survival from droving days when cattle were able to spread out and graze as they slowly progressed.

Coach Roads and Turnpikes

As the nation's economy continued to develop through the early modern period it became increasingly obvious that the existing roads could not cope with demands for moving goods around the country. They were often impassable, especially in winter, and usually rutted and uneven. The diary entry of one clearly miserable traveller on the Lancaster to Newcastle coach road through the Dales paints a vivid picture of how dreadful the experience could be when the elements conspired to do their worst. The rain came down:

Figure 7.7
Contemporary View of a Drover.
Source: as Figure 7.4

> in torrents; for snow to fall in darkened flakes or driving showers of powdered ice; for winds to howl and blow with hurricane force, bewildering to man and beast; for frost to bite and benumb both hands and face till feeling was almost gone; and for hail and sleet to blind the traveller's eyes, and to make his face smart as if beaten with a myriad slender cords.

Most roads in the Dales, as across the country, were totally unsuitable for heavy wheeled wagons and an attempt was made in 1555 to improve the situation as an Act of Parliament made each parish responsible for repairing and maintaining its roads, and every parish had to draw up a list of roads in its care. This did not really work, partly because the local men appointed as overseers could not get their fellow men to put in the hours they were supposed to.

Nevertheless, the mid-eighteenth century saw a considerable increase in cross-country movements as roads were slowly improved, and a recognised network of regional coach roads developed, some turnpiked and some not. In 1784 a mail coach network was implemented to connect major population centres. The roads they followed were the equivalent of today's motorways. A map of Yorkshire, produced by Thomas Jefferys, Geographer to the King, published in 1771, shows the coach roads (pre-mail coach routes) through the Ingleborough area.[29]

The Lancaster to Newcastle coach road came via Clapham then across Long Scar above Crummack Dale, along which stretch it was called Clapham Road (Plate 7.4 and see Figure 7.3), dropped down to ford the Ribble at

Selside and headed up to High Birkwith. This is just a farm now but it was an inn in the days of the coach road. From Birkwith the road headed north and then east, as Langstrothdale Road over to Upper Wharfedale to the next inn at Deepdale. A branch of this headed north from Birkwith over Ling Gill Bridge as Cam Road to join Cam High Road. Jefferys also shows the line of the Ingleton to Gearstones road and a road heading from Gearstones down into Dentdale. At this time, though, the present road up to Ribblehead junction did not exist (see Figure 7.1). The road from Horton to Gearstones swung round after Gauber house to cross the Ribble: it still survives as a public footpath.

Another map, compiled by geologist William Smith in 1821, shows that this road had been changed to the line of the present B road, presumably to avoid the river crossing.[30]

Jeffreys marks what is now Thwaite Lane, then not walled, and Clapham Road heading up what are now Clapdale Lane and Long Lane, but he shows no roads within Crummack Dale. Long Lane, incidentally, was once known as Green Lane, according to the 1847 Tithe apportionment. Through roads here did exist in Jeffreys' time so it could be he – or his surveyors – did not venture north of Austwick, or just omitted to include them.

Coach roads were a big improvement on what had been there before but they were still a handicap to both passenger and goods transport. Road surfaces were dreadful, especially as coaches were not sprung; floods held travellers up at river crossings where there was only a ford; and mud and ruts remained constant problems. Something drastic had to be done. Eventually government bowed to pressure and new Acts were passed allowing Justices of the Peace to establish turnpike trusts. Each trust was granted the right to impose tolls on all travellers on turnpike roads, and gates with toll bars were erected at regular intervals. The trusts were usually set up by prominent local businessmen who recognised that improving roads was the key to stimulating trade and their profits. They invested the money needed to bring the roads up to an acceptable standard and recouped it from money raised at toll bars or by issuing bonds at fixed rates of interest. The turnpike movement was a huge success with over 35,000km being built across England and Wales by 1820.[31] Early turnpikes tended to use existing roads but, as traffic and income increased, new and easier routes were cut. It is easy to recognise some turnpike roads today as all had mileposts,[32] many of which name the trust involved as well as giving the precise distances to the next town in each direction, though not all mileposts have survived. In fact, the metal plate on the first milepost west of Newby Head was hacked off its vertical plinth and stolen early in 2007.

The old Roman road, later the drove and packhorse road, from Bainbridge to Ingleton was created a turnpike road in 1751 as the Lancaster to Richmond Turnpike but the original route over Cam was abandoned when a new line (the present B road) was laid out through Widdale and over Newby Head in

Plate 7.5
Turnpike Milepost on
Old Road, reused as a
wall through.

1795 (see Figure 7.1). From Widdale Head (another former inn) to Ingleton the mileposts still survive; within what is now Craven District they were all metal-plated but in Richmondshire, just over Newby Head, they were only made from stone and are much cruder. This abrupt change may suggest that the old stone posts in what was the West Riding (*ie* west of Newby Head) were later replaced by that county council whereas in the old North Riding the original ones were kept. Turnpikes slowly came to an end with the coming of the railways and were formally abolished in 1878,[33] and for the same reason the Golden Age of the mail coach lasted only twenty years, from the 1820s to the 1840s.

Several towns in the Dales owe their growth and prosperity to the turnpikes. Hawes, for example, only started to grow with the coming of two turnpike roads in the late eighteenth century, first the Sedbergh to Askrigg turnpike created in 1761, and then the Lancaster road. Ingleton partly owes its pre-railway prosperity to being at the junction of this turnpike and the Keighley to Kendal turnpike.

This latter turnpike eventually became the A65 connecting Kendal and Kirkby Lonsdale with Settle, Skipton and Keighley. This formalised an ancient artery that witnessed far more traffic movement than any other road in the Ingleborough area. Large trains of packhorses had long journeyed daily to and from Kendal carrying all manner of goods, and it was a long-established coach road, making this road as important then as the A65 later became as part of the link between the north-south A1 and A6. The old coach road was in dire need of repair or replacement: the Act to establish the Keighley-Kendal Turnpike Trust in 1753 could not have been more damning. The existing coach road was described as 'very ruinous and in great decay and, not only impassable for wheel-carriages, but very dangerous for travellers'.[34] There is clearly a certain measure of hype in a statement like this, as the one who penned it was hardly a disinterested observer, but it was founded on reality. The old coach road is shown on a series of strip maps surveyed by Ogilby and published in 1675,[35] heading from Settle in a very direct line over Paley Green to Lawkland before cutting directly north to Austwick and then Clapham. The 1753 turnpike ignored this line. The new road climbed up Buck

Haw Brow from Giggleswick then took the minor road past Brunton House (said by some to have been a former inn) to rejoin the A65, then followed the present minor road into Austwick and the B6480 into Clapham. There was a turnpike tollhouse just west of the village where the turnpike route began the climb up what is now simply called Old Road which passed through Newby Cote and above Cold Cotes to enter the centre of Ingleton (see Figure 7.3), and another at the south end of the village.

This original turnpike road was due to be modified in 1792, though the change was only effected between 1823 and 1826 when it was diverted by constructing new sections along what has become the A65 (though Settle and Clapham bypasses are late twentieth-century creations). The original turnpike house and bars were abandoned and a new toll bar erected east of the village, as shown on modern Ordnance Survey maps.[36] There are a number of clues that confirm Old Road's former function. Just west of Crooklands, at NGR SD726 708, there is an odd-looking stone poking out of the wall on the north side of the road (Plate 7.5). It has a curving carved end visible on the roadside. On one side of the stone is the numeral 8, and on the other the numeral 9. Close examination of this stone shows that the number 8 was cut parallel to the long edge of the stone while the 9 is at right-angles. It was a milepost and once stood upright in the verge but an enterprising wall builder long since decided it would make a sturdy throughstone. The post told the passing traveller that Settle was eight miles distant and Kirkby Lonsdale nine. Why one numeral was carved sideways is a puzzle – was it perhaps done by an illiterate stonemason who did not know what he was carving?

Further along Old Road near Slatenber there is another similar milepost reused as a through, at SD708 721. Unfortunately, this one was set too far into the wall and the numerals cannot be seen without dismantling the wall. In between these two mileposts there are two further clues. On the parish boundary between Clapham and Ingleton, which is marked by a boundary stone (SD721 713), there is a small enclosure on the north side of the road which contains a spring and trough that used to be known as Blindfold Well where passers-by and their mounts could slake their thirst. Those in need of more than a quick drink could partake of the hospitality afforded by the former coaching inn at Holly Platt near Slatenber. Now a farmhouse, this has a very fine double-story, windowed porch where, it is said, someone could keep an eye out for approaching coaches so the staff could spring into action in good time.

West from Ingleton the original turnpike dropped down by the church and passed through Thornton in Lonsdale but this was abandoned in 1826 when New Bridge, complete with surviving toll bar house, was built over the River Greta on the present A65.[37]

The creation of the turnpike system did not sound the death knell for all earlier coach or through roads. Only major routes were drawn into the turnpike web. There is a cartographic illustration of this in Crummack Dale.

In 1806 Jeremiah Batley commissioned the drawing up of a map of his estate and it marks the routes through the dale.[38] Hunterstye Lane, which linked Wharfe with Horton, is shown as a road but the two other lanes – White Stone Lane that runs south-east to north-west from Wharfe, and Crummack Lane from Austwick to Crummack farm and northwards to join Clapham Lane – are depicted as 'High Roads' confirming that these two were of higher status than White Stone, and also links in long-distance through routes (see Figure 7.3).

Enclosure Roads

From the mid-eighteenth century large stretches of open grazing around Ingleborough were enclosed within new dry stone walls. The idea was to allocate the newly enclosed pastures to those farmers who had enjoyed common grazing rights with the hope that they would improve land quality and thus output. In Ribblesdale Birkwith Moor was enclosed in 1758, and Selside and Shaw Park in 1791; much of Austwick was enclosed in 1814 and Clapham in 1758, though Norber was an early enclosure dating from 1755. (See Chapter 8 for a discussion of the enclosure process.)

Each award made provision for the building of new roads within the newly enclosed areas. Some were designed to allow each farmer access through enclosed fields to still open common pastures or to their own distant fields: such roads were called Occupation Roads. They were for the use of anyone awarded allotments accessed by the new roads, and the farmers concerned were given responsibility for maintaining them. Near Ribblehead Nan Bottom Road was a new occupation road connecting Ashes farm with Thorns hamlet while Nether Lodge Road was remade as an access improvement road from Selside to Nether Lodge farm. Greystones Road was remade, straightened and renamed Selside Shaw Road (the present B6479), again to improve access; while Drain Mires Lane, Back Lane and Moss Lane were also constructed as new walled access roads fanning out from Selside.

New or upgraded roads were integral to the 1814 Austwick Award with roads being afforded different terms according to their status in the hierarchy of routes.[39] Hunterstye Road, running up the eastern side of Crummack Dale; Cromack Road, running from Austwick past Crummack Farm to join Clapham Road; and Clapham Road itself were all designated Public Carriage Roads as well as Public Driving and Bridle Roads. This mouthful effectively meant that any user had legal rights on the new road, whether on foot, on horseback, in a cart or carriage, or driving livestock. Hinkinshaw Peat Road and White Hills Bottom Peat Road were designated Public Carriage Roads, thereby permitting carts; and Beggars Road and Beecroft Road enjoyed the lowest level of usage as Public Footways (see Figure 7.3). Horton Bridle Road, running from Sulber Gate eastwards to join Hunterstye Road, was classified as a Public Bridle Road for travellers on foot and horseback only.

Thwaite Lane is a line of travel with medieval origins though the lane as it is now results from the 1758 Enclosure Award of Clapham Thwaite and Side which makes frequent reference to the 'intended' road.[40] This means the old meandering track was formalised, straightened and enclosed within walls between 1758 and 1759. This element of enclosure is common: many existing and possibly ancient tracks were improved and realigned to fit in with the order and discipline of enclosure landscapes. The previously mentioned map produced in 1619, concerning disputed lands in Crummack Dale, marks and names 'Hunter Stye' along the line of the enclosure award's Hunterstye Road, 'Hortonne Stye' where the Horton Bridle Road was delimited, and 'Horton Stye' along what became Cromack Road. The other roads formalised by the enclosure are shown but not named.

Other roads were designated as Turbary Roads so that villagers could have access to new peat (or turbary) grounds to cut and collect fuel for domestic use. Black Rake Road was one such turbary road beyond Gearstones, and the old square cutting beds can still be clearly seen, especially on Stoops Moss near Newby Head. Fell Close Lane was built so that Selside inhabitants could gain access to their peat ground to the south-west of the hamlet. Again, it is possible to make out the regular cuts of this peat ground. Austwick's inhabitants were provided with three turbary grounds, on the Allotment near the former shooting cabin, accessed by two roads. Hinkinshaw Peat Road is still a clearly delineated and dry green track running parallel to the east wall of the Allotment though it has become overgrown north of and beyond the cabin, while its tributary track, White Hills Bottom Peat Road has been convincingly reclaimed by nature. So, too, have the peat workings which are very difficult to make out nowadays. It should be noted that, in many instances, enclosure agreements were merely formalising ancient rights to dig peat. Hinkinshaw peat grounds were shown on the 1619 map as available for Austwick, Wharfe and Crummack households, while Fell Close was marked for those of Selside (see Figure 6.3), and Hinkinshaw Road is shown already in existence at the time of Newby's map.

*　　*　　*

The remainder of this section of the book will carry the story of how people modified and utilised Ingleborough's environments to the present day, sketching out in cameo format certain apparently disconnected aspects that actually seem to knit together to complete the overall picture I set out to paint. I should say, though, that I have been discriminating in what I have chosen to include, and in no way are the chapters that follow meant to be comprehensive in their coverage. To a certain extent they must reflect my own particular interests and research themes.

EIGHT

Developing Landscape: Ribblehead

Commons and Stinted Pastures

As the Middle Ages merged into the early modern period the rural landscape at Ribblehead settled into a pattern that remained largely unchanged from the end of monastic control until the late eighteenth century. We can picture a scene of isolated farms, worked by small landowners or tenant farmers, dominated by stock rearing, with cattle grazing on the lower and sweeter pastures and sheep spending much of the year on the fells. To complete this image we must remove many of the field walls and mentally merge the fields we see today into much larger units, especially in Ribblesdale. Around each farmstead the fields had been created in monastic times by installing drainage ditches and spreading manure and maybe lime to improve the quality of the soil by reducing its acidity. Beyond this ancient intake land much of the area remained as open pastures held in common by tenants and landowners within each manor. These were the commons.

Each manor formulated regulations for the proper management of the commons, and infringements were dealt with by the manor court. Two main ways were devised for controlling stocking rates: it would have served nobody's interests to allow over-grazing. In much of the Pennines the rule of levancy and couchancy was applied to stock control. This meant that no grazier could let loose on the commons in summer more sheep or cattle than he could over-winter back at his farmstead using the fodder he had reaped during the previous summer. This was a self-controlling mechanism. Alternatively, a system of stinting was employed. In this, each farmer was allowed a specified number of stints or gaits. One stint or gait (or gate) represented a defined number of animals. One cow was one cattle gait or beast gait. Manor courts laid down how many sheep one cattle gait was the equivalent of, and farm tenancies were advertised as having a given number of beast or sheep gaits. Although, given human nature, manor court records tell of some people trying to beat the system, it did generally work to everyone's interest.

Some stinted pastures were known as Cow Close. One such pasture still bears the name though it long since ceased to be stinted. Cow Close is named on the Ordnance Survey 1:25,000 map in the area between Ling Gill and Brow Gill (centred on SD797 778). Other former stinted pastures include Selside Shaw (SD782 765) and Lamb Pasture (SD775 752) either side of the hamlet of Selside (Fig. 8.1). We will return to present stinted pastures around Ingleborough in Chapter 10.

Stinting as a management tool dates from at least the late medieval period[1] but it would be fortuitous indeed for a researcher to happen upon dating evidence for the establishment of any individual stinted pasture. Manor court records do occasionally hint at length of usage. Two examples will illustrate this point. An entry in the Newby manor court records for 1543 refers to stints on a common pasture near Chapel le Dale called 'le sleyghtes'.[2] It involved tenants from Southerscales and 'Inmanloge' (Ingman Lodge or Lodge Hall). Place-names on modern maps indicate that Sleights Pasture extended on both sides of the road. Secondly, Winterscales near Ribblehead was described as comprising both Old Close and New Close in 1591.[3] Close means enclosure and this particular enclosure had clearly been walled quite recently before 1591 and in the more distant past. It is shown on modern maps as Winterscales Pasture and the irregular lines of the ancient walled boundary can be traced on the map, stretching from the railway to the top of Greensett Crags. Scales Moor, between Chapel le Dale and Kingsdale, was an unstinted pasture until 1810 when, by agreement of the common holders, it was converted to a stinted pasture.[4]

Despite theoretical rules and regulations being in place to monitor misuse of stints and commons, and even though all gaitholders had access to the pastures, the arrangement was not without problems. As time went on, these drawbacks became increasingly apparent. After the Restoration of the monarchy in 1660 the rural (and urban) economy began to show signs of recovery. Farmers felt secure enough to invest in their land, and in many cases to rebuild their old houses in stone, and farming was transformed from a subsistence to a commercial basis. As happens in all walks of life, some farmers were more progressive than others; some saw the potential of their holdings in terms of surplus leading to profit. Through the late seventeenth and eighteenth centuries the processes of land improvement were stepped up. Those farms having the easiest access to the outside world by being on through routes, as well as high quality pastures and, even better, riverside meadow land, were at an advantage compared to those more remote and less favoured. The larger farms were entitled by the age old system to a greater number of gaits, which again put them at an advantage.

Management of the commons could also be compromised when neighbouring manors were in dispute over boundary lines. We shall

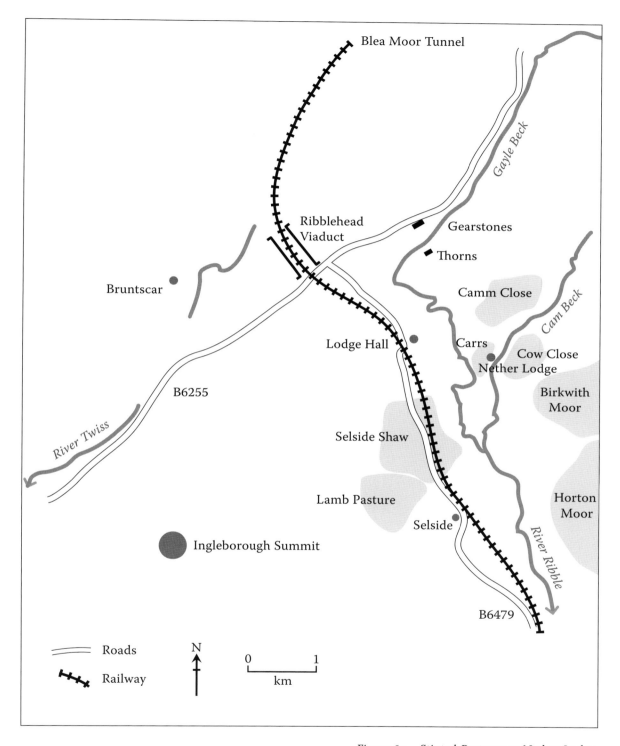

Figure 8.1   Stinted Pastures at Nether Lodge.

investigate one such dispute in Crummack Dale, from the first years of the seventeenth century in the next chapter, and there was one later that century between the residents of Kingsdale and Deepdale. The latter were laying claim to a substantial area of land at the head of Kingsdale and, to try and hammer their point home, a boundary perambulation was undertaken and committed to written form in a legal document, signed by eleven disputants in 1656. It is worth quoting part of it:[5]

> It is to be remembered that the most part of the Inhabitants of the Mannor of Deepdale in Dent ... did the day and yeare above written ride their Bounders upon the Commons belonging to the said Mannor ... and these adioyneing neighbours haaving Notice before of our Rideings did meete us ... and did neither contradicke nor molest us and Ingletonfellmen did likewise meets us with a fox head which they said was killed in that libertie which we challenged who did not say we went wrong and likewise Mr Rippon Chieffe lord of Thornton with some of his neighbours came to meet us who said they would neith stopp us nor sue us for a trespass.

It then goes on to describe in detail the route that the eleven men had ridden, in their word without opposition, from the top of Whernside down Buck Beck to where Kingsdale Head farm now stands, then up Backstone Gill to Gragareth there turning north to follow the present boundary. They were effectively laying claim to almost 5km² by this deposition, dated 10 May 1656.

Put all these elements together and it is not difficult to imagine the more successful farmers wanting to advance their own cause with the disadvantaged being left behind. Add to this the growing realisation that commons and stinted pastures could never be improved in that state. Why should any one farmer expend money and energy in improving the quality of the pasture if others contributed nothing yet still benefited? There simply was no incentive to do anything to these commonly grazed areas.

Enclosure

There was an alternative, however – enclosure and division of the commons within walls and subdivision of the stinted pastures into smaller units. There had been piecemeal encroachment onto the waste throughout the monastic period, as individual tenants nibbled away at the commons, preferring to pay the manor court fines imposed on them but, from the late eighteenth century, we are talking of an organised and systematic approach. Those farmers and landholders who already had the largest number of gaits, and the largest area already privately enclosed, were effectively in a position to dictate to their lesser mortals what was going to happen. In the early years of enclosure legal agreements were drawn up, sometimes by private agreement if most gaitholders agreed, or by Act of Parliament if not, to carve up the commons and stinted pastures by Enclosure Awards, though from the 1770s most awards resulted from parliamentary action.

Each award had its designated commissioner, whose word was law, and he surveyed the area to be enclosed, allocated allotments to the gaitholders according to how many gaits they held, determined where the new walls would run, laid out new roads or straightened old ones, inserted drains or diverted water courses, laid down precise specifications for the walls, and designated specific areas as public quarries for wall and road building, for domestic use and in some cases for burning into lime. This was a major re-drawing of the landscape. It was land privatisation and the ultimate objective was to improve the newly enclosed land so as to boost farm output and profit and, at the end of the eighteenth century, to ensure the nation could feed itself during the long years of war against France. Vast areas of the country, never mind the Dales, were duly carved up and allocated. Selside Shaw and Lamb Pasture were de-stinted and enclosed in 1791; Horton Scar and Harber Scar in 1804; and Horton Moor in 1847 (see Figure 8.1).[6] Some field walls are ruler-straight while others are curvilinear and irregular. Generally speaking, the straight ones resulted from formal enclosure, and the higher the enclosures, the later the process had been put into effect: compare, for example, the altitude and field size of Selside Shaw with the two Scars and then with Horton Moor. There is a clear progression through the years.

Barns, Byres and Boskins

One element of that newly enclosed landscape that still typifies much of the Yorkshire Dales is the field barn. Swaledale and Littondale have the highest density of barns but Ribblesdale also has its fair share. There is a particularly good example at Thorns with another one (SD785 790) next to the right of way over Back Hools Hill to the south of Thorns, though this one has now lost its roof. Many field barns across the Dales have been converted into houses but others less accessible have decayed beyond repair. Roofing slates fall off, rain and frost get inside the building fabric and, very soon, the walls begin to crumble and the roof caves in. The barn is effectively lost. The reason is simple: field barns are now redundant. They no longer fit into the modern farming scheme.

Field barns were an essential aspect of the farming scene right up to the mid-twentieth century. They were built to house cattle over winter when they could not be left free to graze in the open fields, and were basically self-sufficient. Hay was cut and turned over for drying in the meadow, either by scythe and hay fork, or by horse-drawn mowing machine and tedder if the terrain was favourable and the meadow large enough. The hay was gathered up and transferred to the barn to be stored in the dry and fed to the cattle on a daily basis through the winter.

To enable field barns to work effectively the interiors were carefully designed and each part had its own dialect name (Fig. 8.2). The barn itself was often called a *laithe*, though not commonly in this area, and it contained the *byre* or cow house. Larger barns, like the one at Thorns, had a ramp leading through a large arched doorway into the central part of the barn which was the *sink mow*. This ramp allowed hay carts to be unloaded within the barn, in the dry, thus saving time and effort. Men stood on top of the hay and forked it straight onto the *mew stead*. The sink mow was also the place where oats were threshed and winnowed in the dry. Below the mewstead was the actual byre with its stalls or *booses*. Each boose held one or two cattle which were tied to a sliding ring on a vertical pole called a *rudster*. This prevented the cattle from moving around too much and possibly injuring themselves. Individual stalls were divided by partitions made of slate or wood: these were the *boskins*. Larger barns had two or more parallel rows of boskins, often with a feeding passage (or *foddergang*) in between. In this case the back section of each stall was called the *skelboose*. To help maintain a degree of cleanliness within the byre there were small *mucking holes* in the outer walls through which the farmer or cattleman tossed solid waste, and a drain or *group* to allow liquid waste to run away. Larger barns on more prosperous holdings had lean-to structures tagged on to the outer walls. These were the *calf-houses* where young stock were over-wintered. Again, the larger ones often had a *fold yard* where the animals could be let out temporarily.

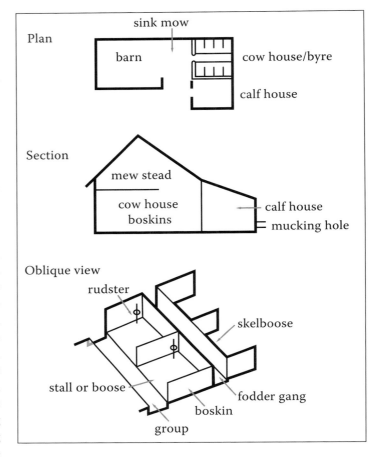

Figure 8.2
A Traditional Dales Field Barn.

Barns are being lost because farmers cannot justify the expense of maintaining them; and the dialect terms are also being forgotten.

Nether Lodge and Ling Gill

One family benefiting from the Selside enclosure was that headed by Christopher Bateson, described as a yeoman farmer resident in Selside. Apart from land in the Shaws he held almost 25ha on his 'Estate at Netherlodge', which did not amount to much, but he also had 295 sheepgaits and 24 beastgaits on the unenclosed Carrs, Cammside and Cow Close stinted pastures. In 1821 he was able to pay for a detailed farm survey (Fig. 8.3).[7] In 1830 Christopher's widow, Elizabeth, sold the land to two landowning and highly ambitious brothers from Clapham for £1935 (£9500 at today's rates, a bargain indeed). James William and Oliver Farrer had been buying up land and farms all over Ribblehead and Gearstones and in 1851 they, too, commissioned a map of their 'Netherlodge Estate' (Fig. 8.4).[8] This was done because they had bought two more farms, Syke and Dry Lade, to add to Nether Lodge and Ling Gill farms, making a discrete estate, now of 220ha plus stints, which they duly tenanted out.

Something of a myth has grown up over the years that the Dales population was stable and unchanging for decades. If the Ribblehead area was in any way typical, this was definitely not the case. Perusal of parish registers, manor court records and census records from 1615 to 1891 emphasises how mobile the tenantry was. Dry Lade farm, for example, housed five different tenant families in the century from 1745; Syke had seven between 1729 and 1871; Nether Lodge eight from 1736 to 1871; while Ling Gill had no less than eleven from 1719 to 1834. Some families came and went – they eventually disappear from the record – but others seem to have moved around within the area.

Figure 8.3
Netherlodge Estate in 1821.
Source: North Yorkshire County Record Office ZTW XI

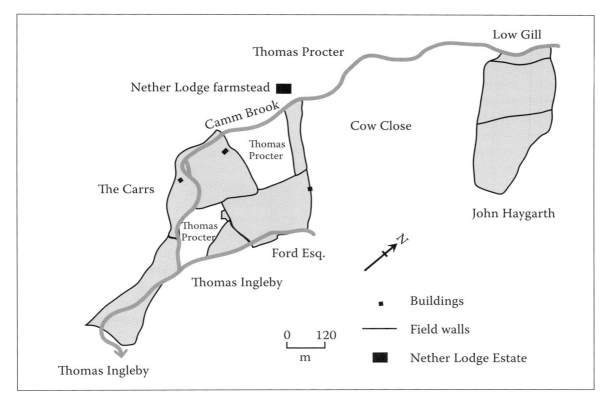

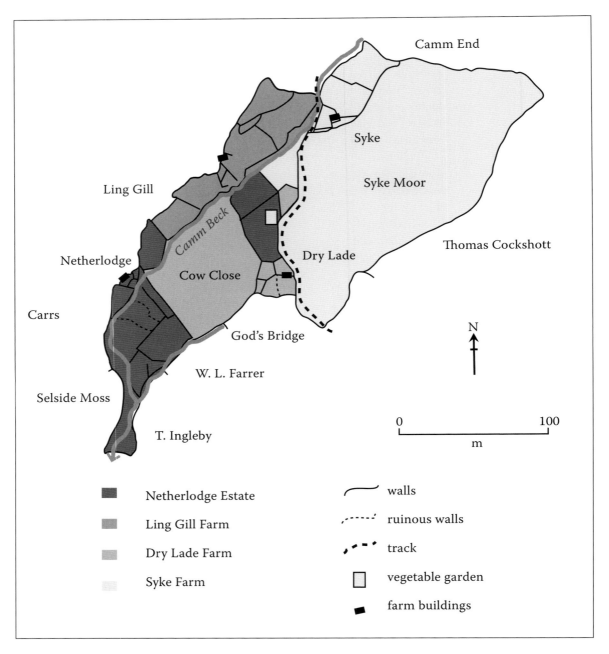

Figure 8.4
Netherlodge Estate in 1851.
Source: North Yorkshire County Record Office ZTW XI

The Sidgewick family were one such. In 1617 they were living and working at Syke but were recorded at Nether Lodge by 1654 and at Dry Lade in 1745.

A Probate Inventory drawn up on the death of Cicely Bentham, spinster, in November 1690 valued her total estate at £18 9s 10d, most of which was taken up with debts owed to her.[9] Cicely had lived at Dry Lade, though not alone. In her will she bequeathed sums of money to Richard Lancaster and his wife and to Anthony Dodgshon, all of whom were recorded as living at Dry Lade. Cicely must have earned her keep by knitting socks as the inventory valued '1 doz. pr. of stockings' at 2s 6d (£9.34 in today's values) and 'yarne'. The parlous state of her existence is illustrated by the total value of her 'apparel and money in purse' at one guinea and the entry 'one only shift'; while her end is hinted at by two entries of debts owed by her estate, namely the sums of 9s for 'attendance in her sickness' and 7s 'for physik'. Life then was not easy in remote farmsteads such as these.

The manor court records for the Higher Division of Newby Manor have survived for the period 1739 to 1810.[10] The court sat annually, usually in April, and a major part of each sitting's business was to record admittances. Every time a tenancy changed hands, either passing to a widow or son on the death of the father, or when a tenant no longer wished to keep up the tenancy, an admittance had to be recorded and payment made to the lord of the manor. In those seventy-one recorded years Dry Lade and Syke were only recorded once each, and Ling Gill three times, whereas Nether Lodge appeared in eleven entries.

Frequent changes of tenancy here may reflect the marginal nature of upland farms such as these. Each of the farms was very small, stinted pastures excepted, and the low quality of grassland not able to support high stocking levels. They were living on the edge in a sense and it did not take much to push them over: an increase in rental, a cool and wet summer, a family crisis, could force them to forgo the tenancy. Macro-economic forces also drove many tenant farmers off the land. Food production may have been high in direct response to high prices during the French wars and for a short time afterwards but by the 1830s farming across the country was in recession and it did not really recover for the rest of that century. In fact the mid-1870s saw a deepening of the depression and many isolated farms were deserted for ever.[11] Add to all this the coming of the railway here in the 1870s, and the consequent abandonment of the old road network through Nether Lodge, Syke and Dry Lade, and we can perhaps understand why the farms were given up. Ling Gill does not appear in the records after 1834, Dry Lade after 1852 and Syke after 1871. Nether Lodge survived to the present day partly because of its easier access to the modern road and partly owing to its higher quality pastures.

In the space of little more than half a century a distinct estate had come and gone. The three 'lost' farms can still be seen in the landscape but only as scant ruins, mere foundations now. Dry Lade farmhouse (SD8018 7786) stood between Cam Road and the still standing barn; ruins of the much larger Syke farmhouse (SD8040 7874) with attached barn and byre lie on a right of way up Syke Gill; ruins of Ling Gill farmhouse (SD7979 7854), which was even longer than Syke, are adjacent to the right of way from Nether Lodge to join Cam Road at New Head Hill.

The Hamlet of Thorns

Also now 'lost', and tucked away in a hollow in the hills, is the former hamlet of Thorns (SD781 794), invisible from afar, though its copse of trees can be seen from all directions. It started its life, as far as we know, as a monastic lodge for Furness Abbey and remained as an important stop-off point on the packhorse route running from north to south. Now it is a mixture of rather picturesque and atmospheric ruins, most of its buildings having long ago been reduced to foundation level (Plate 8.1). Only one house still manages to withstand the attack of winter weather, with its frontage facing the former village 'street', but two barns remind us of its past function. A small still-standing outhouse was an old wash house, complete with copper set-pot and furnace, and across the street is the roofless 'little room'. Running from the large barn in the centre of Thorns is a walled lane: this was Nan Bottom Lane.

The manor court proceedings for the Higher Division record only ten admittances at Thorns from 1740 to 1810, while in 1841 the hamlet was occupied by three households. Two families of Fothergills and the Bentham family had between them 21 people recorded in the census of that year. Ten years later this was down to 14 with only two families, the Fothergills farming a tiny holding of 8ha and the Benthams with a more viable 72ha.[12] The 1861 census records only two Fothergill brothers living there farming 36ha and by the next census one of the brothers had a family and the other had left. The total population of Thorns was only five in 1881, comprising the Parker family, and the last available census for 1891 has the sad entry 'one uninhabited dwelling'. That was the end of the village. The abandonment of the road through Thorns, the end of the Gearstones fairs, outbreaks of cattle murrain and severe depression in farming conspired to drive the families away for good. Until little more than a hundred years ago Thorns and Gearstones were a thriving self-contained little community with houses, farms, inn, shop and school, linked to the outside world by packmen, drovers and merchants and then, with what must have been traumatic rapidity, it all imploded and shrank to a shadow of its former self.

Lodge Hall

Lodge Hall (SD780 779) has had a rather different history since its demise as a monastic lodge. The land here has much more potential and access is obviously easier, so it did not suffer from the same drawbacks as Thorns. At one time it was occupied by a family of Quakers and there is a burial ground under a canopy of trees. It was not their tradition to mark graves so you would never know it was a burial ground just by looking at it.

An alternative name for the house is Ingman Lodge and this is a mystery, though legend claims to know why it is so-called. The assize court judges

Figure 8.5
Lodge Hall, etching by
Godfrey Wilson, 1939.

stayed here, so the story goes, and on occasion they condemned criminals to death so the house came to be known locally as the 'angman's lodge. To add to the house's gruesome image a murder was committed in one of the bedrooms and – predictably – blood stains can, allegedly, still be seen on the floorboards!

The house bears a datestone 'CW 1687' (Fig. 8.5). This was Christopher Weatherhead and there is a genuine, if troubling, story attached to him.[13] Christopher had owned considerable property in Ribblesdale, including Knight Stainforth Hall, and his son, also Christopher, inherited Ingman Lodge, though his father's will, dated 1732, had left land there to another son called Thomas. (Knight Stainforth had gone to a third son called John who also received much land between Selside and Horton.) Christopher junior had business interests in Liverpool and he was a prominent owner of plantations in the West Indies, but his grand scheme did not go entirely to plan. He was declared bankrupt in 1774 and lost everything, the house being sold to another Liverpool merchant with Giggleswick connections, Thomas Backhouse, to help pay off his debts. An inventory of Weatherhead's assets was compiled and listed among his possessions were quantities of slaves, all individually named. No doubt they would have regarded his downfall as poetic justice though they, too, were sold on to the new plantation owners.

Bruntscar and a Fishy Tale

The valley of Chapel le Dale, too, was much more thickly populated in the recent past. Bruntscar farm (SD738 788), for example, is now just a single farm at the end of a road. At one time it had a school for children from surrounding farms. It also has a cave, 853m in length, one of many under the fells that surround the dale. There is a local legend attached to this cave.[14]

In the days before piped water and taps Bruntscar's neighbours used a pool in the stream that issues from the cave as their source of water. Two hundred

Plate 8.1
The Deserted Hamlet of
Thorns, once a lodge for
Furness Abbey.

years or so ago this pool was home to Dick. He was a trout – a tame trout, the playmate of the farmer Francis Kidd. Francis used to throw morsels of food into the pool for his friend and, apparently, Dick had a particular penchant for beef and mutton. The fish slowly came to trust Francis and would eat out of the palm of his hand while being tickled and caressed by the other hand. Dick seemed to spend almost all of his life inside the cave passage, rarely venturing out until one day a local girl who came to collect water in a bucket scooped him up without noticing and went off home with him. Amazingly, no one saw Dick until the girl was about to hang the bucket over the open fire to boil it at which point Dick leaped out onto the fireside rug. If we are to believe the story, Dick was clearly more intelligent than that family and almost certainly the only telepathic trout in the world. He died at the grand old trout age of sixteen, much lamented.

Shanty Town

The quiet slumbering of the accumulated ghosts of lay brothers, farmers, drovers and packmen was rudely interrupted in 1870 when work began on the construction of Ribblehead viaduct, part of Midland Railway's grand scheme to drive its own rail link from the south to Scotland. Though it would probably not be granted planning permission today, this viaduct has to be one of the country's best known and most photographed, and it is now a Scheduled Ancient Monument. It is an impressive feat of engineering regardless of the equipment and technology available at the time. The statistics speak for themselves: its twenty-four arches span over 400m in total length and at the highest it rises 32m from the ground below. Before each pier could be built a shaft 8m deep had to be hacked out of solid rock to take the weight of the masonry, with the bottom 2m being filled with concrete. There is an old story about this viaduct – and of Garsdale Head viaduct as well – that the piers were seated on wool. In practical terms, of course, this would have been impossible and the story must relate to investment in the new railway by woollen manufacturers of the industrial West Riding.

In order to build the viaduct an enormous quantity of materials had to be located and assembled on site. With the boggy conditions and notoriously wet climate up here, this must have been a logistical nightmare. The stone for the piers and trackbed plinth came from quarries to the north in Little Dale and Force Gill. In both, the stone was quarried from the stream bed rather than from the hillside. In Little Dale alone some 23,000m^3 of black limestone were hewn out, cut to size, shaped and hauled down to the viaduct on a specially built tramway.[15] A brickworks was built east of the viaduct, using clay dug locally, and this had the capacity to churn out up to 20,000 bricks each day.[16] These were moved on a network of tramways (Fig. 8.6) which also carried in coal to fire the kilns and a host of other necessities. Where tramways could not reach, they resorted to bog carts which were small and light and set on a large rotating drum rather than wheels to stop them getting stuck in the mire.

The scaffolding and supports for the arch tops were made of timber (Fig. 8.7), as were almost all the buildings on site, and this all had to be brought in from outside the area. If you were to make a list of all the materials that were needed, from nails and shovels to steam cranes and tramway locomotives, the amount would be truly staggering. It obviously could not be brought in by rail and the road up from Settle was still just a rough track and the distance from the nearest rail head at Settle Junction was far too great anyway, so it all came in from the station at Ingleton. That journey is long enough and its two long and steep inclines proved to be obstacles for the heaviest loads, though the foremen and horse leaders knew their job well. Local inhabitants and travellers on the turnpike road, though, cursed and complained at the dreadful state of the road during the five years that construction of the viaduct took.

On a tour of the whole site during construction you would have seen a range of essential buildings: stores, blacksmith's shop, wheelwright's shop, saddler's, farrier's (they fitted horse shoes), locomotive sheds (an inspection pit can still be seen on the ground), carpenter's and joiner's shops, not to mention domestic quarters ... the list is endless. Nowadays the only sounds, apart from passing trains, are the howling of the wind and the call of

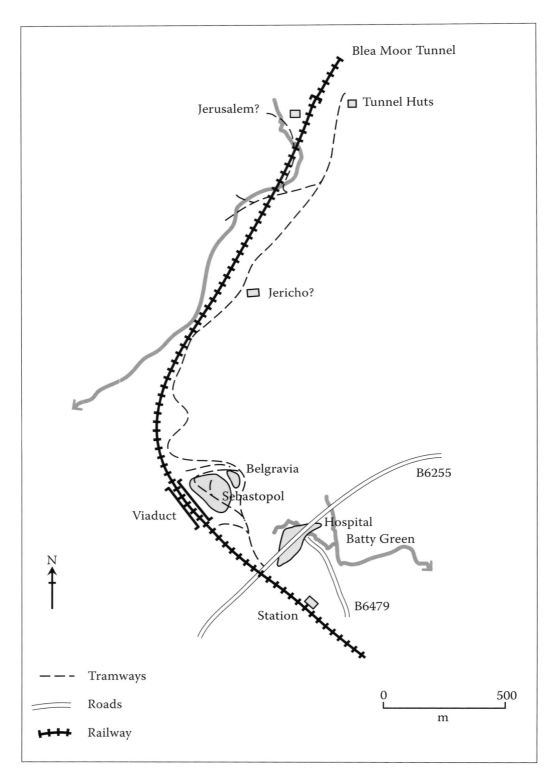

Blea Moor Tunnel

Jerusalem?

Tunnel Huts

Jericho?

Belgravia

Sebastopol

Viaduct

B6255

Hospital

Batty Green

N

Station

B6479

- - - Tramways

Roads

Railway

0   500

m

Figure 8.6
Ribblehead Construction
Camps.
Source: Cardwell et al.
(2004), pp. 197, 199

moorland birds but in those five years the commotion would have been at a crescendo all day long, Sundays excepted.

A broad array of accents would have been heard on site. None of the workers on the viaduct, or their families, were local folk and there were certainly no houses here before construction started.[17] While work was going on a national census was held, in 1871, and this has provided important detail about who was here. The census records how many lived in each household, what their names were, how old they were, what they did, and where they were born. It is important not to accept everything in the census records as reliable fact: many construction workers at the time tended to be rough diamonds and some had secrets from their past that they were not willing to reveal. The answers they gave may have been false. Others were illiterate including, apparently, census enumerators. How else can we explain why one man's birthplace was recorded as 'Kent, Bournemouth' and another's as 'Lestor, Lestorshire'? Almost every part of the country was represented in the census. Railway workers by and large led an itinerant life, moving from one construction project to another in search of continued employment. We have often been told that gangs of Irish migrant workers slaved on projects such as this and I actually found a clay pipe hidden in one of the dry stone walls running along the edge of the track. It was finely engraved with an Irish harp and a shamrock leaf and has been firmly dated to the 1870s. It had been made, however, in Scotland by an enterprising factory owner who mass-produced pipes for homesick Irishmen. Having said this, you might

Figure 8.7
Ribblehead Viaduct
under Construction.
Source: F. S. Williams
(1876) 'The Midland
Railway: its Rise and
Progress', London:
Strahan

BATTY MOSS VIADUCT.

expect the census to confirm the Irish connection but out of 142 households only six were Irish.

We can dispose of a second myth while we are at it, namely that gangs of thousands of navvies lived and worked along the railway while it was being built. For a start the numbers bandied about are far too high. The 1871 census has only 455 workers at Ribblehead, though this number could have reached double that at the peak of construction: in 1871 work had not yet peaked here. Of these 455 (mainly) men – and boys, of course – only 63 per cent were classified as labourers. In other words 47 per cent were not navvies at all. They were skilled craftsmen in the host of trades mentioned earlier, or those performing service occupations, or in management positions.

Many of the labourers were single men (305 out of a grand total of 902 people) who took up lodgings on site with other families.[18] Regardless of their age or work status they all had daily needs that had to be met, and these were indeed all catered for. Fresh food was brought in by provisioners from Ingleton and Horton, but many needs could be satisfied from within the community. In 1871 there were drapers, seamstresses and dressmakers; butchers, bakers and grocers; tailors and shoemakers; and a hairdresser. People, men in particular, tended to develop quite a thirst and enterprising people provided the wherewithal for them to fritter away their hard-won wages and to let off steam.[19] There were the *Welcome Home* and *Railway Tavern* (later the *Travellers Rest*) beer houses and another that one visitor dismissed as a 'chaotic heap of stones'. A year or two after the 1871 census, the teacher from Chapel le Dale school decided he needed a change of career so

Plate 8.2
Aerial View of the Ribblehead Construction Camps.

Plate 8.3
Fully excavated
Office-Storeroom at
Ribblehead. The right-
hand third – the office
– has a lime mortar
floor set on limestone
slabs.

built a large house for himself at Ribblehead with rooms to rent out to single men, which later was licensed as the *Railway Inn*, now the *Station Inn*.

For those with a rather more sedate mien there was a reading room with books and newspapers, a mission room run by James Tiplady whose ambition to save the labourers' souls must have been as unrealistic as police officer Archie Cameron's aim of keeping the peace between drunken men on pay day.[20] Some – and it was only some – of the children were taught the basics in the school room by Miss Herbert, and there was a surgeon on hand to attend to the many injuries that were an inevitable part of constructing a viaduct as big as this one. A hospital had also been built in 1871 (see Figure 8.6) to house the many who fell victim to a smallpox epidemic that swept through the area like wildfire.

The men and their families were housed in temporary settlements that the railway company had built along the route from Settle to Carlisle. On the Horton road there is an isolated house, called Stone House (SD779 771), which is said to be so named because it stood in a sea of temporary wooden huts. There was also a settlement where the former railway cottages at Salt Lake now stand (SD774 785). Because there was a lot more work to be done at Ribblehead, especially with the cutting of the 2420m-long Blea Moor tunnel, the population here was much greater. Nine temporary settlements – so often disparagingly called shanty towns – housed the hordes here (see Figure 8.6). Most of them were simply collections of living huts, built of wood with a felt roof, and divided into three sections. The resident family slept at one end, the lodgers at the other, with the central area being a communal kitchen, eating and sitting area. Lodgers, incidentally, were seen as a vital source of extra income for families with many young mouths to feed. Coming south from the entrance to the tunnel there were Tunnel Huts and Bleamoor Huts, then Jericho and Jordan, Inkerman and Jerusalem. Because the huts were made of wood, they have left little impression on the ground and the location of some settlements can only be guessed at.

The precise location of three townships is known: Batty Green (at first Batty Wife Hole) spread across the generally flat area either side of the road junction at Ribblehead.[21] This contained rows of terraced houses between the present B6479 road and the junction with the vehicle track to the viaduct; with the public and civic buildings, and maybe company offices, just west of the road junction. The stone foundations of five such buildings can clearly be seen as linear earthworks. Between the Horton road and the stream there are more linear earthworks: these were thought to be shops and trade workshops. Beyond the large parking area east of the road junction, at the foot of Sandy Hill drumlin, there are the footings of a rectangular building, 13m by 9m, which is thought to have been the hospital built during the smallpox outbreak. It was probably the case that some of the houses in Batty Green housed those who were tending to the varied needs of the construction workers and their families.

To the east of the viaduct was a large settlement called Sebastopol. This was a residential area and the faint traces of terraced rows of wooden huts can be made out on three levelled platforms, but it was also an industrial zone with the brickworks (whose remains can still be seen), engine sheds, quarries and who knows what else scattered around. To the east of Sebastopol was a settlement called Belgravia (the men had a droll sense of humour) that lay just east of the ruined, pre-railway lime kiln (Plate 8.2). Archaeological surveying and a rare surviving photograph revealed a series of individual wooden huts here, each with a porch. Belgravia is on higher and drier ground than Sebastopol and the former's inhabitants would have been able to look down on the latter's. No doubt they would have found this perfectly acceptable: after all Belgravia housed management and its families.

Immediately north of Belgravia there are the scant remains of a stone-built structure, building n6 in archaeospeak (Plate 8.3). This was fully excavated and recorded in 2007.[22] Before the excavation it just consisted of a heap of limestone rubble; by the end the group were able to interpret many details of the building's usage. It served a dual function. The eastern third was an office with a window in the front wall and a floor covered in lime mortar to help reduce rising damp. The western two-thirds had been a storeroom. This building was ideally placed for those inside to observe progress on the viaduct.

On Saturdays the elevated section of society may have observed a locomotive hauling carts down the main tramway from the tunnel full not of stone or coal but of people. This was the shoppers' special taking them down to Batty Green for their weekly treat.

They may also have felt a little bemused at another little known aspect of

Ribblehead. The land owning family, which still owns this area, insisted that all telegraph wires across the site had to be buried in a trench.[23] This was not for aesthetic reasons but was far more prosaic. Their main source of income from these bleak moors – apart from rent from the railway company – was in grouse shooting and they were concerned that birds might come to grief on the wires, thereby reducing their potential income.

The viaduct was completed in 1875 and the men moved elsewhere with their families.[24] Most of the huts and the infrastructure were dismantled soon after and, by 1879, all that remained were the ex-teacher's inn, the station, and two cottages at Blea Moor signal box. The weather and vegetation soon reclaimed the area ensuring its secrets remain largely hidden.

Those involved in constructing the viaduct cannot have imagined that it would one day achieve iconic status and become a major tourist attraction in its own right. Neither, one suspects, could they have imagined that the powers that be would have used the supposedly precarious state of the viaduct as an excuse to try and shut down the entire Settle-Carlisle railway. However, they would surely have been delighted at the determined efforts made by so many people across the country – including prominent politicians – to keep the line open. Detailed investigations of the structure in 1988 proved that the earlier cost estimates had been much exaggerated and renovation work commenced soon after, with the closure proposals being withdrawn in the following year.[25] Since then the line has gone from strength to strength with constant freight traffic in addition to passenger services, diversions from the West Coast line and steam specials.

NINE

Developing Landscape: Ingleborough South

Turbary Rights and Fights

Inhabitants of any medieval or post-medieval township enjoyed certain inalienable rights that were monitored and regulated by the local manorial court. Anyone infringing these rights was quickly hauled before the court and amerced, or fined a set amount. Medieval manor courts had a bewildering array of rights to keep in check and each right involved payment by the tenants. The rights of *estovers* would have been a jealously guarded right in certain parts of the Dales as they included the right to gather bracken and rushes for animal or domestic bedding. One of the reasons why bracken is perceived to be such a problem nowadays is the reality that no one has any need to gather it anymore. If it is not actively managed, it will naturally do as nature intended.

Many ancient rights had all but disappeared by the late Middle Ages as land management practices and the legalities of land ownership and tenancy adapted to changing demographic and political circumstances. Other rights persisted well into the early modern period; indeed some still survive. *Turbary* gave tenants and freemen the right to cut turves – peat – on the moors for fuel and this right was of great importance in the Ingleborough area owing to the acute dearth of woodland. *Stonary* allowed them to collect, and in many cases, to delve (dig) for stone for building houses and boundary walls and burning into lime. In all cases, the manor court verdicts stipulated that the materials were strictly for tenants' own use and were not to be sold elsewhere.

Ingleborough's acidic foothills, where either impermeable sandstones or glacial till dominate, have large expanses of peat that were exploited for many centuries. Until the parliamentary enclosure process carved open commons into individual allotments people could go and cut peat – at the appropriate time of the year and in the allotted places on the commons – as they wished. Problems frequently arose when individuals or groups of people deliberately transgressed by straying out of their allotted patch or beyond the stipulated time slot. Whenever the transgression affected a neighbouring township it was no longer simply a matter of bringing it before the manor court. External adjudication was sometimes the last, and only, resort. Such an instance is well documented in the records for part of southern Ingleborough and it became a *cause célèbre* four hundred years ago.

A dispute between the inhabitants of Austwick, Wharfe and Crummack on the one hand and Selside in Horton parish on the other dragged on for nearly eighty years and involved the legal advisers of Kings James I and Charles II. It also brought into play Christopher Saxton, the famous map maker. The dispute first came to light in the area in 1602 when contrary land claims for common land in the vicinity of Sulber were lodged by the two sets of contestants. Surviving records do not document why the dispute arose but there can be only two possibilities: it concerned either access to pastoral land or turbary plots, or both. Certainly Thieves Moss was the turbary ground for the inhabitants of Austwick through the nineteenth century, and what was to become The Allotment in the later Enclosure Award is shown on a map in 1619 as turbary grounds for 'Austwick, Cromak and Wharffe'. The contestants would not agree where the boundary lay as each party wished to further their own interests at the expense of the other. Saxton was granted a royal commission to prepare a 'rough draught' of the disputed grounds.[1] The map carries a wordy legend – 'A plot of the common in question betwixt the tennantes of Selside and Austwick made by Christopher Saxton for and with ye … consent of the persons hereunder named …' and is dated October 1603. It encompasses all common and enclosed land from Lord's Seat on Simon Fell in the north through Sulber Gate to Crummack Dale and Moughton in the south. The purpose of the map was to help in settling the dispute but it clearly had not worked as court records confirm the appointment of commissioners to draw up a further map of 'commons and wastes' in 1619 (see Figure 6.3).[2] The descriptive detail accompanying the map referred to land 'now in variance' between the two sides. As so often happens with historic legal disputes, extant records inform us of the problem and the process but not the outcome.

It seems that the feud between the residents of Austwick and Selside might have been a generational matter. A feigned court case was held at York in 1682 to record a dispute between John Green of Selside, defendant, and James Banks of Austwick, complainant, on common land above Crummack Dale.[3] The case record listed the areas concerned, including Horton Stye, Dudderhouse Hill, Lord's Seat, Long Scar and Hinkinshaw. The dispute was about grazing and turbary rights and the point of a feigned case was not to find in favour of one party or another but to ensure that the dispute, or matter, was duly recorded in a formal manner.

Another map has survived concerning land disputed between Austwick and Horton in Ribblesdale.[4] Though undated, it was probably drawn up in the late eighteenth century: part of it is shown in Figure 10.2. The disputed area stretched all the way from Moughton Nab above Helwith Bridge, across Moughton and Hunterstye Head to Thieves Moss. No reason for the disagreement is stated on the map but there is the telling hand-written remark 'Thieves Moss. Peats got here by Austwick.' Horton's inhabitants presumably still felt aggrieved even though by then the Moss was clearly part of Austwick.

Thieves Moss

Modern detailed Ordnance Survey maps still name Thieves Moss. It was similarly labelled on Saxton's map so the place-name clearly has ancient origins. It is set within a natural limestone amphitheatre between Moughton Scars to the south and Sulber to the north, and it forms a dramatic contrast with the expansive limestone pavements on all sides of the dale. Thieves Moss is an area of wet ground on a covering of acidic and poorly drained glacial till. The place-name must have been accorded to the moss for a reason. Could it be that this was a hideaway for stock thieves or opportunist robbers who preyed on passing traffic along Clapham Lane? Certainly in those distant days strangers would have been repelled by the drama and complexity of the landscape within upper Crummack Dale and would-be Dick Turpins or rustlers could soon lose themselves among its hidden nooks and crannies.

The Legend of Alice Ketyll

The Thieves Moss story is pure speculation whereas Alice Ketyll is the central figure in a supposedly local story with a long history. It is set during the long-running Wars of the Roses when Lancastrians and Yorkists feuded and fought, causing intermittent consternation and disruption for all and sundry between 1452 and the defeat in battle of Richard III in 1485. The local context is Clapdale. The two central figures are Dame Alice Ketyll and her foster-son John de Clapham. It all happened in 1467 or 1468.

Clapdale is a house (formerly Clapdale Hall) at the head of Clapdale valley (Plate 9.1). Until the 1960s it was a working farm and it has been rebuilt several times during its long history. Any building set on a stone plinth as massive as Clapdale's has to be very old, to say the least, and history – or legend – has it that it was first erected for the de Staveley family around 800 years ago. Legend also insists that it was Clapdale Castle though we can be certain that it was no such thing – a stronghold maybe but not an actual castle. By the 1460s the house was in the hands of the wealthy and powerful John de Clapham. Alice, so the story goes, was his foster mother and she lived in a little cottage in the valley below. Now, many legends have a tiny kernel of truth hidden within the froth of invention and she may well have been a real person. Whenever this story has been retold in print the question never

Plate 9.1
Clapdale Farm, with
seventeenth-century
dovecote adjacent.

seems to have been raised about her status. Her being John's foster mother is completely at odds with his wealth and position, assuming he ever existed, which is not really relevant to this line of thought. It seems more likely that she had been his wet nurse in which case their relative social distance would not be a problem in trying to square this particular circle.

Alice had been thoroughly bewitched, at some point before our story begins to unfold, by carrying out a number of devilish deeds in Clapham and, by way of reward, she was assured of Satan's services in perpetuity. In 1468 John found himself on the losing side in the wars and an inevitable outcome of losing in this way was to have one's wealth and property sequestered by the crown. In desperation he called on Alice to help him out of his predicament. She obliged, conjuring 500 troops out of thin air to fight alongside John against the Yorkist earl of Pembroke. The latter was captured and John slew the earl and his brother in the porch of Banbury church in Oxfordshire. For this he was eventually captured and executed. Alice, meanwhile, sent her mysterious men on their way back to the other world while using her powers to rescue his head from the stake and his body from where it had been cast so she could give it a decent burial in the family vaults at Bolton Priory church in Wharfedale.

Clapdale was burnt to the ground and Alice was arrested and tried but spared execution. Instead she had the devil cast out from within her and, having completed due penance, is said to have ended her days in a nunnery at Twistleton south-west of Chapel le Dale.

A story worthy of any romantic's library it may be but there is one major flaw in it all. Recent meticulous detective work by two local residents has torn the story to shreds, at least as far as Clapham is concerned.[5] The archives have no record of John but they do have the proceedings of the trial for witchcraft of Alice Kettle (or Kyteler) but this trial was in 1324 and in Kilkenny in south-east Ireland. R. Balderston Cragg, author of a book published in 1905, had lifted the story with its every detail and transplanted it to Clapham.[6]

It does not matter, therefore, if Alice was John's foster mother or his wet nurse: she was not from these parts. However, Clapdale – whether burnt down or not – was held by the Ingleby family from 1573 to 1852 and the house's solid plinth no doubt dates from their early days here.

Robin Proctor

This is a very short, but sad, tale and this time largely a true one. Robin Proctor has a prominent landform named after him, namely the scars that bound the southern edge of Norber north of Austwick. Robin, so the story goes, was a local well-established yeoman farmer from somewhere south of Ingleborough. One day he was returning to his home, taking the direct line over Thwaite Scars rather than sticking to the safer but longer track, when he was caught out in thick fog. Sadly he lost his bearings and tumbled with his steed over the edge of the cliffs, both being dashed to pieces on the rocks below. It is a nice story but has at least one major pitfall: the ground up there is so rough and rocky that no one would knowingly ride a horse across it. On the other hand there is an entry in the Clapham Burial Register, dated 12 August 1677, recording the death of Robert Procter of Hazle Hall farm (now near Clapham Station) 'falling from a cliff at Norber'. There is no proof that he was riding a horse, but the story in essence is absolutely true.

On top of Thwaite Scars and Long Scar there are many stone piles, or cairns. A few may have their origins as prehistoric burial cairns; the majority seem to serve no logical purpose and they may simply result from the efforts of whoever had time to spare at some point in the not too distant past. Yet others were constructed just above cliff lines: were these erected after Robert's death as a kind of early health and safety warning?

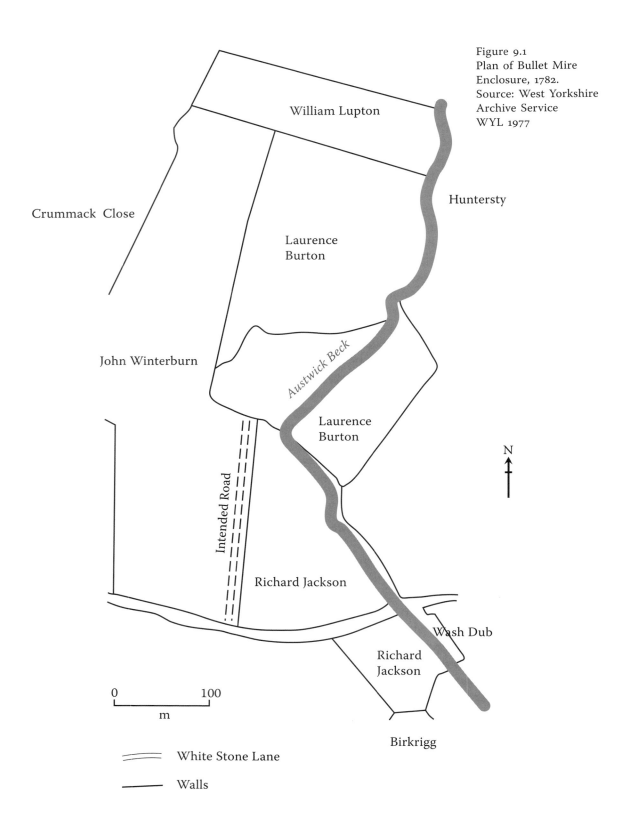

Figure 9.1
Plan of Bullet Mire
Enclosure, 1782.
Source: West Yorkshire
Archive Service
WYL 1977

William Lupton

Crummack Close

Huntersty

Laurence
Burton

John Winterburn

Austwick Beck

Laurence
Burton

N

Intended Road

Richard Jackson

Wash Dub

Richard
Jackson

0   100
m

Birkrigg

White Stone Lane

Walls

Bullet Mire

Not far from the Scar is Bullet Mire, an area of ground in Crummack Dale between the two north-south lanes and the east-west White Stone Lane (Fig. 9.1). Austwick Beck forms its eastern boundary. In July 1782 an agreement was drawn up by the four farmers who held common grazing rights on the Mire to carve it up into discrete holdings.[7] Hitherto it had been a stinted pasture, surrounded by 'old inclosed lands', within which the four had inalienable rights to specified numbers of cattle- or beastgaits, one gait representing one cow. John Winterburn held six gaits, Richard Jackson and Laurence Burton two each. All three were yeomen farmers living in the nearby hamlet of Wharfe. In addition two were held by the trustees of the late William Lupton who was described as a merchant in Liverpool. One wonders how he came to hold grazing rights in Crummack, especially on such a small scale, though Lupton was a prominent family name west of Kirkby Lonsdale.

The Mire cannot be described as high quality pasture. The northern and southern sections have much bedrock outcropping very close to the surface and the rocks break down to form acidic soil which, in turn, can only support limited grass growth. The central section lies in a natural dip and tends to be very damp. Under a stinting regime no individual gait holder would have felt inclined to improve the sward because his fellow gait holders would benefit at his expense, hence the agreement. Each could improve what he was awarded and it was up to the others to do as they wished with their allocation.

The agreement stipulated that the Mire should be divided up internally by dry stone walls '6 foot high at the least' and it was all to be completed by May 1783 with each of the four parties attending to the task 'in due and fair proportion' to the number of gaits they had held and the size of their new holdings. It was up to them to either build it themselves or to pay someone to do it for them. The total length of new wall was a fraction over 1km so the building work would have been split at the rate of 100m per individual gait. At that time it was reckoned that a competent waller could put up a rood of seven yards (just under 6.50m) in a day, assuming stone had been delivered to site and laid out along the intended line. Winterburn was responsible for 600m which required 93 man-days which could easily have been accomplished within the time limit. But that was not all. The agreement also required them to build new walls along the 'High Road', ie White Stone Lane, bounding the divided land. This added a further 280m. Only two of the four had new land bordering the road but the agreement does not say if all were to undertake this task.

Furthermore, they were bound by agreement to maintain the road past the Mire and to widen Austwick Beck on the eastern side of the Mire to reduce the frequency and severity of floods across the Mire, and thereby help to dry it out. They were also required to make a new cart road across the Mire to give access to the upper parts of the enclosure. This was to run through Winterburn's allotment. On the other hand, though, their ancient and inalienable rights of free liberty to make use of the sheepwash 'at the antient Wash Dubb' were confirmed.

Examination of the Mire today shows that there are discrepancies between what the enclosure surveyors set down on paper and what the allotment holders actually did afterwards. The walls are not 'at least six feet' high and there is no trace on the ground that the cart road was ever laid. It also casts doubt on the wisdom of some such agreements and on the folly of the often hopeless optimism of those pushing them forward. Even if the beck had been widened – and it is difficult to tell – the Mire still gets very wet and the rocky northern allotment, granted to Lupton's trustees, is incapable of meaningful improvement. Winterburn ended up with the greatest area, as rightly befitted his proportion of stints, but he also came out with the driest and best quality bits. Perhaps he was able, for whatever reason, to put pressure on his neighbours to go along with what might have been his sole idea designed to be of benefit to him. It is difficult to see how the expense incurred by the others could ever have been justified on purely economic grounds.

The embodiment of the enclosure process was carving up communal pastures and allocating parcels of land to those who already possessed advantages over their fellow men, or extinguishing rights of common by reducing open pastures to controlled stinted pastures. It was not an egalitarian exercise, doling out land in equal shares to all men. The 1814 enclosure of Austwick's commons – much of Ingleborough, all of Moughton, Swarth Moor at Helwith Bridge, and Oxenber south-east of the village – bears this out graphically.[8] Charles Ingleby was a man of substance, from a family with a long lineage, and he received 301 sheep gaits from the great carving up. At the other end of Austwick's social hierarchy was Roger Bickerstaff who was allocated a mere two: one can well imagine how hard life would have been for him and his family, unless he had property elsewhere. Equally distressing must have been the outcome for sisters Alice and Isabel Winterburn who received just two and a half gaits each. The adage 'to those that have, let there be given' has a long pedigree.

Enclosure was not a universally popular phenomenon for the very reason that it was perceived to be socially divisive and those at the lower end of the social scale certainly lost their communal rights to peat, stone, bracken and grazing. On occasion, it became the butt of satire. One anonymous bard was moved to compose a long satirical – yet true? – diatribe against the enclosure of his home area elsewhere in the Yorkshire uplands in the 1770s, in which he wrote:

> No longer would the dismal cries
> Be heard, for want of due Supplies:
> Instead of dangerous Bogs and Rushes,
> Of Fens & Briars, Whins & Bushes,
> Plenty of Grass & Corn would spring.[9]

Plate 9.2
Wash Dub in
Crummack Dale, with
its ancient clapper
bridge spanning
Austwick Beck alongside
the ford.

He was casting doubt here on the very thesis of enclosure, that waste land could be miraculously transformed into productive farm land, either by carving it up as at Bullet Mire or by reducing unregulated common pastures into stinted agreements as on Ingleborough. Certainly, much land was duly brought into arable or pastoral production in the Dales and elsewhere, but to assume areas such as Bullet Mire could be fully improved was too ambitious.

The 'antient Wash Dubb' referred to in the Bullet Mire enclosure lies within a rectangle of very broken ground alongside the lane where it crosses the beck by an ancient but undateable clapper bridge (Plate 9.2). Wash dubs (dub means pool) were used in the days before chemical dips were introduced and were only abandoned in the first half of the twentieth century. In those days farmers came together as washing was an arduous business. Sheep were driven from the various pastures and corralled within the enclosure. One by one they were thrown into the temporarily dammed stream where the more hardy men stood, often chest-deep in water, manually scrubbing the sheep to rid their fleeces of parasites. It was a communal and co-operative affair as well as one of those great social occasions of the farming calendar, the like of which are rarely seen today.

The Farrers and Clapdale

The Farrer family have been lords of the manor and resident in Clapham village for just two hundred years.[10] In the decade before Victoria came to the throne the family replanned not only the village but also much of the estate in Clapdale. Apart from wanting to improve the estate, to add value and for aesthetic reasons, they also deliberately provided work for local men during a period of depression in farming with its consequent social ramifications. The brothers James and Oliver had a dam constructed across the valley to transform an existing small lake into the present one. The main track from the village to Trow Gill was laid out as a carriage drive (Clapdale Way) with features of added interest to the gentry of the day, such as a grotto, as well as to allow visitor access to Ingleborough Cave.[11] Woodlands were created and planted with an integral network of paths. In 1834 they opened up and explored Ingleborough Cave releasing an underground lake to achieve this;[12] and they had Thwaite Lane re-routed and hidden away in tunnels where it drops down into the village.

Reginald Farrer, who lived from 1881 to 1920, is perhaps the best known member of the family as he was a keen botanist and collector of exotic plant species many of which he tried in Clapdale, as well as being a painter, an author and a Buddhist convert.[13] This inner change arose from experiences on his many journeys to Asia in search of plants. His rock garden became famous and attracted visitors from far and wide but he made a more visible and long-lasting impact on Clapdale itself. He wanted to establish exotic species on the inaccessible cliffs above the lake and resorted to shooting seeds from a shotgun to achieve his aims. Just upstream of the lake he planted various species of rhododendron in what he came to call Ceylon Gorge as the landscape reminded him of that island. In the flush of summer growth the valley from the village to the top end of the woods is a riot of native and totally alien species yet these do not look out of place here; they have moulded the micro-landscape in a particularly attractive way.

At the height of their fortunes the Farrers owned land from Burn Moor south of the Wenning valley, and across Ingleborough to Ribblehead, Newby Head and Ling Gill. Death duties and changing times have necessitated the piecemeal dismemberment of selected parts of the estate, though it still remains extensive on the Ingleborough massif.

Quarries and Delfs

Certain parts of Ingleborough South have been greatly affected in modern times by large-scale quarrying, especially at Helwith Bridge, Horton in Ribblesdale and, to a lesser extent, above Newby Cote. Elsewhere, quarrying activities have had a less visible and intrusive impact on the landscape; indeed it could be argued that medieval and early modern quarries can blend almost imperceptibly into the landscape and even add to it. Such quarries are much smaller in extent and depth, they were laboriously worked by hand tools often with no explosives, and they are perhaps better described as delfs (or delves or even delphs) which are shallow diggings or workings rather than the quarries that the word conjures up in our minds.

These small-scale workings were often seasonal and part-time, undertaken not by dedicated quarrymen but by farmers or others who slotted stone-getting into the routine of their busy working lives. It could be a family affair with the men doing the actual quarrying, prising blocks of stone from the bedrock. From medieval times this was achieved by chiselling out small depressions along the intended break-line and then ramming in iron wedges into each hole. These were struck one after another with a sledge hammer. This was a laborious process and the finished edges were rarely even so, around 1800, a refinement was introduced using the plug and feather method. The initial task now was to drill, rather than chisel, a line of shallow holes where the stone was to be broken free. This was done using a jumper, a long sturdy iron bar, half-rotated every time the jumper man's partner hit it with his sledge hammer. Then the plug, a tapered metal wedge, was driven into the hole between two half-round pieces of iron which were the feathers. If the plug and feathers were hammered squarely, the stone would (hopefully) crack along the line of holes, after which it could be prised apart. It was still laborious and back-breaking work, but required a higher level of skill and dexterity. If any stone needed to be broken up into smaller pieces, this was often given to the women and children as it was deemed unskilled work and thus paid at a lower rate.

In the Ingleborough area such workings supplied building and walling stone locally and they tended to leave untidy and chaotic jumbles of hollows and stone heaps as can be seen on the southern crest of Little Ingleborough (Plate 9.3). Environmental conditions here make nature's process of reclaiming these delfs slow and hesitant.

This is not always the case, though. At the head of Crummack Dale there is a spot known as Moughton Whetstone Hole where Hunterstye Lane begins its ascent out of the valley bottom. Lying in the stream bed are small pieces of stone coloured in alternate bands of purple and green (the liesegang rings discussed in Chapter 3), best seen when moist. This is the whetstone, which is a quarryman's term rather than a geologist's. Whetstones were used for sharpening steel blades and edges and any stone with a surface of sufficient and consistent hardness did the job. This particular stone was in great demand at one time but no one seems to know the full details of when, or how anyone came to discover it here. The stone was not quarried within the stream and therein lies another mystery – where exactly was it quarried? There are no obvious quarrying remains here.

Early Lime Burning on Hagg

The open commons of Ingleborough Fell reach down to the enclosures above Newby Cote, and the level ground between Clapdale Scars and these enclosures are called Hagg. It gives the appearance now of being lightly grazed unimproved pasture separated from the enclosed pastures by a high dry stone wall. It is quiet and undisturbed. In the seventeenth century, however, it was all very different. This was a hive of proto-industrial activity based on the burning of limestone to produce quicklime.[14] Less than one hundred metres from the headwall is a quarry, or rather a delf. It is shallow (never more than 2.50m deep) and completely grassed over. It extends for 100m in length and up to 40m in width. Assuming that the pre-quarrying ground surface was as level as the surrounding land, simple computer calculation shows that around 3200m³ of stone have been removed from this delf. This is a staggering volume.

The stone was destined for a series of lime kilns that lie in a line just above the headwall, west of an L-shaped plantation (Fig. 9.2). There are six kilns here, a seventh just round the wall corner hidden among the network of holloways running up from Newby Cote, and two others below the

Plate 9.3
Stone Delfs on Little Ingleborough, exploiting flagstone beds.

limestone outcrop to the north-east. These two obtained their raw material from this outcrop; the six (and possibly the seventh) obtained it from the delf. Even with this number of kilns burning lime regularly, the amount of stone removed from the delf represents many years of usage. There is a ruined, stone-built lime kiln tucked into the corner of the field called Cote Side to the west of the holloways (at SD7334 7097), which had its own quarry on the open hillside, but this is a relatively modern kiln. It probably dates from the late eighteenth or early nineteenth century. The nine kilns on Hagg are much earlier. Two were excavated in 2005; one was carbon 14 dated to the period 1545 to 1605 though, strictly speaking in archaeology, the full calibrated date range of 1440 to 1640 should be used. (Calibrating dates is an archaeological technique that gives broader date ranges with a stronger chance of these dates being correct, so the 1440–1640 range here has a 95.40 per cent probability of being accurate. The 1545–1605 gives a much less rigorous probability.) Whichever date range is preferred, that kiln is early. All nine are probably broadly contemporary.

The Newby manor court rolls have survived for the years 1739 to 1810, and they have proved useful in determining the extent and significance of lime burning in the area, and the lengths to which lime-burning villagers were prepared to go.[15] For example, the court hearing in April 1748 imposed a fine of 10s on anyone who might 'Cut up and Burn any Sodds or make any Soddkilns' on the moor, and that of May 1758 decreed that a fine of 1s 6d was to be levied against anyone digging on the common 'either for fewell for the fire or for the tillage of ground'. It does not state what was being dug but it clearly referred to turf or peat used as fuel in local lime kilns or domestically. The court proceedings from 1774 to 1784 contain identical rulings which imposed heavy fines on transgressors for the 'great damage' they had caused:

> Whereas several persons of late years have digged delved and graven up great quantities of the Commons and Wastes Grounds ... to burn into ashes and mix the Soil with Lime and sometimes lead the Soil into their Inclosed Grounds for the Improvement thereof to prevent such Practices for the future We Present and Amerce each person ... the sum of five Shillings for every Yard they shall dig delve and grave up.[16]

What this quotation is referring to is the then common practice of paring and burning: the turf layer was removed (ie pared off) with a special type of spade and piled up to dry. These piles were later burnt, the ashes were raked out across the pared area and burnt lime was ploughed in to the soil/ash mixture. The sheer size of these fines bears witness to the scale of the problem, as perceived by the lord of the manor, on the one hand and to the importance attached to land improvement by ordinary farmers in the eighteenth century.

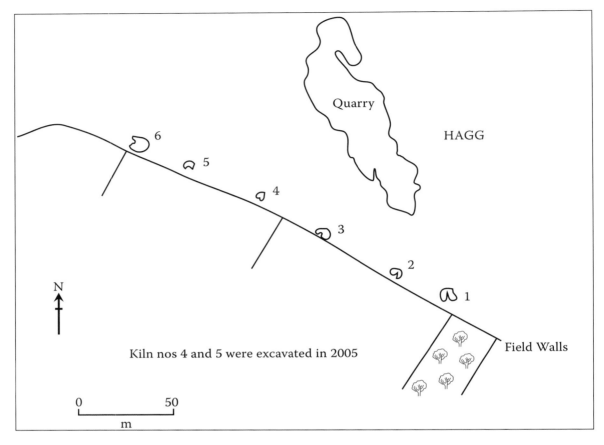

The type of kiln in use here is known as a clamp or sow kiln (Fig. 9.3). They show on the ground as small bowl-shaped hollows, each with an opening on the lower side. When excavated, depth varies: one of these was just below the turf layer; another was 1.50m deep; but bowl diameter, at the top, was about 2.50m in both kilns. When in use, they were filled with alternate layers of fuel and small pieces of limestone with this material being stacked up above ground level in the shape of a dome. When complete, the whole mass was sealed with turf to prevent it burning through too quickly, the fire was lit through the front entrance, or stoke-hole, and it was all left for a few days, depending on the vagaries of the weather, until ready to be dismantled. The purpose of burning lime was to spread it on pasture and crop land to improve the soil and thereby to increase output.

The study of clamp kilns in the Dales is very new and this archaeological work is pushing back the boundaries of knowledge. It is in fact pioneering work, with clamp kilns having been located all round the Ingleborough area as well as more widely through the Dales.

One of the excavated kilns revealed a strange secret, one that it shared with another excavated clamp kiln near Feizor, south-east of Austwick.[17] The

Figure 9.2
Location Plan of Clamp Kilns and Quarry on Hagg, Newby Cote. Surveyed by Jeff Price

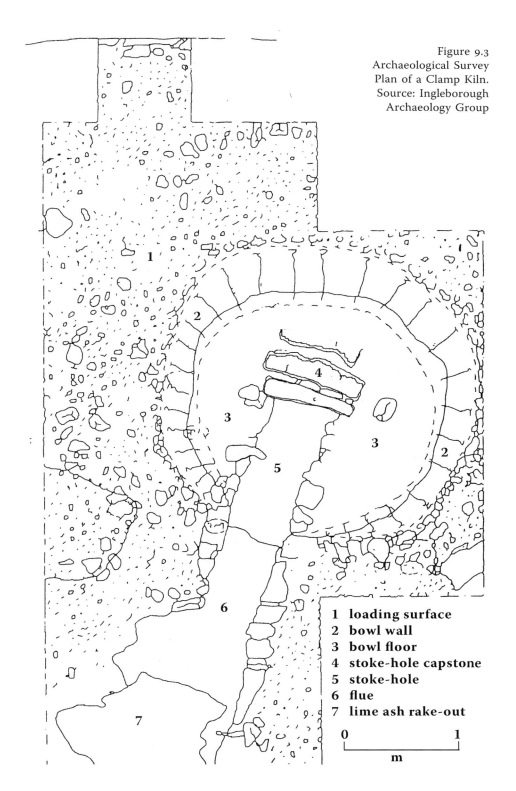

Figure 9.3
Archaeological Survey
Plan of a Clamp Kiln.
Source: Ingleborough
Archaeology Group

1   **loading surface**
2   **bowl wall**
3   **bowl floor**
4   **stoke-hole capstone**
5   **stoke-hole**
6   **flue**
7   **lime ash rake-out**

0   1
        m

stoke-holes mentioned earlier run through the kiln base like a stone-lined culvert. Their purpose was to allow the ingress of oxygen to feed the fire and to make it easy to rake out waste lime ash after each burn. Within this particular kiln, and the Feizor kiln, there were bones, part of the front end of a horse. It was not the entire skeletons by any means, just the skull, front leg bones, a few vertebrae and a collar bone. They had been deliberately stacked in a small neat pile within the stoke-hole. It was definitely not a matter of someone wanting to get rid of a knackered or diseased nag. These bones were carefully examined by an osteoarchaeologist who found no signs of disease and none of burning, which proves that the bones were interred within the kilns after they had been abandoned.

There is only one logical explanation for these two burials and it necessitates use of the stereotypical archaeologist's favourite, yet dreaded, word ritual. There can only have been a very convincing reason why these limeburners decided to carry out this act. We cannot know it, but there is a plausible explanation. In times past the stoke-hole was sometimes called a 'horse', in the sense of an old-fashioned A-frame clothes-horse. We can surmise that these men were placing key parts of a real horse within the stone horse in an attempt to ward off the evil spirits that their superstitious minds believed in. It was, in short, a closure ritual. To have found one such burial would be odd in itself: to have two virtually identical situations almost defies rational understanding, and it seems to have no parallel elsewhere.

More recent lime kilns can be seen, in various states of disintegration, right across the Dales and over one thousand have been located and surveyed within the National Park. There is an especially fine example, with its Romanesque arch, above Robin Proctor's Scar, at SD7614 6995 (Plate 9.4). This would have produced many times more lime than the clamp kilns and the scale of the operation here is attested by the size of the quarry just behind the kiln and by the degree to which the bowl lining had been burnt deep red. The clamp kiln on Hagg that contained the horse burial had an estimated volume of 4m³ while this kiln had a capacity of about 22m³. This type of lime kiln was much more fuel- and labour-efficient, and therefore more profitable. Given its isolated situation, it may have been built after the 1755 enclosure of Norber or the enclosure of Clapham Thwaite three years later, to improve the quality of the pasture.

Wharfe Mill

Wharfe was once associated with an altogether different type of economic activity. Though it is marginal to the Ingleborough massif, this depended entirely on water coming off the mountain. Between Wharfe and Silloth house is the site of a cotton mill, shown on the Ordnance Survey First Edition Six Inch map as a ruin (SD779 693). All that remains to be seen are earthworks where the mill and attendant row of cottages stood, a raised causeway from

Plate 9.4
Lime Kiln above Robin
Proctor's Scar, with
the draw arch through
which burnt lime was
drawn,

the modern road to the mill, a faint trace of the pit which housed the 9.20m diameter water wheel, and a stone pillar that was the last support for the launder which brought water from the mill dam in the wooded area across the fields to the north.[18] It had been a large mill, measuring 18m by 10m. It is possible to piece together its history from legal documents. It had originally been a corn mill and as such would have had medieval origins, as did so many water-powered cotton mills in the Yorkshire Dales. It was converted to cotton in the early 1790s which is when the launder seems to have been constructed to replace the earlier surface leat. It changed hands by 1797 when an insurance valuation put buildings and machinery at £750 and stock in hand at £250, both substantial sums for those days (£1 in 1750 was worth £80 and in 1800 over £30 at today's values). It was advertised to let in 1816 and the new lessee converted it from cotton to silk manufacture. Twenty

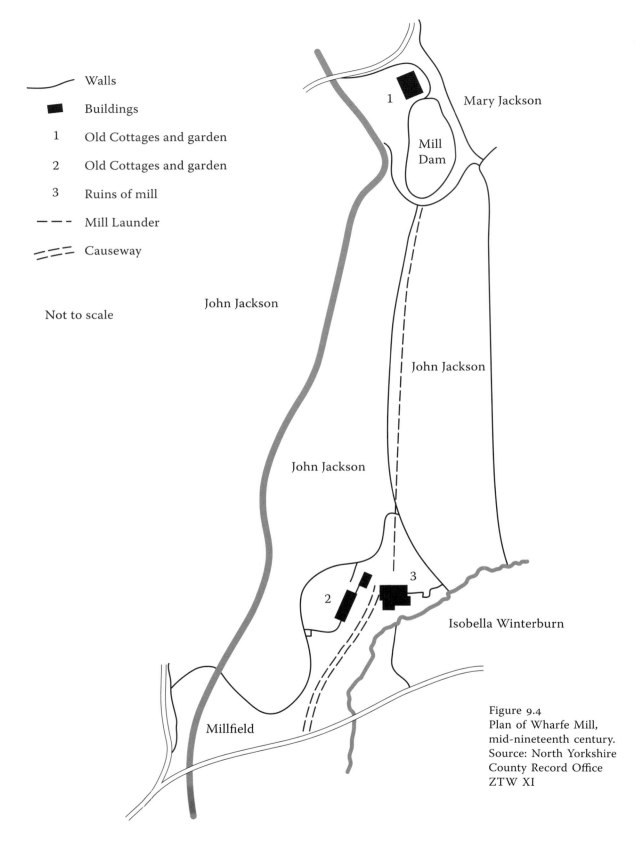

Walls

Buildings

1   Old Cottages and garden

2   Old Cottages and garden

3   Ruins of mill

Mill Launder

Causeway

Not to scale

Mary Jackson

Mill Dam

John Jackson

John Jackson

John Jackson

Isobella Winterburn

Millfield

Figure 9.4
Plan of Wharfe Mill,
mid-nineteenth century.
Source: North Yorkshire
County Record Office
ZTW XI

years later it was all up for sale again as part of a bigger estate, though this did not necessarily affect the lessee. By 1846, however, it was in ruins. Fire had consumed it.

This was not the first mill site on Austwick Beck. Adjacent to Mill Dam, on the north side, are the severely overgrown ruins of another building, with a surface leat leading to it through fields to the north, and a possible wheel pit. Nothing is known of this mill but the wording of the 1793 agreement suggests that the new cotton mill replaced a corn mill 'on the same place' and it is unlikely that there had been two contemporary corn mills so close together. Further upstream still are the remains of yet another structure close to the beck which could have been a much older water-operated corn mill with a hydraulic ram rather than a wheel.

Interestingly, an undated map (Fig. 9.4) names Isobella Winterburn, as owner of the field next to the ruined mill.[19] We have already met her (with a different spelling) as recipient of sheep gaits in the 1814 Austwick enclosure award. In the 1851 census she is noted as being 76 years of age, indicating that she was born in 1775 and was 39 at the time of the enclosure award. In the 1851 census she was noted as an 'unmarried landed proprietor' resident in Wharfe. Isobella had obviously done well for herself, after all.

Modern Land Use

The Present Settlement Pattern

There are no real villages, and certainly nothing approaching a town, in the Ribblehead area today. The most you will come across are aggregations of two or three houses; and Gearstones, with its single farm, bunkhouse and small row of cottages, is second in size only to the hamlet of Chapel le Dale which has a scattering of farms, former farms and cottages centred on the church. You will not find a shop anywhere but two public houses still survive, largely based on the tourist trade. Otherwise the area contains only isolated farmsteads, though it is possible to recognise a distinct pattern of settlement made up by these farms: they tend to occur in 'linear nucleations'. The more open valleys of Ribblesdale and the Wenning, however, have long been able to support larger centres, such as Horton in Ribblesdale, Austwick and Clapham.

There is a discontinuous string of ten farmsteads extending south-west to north-east along the foot of the Whernside massif from Ingleton through the hamlet of Chapel le Dale to Winterscales and Gunnerfleet near Ribblehead viaduct. Another loose line, with four farms, spreads south from Ribblehead towards Selside; and there is a nucleation around Gearstones. All these farms lie more or less on the 300m contour which is about as high as farms get in this part of the Dales. Go higher and nature really begins to make its impact felt with longer and harsher winters, shorter growing seasons and a high average annual number of days with cloud and precipitation. Farms above this general level must be considered marginal and it is no surprise that at least seven farmsteads above 300m have long since been given up: they are either ruinous now or the houses have been sold off with the fields being amalgamated into larger units. Colt Park in Ribblesdale, Winshaw beyond Gearstones, and Scar Top and the Scales farms above Chapel le Dale are now ordinary houses for get-away-from-it-all folk. Apart from Thorns and the Ling Gill farms, Ribblehead House, Goat Close, and Low Gayle now appear in the landscape only as field barns; the houses have gone. Around the mountain's southern flanks most of the long-established farms are still working farms. Only Know Gap has disappeared completely, but the hamlet of Wharfe is no longer a farming community.

The total population of the Ribblehead area is probably smaller now than at any time since the Middle Ages and major differences between present and past population structures can be recognised, representing changes that are very recent. Even in the 1950s – and arguably rather later than that – most people who lived up here were tied to the land or to some form of local employment. All the long-established farmsteads were still occupied by farmers and their families; Salt Lake and Blea Moor cottages were occupied by railwaymen; other houses were occupied by the school teacher at Chapel le Dale, by those engaged in service functions, and by quarrymen. They were all here because this is where they worked. Nowadays it is very different. Among the resident population now are retired professionals, those able to work from home courtesy of broadband, and those who commute to Lancaster or wherever. Many are here because they made a rational decision to move here. The changes seen over the last few decades have been profound by any definition.

The Upland Farming System

The Ingleborough area supported limited arable cultivation throughout much of its history and prehistory but all you will find now is grass, and this area displays the variety of Dales grassland forms in microcosm. Across the National Park as a whole 29 per cent of the area is classified as neutral grassland which translates in farming terms to heavily managed hay meadows and valley bottom pastures.[1] These can be seen associated with the string of farms running along the foot of Whernside, around Gearstones and south of the mountain. Acidic grassland makes up 24 per cent of the Park and this can be seen in much of upper Ribblesdale on the drumlins and on the slopes of the moors (Plate 10.1). A similar sized area consists of wet bog on open moors and this can be seen around Whernside Tarns and Greensett Moss on Whernside, and Newby and Hurnel Mosses on the southern slopes of Ingleborough. A further 4.6 per cent is classed as calcareous grassland developed on limestone bedrock, as on Philpin Sleights near Chapel le Dale, in small pockets immediately north-west of Thorns, and in a swathe from Sulber through Moughton and Crummack Dale to Clapdale. These variations in dominant vegetation are reflected in agricultural land use.

On such land between Sulber and Selside rare cattle breeds have been introduced through the Limestone Country Project (see below) as they can withstand the hostile weather conditions and will eat off what more selective breeds would shun.

High quality improved pastures are rather limited on Ingleborough's southern slopes. There is a narrow line of improved enclosed land above Old Road between Ingleton and Clapham, rarely more than one field deep, with dramatic vegetation change either side of the enclosure headwalls. This narrow band extends northwards up the western side of Clapdale to the former farm that bears that name and to the now totally ruined farmstead of Know Gap House (SD743 706) with its rich and still maintained enclosures. This is but one of many upland farms that was abandoned during the dreadful agricultural depression at the end of the nineteenth century. Know Gap, as we have seen, was certainly still occupied in 1885 but was already doomed.[2] Further high quality pasture is to be found in the dale bottom around Crummack farm and Wharfe, though place-name evidence here hints at this area's former natural state: the name of Sowerthwaite Farm may derive from Old English and Norse words meaning the clearing with sour (*ie* acidic) land, though it could conceivably derive from dialect pronunciation of the word south.

Signs of past arable cultivation are even rarer than decent pasture ground. There are such clues around Wharfe and on Clapham Thwaite to the west of Austwick but the most extensive area of, probably medieval, field systems extend westwards from Clapham towards Cold Cotes on the series of plough terraces, or lynchets, either side of Old Road. Tithe apportionment maps from the 1840s indicate what each field was used for and very few north of Old Road were under the plough at that time.

Variations in vegetation and land quality are also reflected in agricultural land values. These tend to fluctuate depending on demand for land and on locality but ballpark figures do give some idea of basic values and provide useful comparisons with the recent past.[3] Rough fell pastures, for example, currently fetch up to £1250 per hectare (£350 in 1991), improved lower level pastures up to £11,000 (£7750 in 1991) while small 'pony paddock' pastures can sell for as much as £25,000. The average cost of a sheep gait is now between £100 and £250 (£150 to £180 in 1991) which shows remarkable consistency over this period. Ingleborough does not have much top quality dairy grassland but prices in this sphere of the farming market have seen a marked upturn since the middle of 2006 and, while house prices may have plateaued in 2008, land values maintained their vigour.

More than one third of the land area of Britain is utilised primarily as sheep grazing but this proportion rises considerably in our area where most of the farms now concentrate on raising sheep. Stocking density depends on the quality of the pasture: on neutral grasslands it is in the order of three sheep to the hectare but this falls to 1.5 animals per hectare on acidic fell grassland. The nutrient level in soil and plants is too low to sustain any more stock, and in any case it has to be supplemented for much of the year with hay or additives. Over the last fifty years there were marked variations in the number of sheep in the Dales. In 1954 there were 470,000 within the National Park, rising to 750,000 by 1987, an increase of almost 60 per cent, but falling to 355,300 by 1996. Cattle – either dairy breeds for milk or store cattle for beef – figure less prominently in farm statistics. The number of cattle across the Park grew from 68,000 in 1954 to 75,000 in 1987, an increase of just over 10 per cent, while in 1996 the total had dropped to nearly 41,400.

Plate 10.1
Acidic Grassland,
offering low-density
stocking.

(It should be borne in mind that statistical surveys at different times do not always use the same methods of counting so direct comparison here may not be valid.)

Other trends can be recognised over the last five decades. We have seen above that many farms have gone out of business with their lands being aggregated into larger units, and this process has been mirrored all through the Park. Since 1954 there has been a fall of about 35 per cent in the number of farm units and this is reflected in average farm size. In 1954 half of all farms were less than 20ha in area and 80 per cent were below 50ha; for 1996 the figures were 22 per cent and 43 per cent respectively. In 1996 almost 37 per cent were over 100ha.

In these highly competitive days the old and small units are not economically viable. In farming 'big is beautiful'; economies of scale on larger units allow them to survive and, occasionally, to prosper. They earn enough (just enough or not enough, some would contest) to be able to invest in new machinery and equipment, to increase the size of their holdings, and to improve the quality of the pasture. If a small farm has survived, it is probably because someone in the household has another source of income, be it bed and breakfast or another job altogether. There is nothing new in this, of course. For centuries small farmers within the Dales ran their holdings alongside other forms of employment, such as mining, stone-getting and weaving.

Farmers are often accused of grumbling for the sake of it but it is beyond dispute that nature is against them in the Ribblehead area. The weather presents a multitude of constraints in itself. The year 2006, for example, produced a very wet spring followed by a really hot and parched summer, topped off with a drenching late autumn and early winter. The ground was either too wet to get onto to carry out necessary tasks or else the grass was tinder dry and almost barren in parts. As for 2007 and 2008, those drenching summers are perhaps best forgotten. 'Normal' years seem to be a thing of the past!

Access is another constraint that pushes up costs and reduces profit margins. The nearest stock markets are in Bentham, Hawes and Lancaster all of which are a considerable distance away from Ribblehead and Gearstones. Annual sheep sales were held at Ribblehead from 1931 to 1981, and this tradition was resurrected in 1988 as the annual Sheep Show held in September, though the Foot and Mouth outbreak meant that the 2000 show was the last one to be held. Bread and butter animal sales, however, are negotiated at the various weekly stock markets.

One small but significant indicator of the health of upland farming in the Dales, which is mirrored in our area, is the fact that the average age of farmers is in excess of fifty. Many sons and daughters have either decided, or been persuaded, that there is no secure long-term future in upland farming. They may have kept in mind that a survey carried out in 1992 concluded that the average weekly wage of farmers was only £100, substantially lower than for trades in general, and the suicide rate among farmers was rising.

Much of Ingleborough South is still managed as stinted pasture. It is grazed in common by gaitholders each of whom has the right to let loose a specified number of sheep, and the system has not really changed in substance since the original enclosure awards were formulated two centuries ago. The southern and eastern flanks of Ingleborough are not run as one huge stinted pasture but are divided into individual pastures, each with its own management structure (Table 10.1). Newby Moor is one such, Ingleborough Fell another, Clapham Bottoms a third, and Moughton and Scars yet others. Each should call an annual gaitholders' meeting which is responsible for coordinating the following season's stocking arrangements, and ensuring that those who have stocking rights adhere to the rules.

Plate 10.2
Hodge Hole Barn,
Chapel le Dale,
renovated and saved for
the future.

Table 10.1 Stinted Pastures, Ingleborough and Ribblehead

Name	Area (ha)
Ingleborough	
Ingleborough Fell	760
Clapham Bents & Newby Moor	740
Clapham Bottoms	180
Moughton	c350
Scars	283
Ribblehead	
Blea Moor	435
Cam End	690
Carrs	150
Littledale	612
Winterscales	267
Scales Moor	414

Source: Ingleborough Fell Stint Book and Austwick Stint Book, courtesy of the gaitholders committees; http://commons.ncl.ac.uk

The rules established for one stinted pasture were much the same as for any other. On the Little Dale stinted pasture, at Ribblehead, the rules were formalised in the annual meeting of 1934 and they were broadly the same as those for Ingleborough Fell and Austwick.[4] Times when sheep were to be dipped and washed were laid down 'as near as possible to the second Wednesday in October' and the timing and frequency of gathering on the fell was also set down for all to observe. Common holders contributed, in proportion to the number of gaits they held, to the wages of the shepherd who was employed from March or April to November each year, and they were similarly bound to maintain boundary walls. Perhaps surprisingly, no gaitholder could go onto the fell to look to his sheep without first obtaining the shepherd's permission, except in an emergency such as deep snow. One beast (cow) gait was equated to four sheep gaits; one horse gait to eight or ten sheep gaits. A lamb counted as nothing before August after which it equalled a half gait until November when lambs were removed from their dams and reached their majority as a full gait.

If all gaitholders were to assert their rights every year, the commons would be in dire trouble from over-stocking but this does not happen. Indeed, it is not unknown for one gaitholder to buy up someone else's quota, with no intention of ever taking it up in practical terms, as a means of ensuring that stocking levels are maintained at a low level with the aim of promoting environmental recovery. Such, recent, attitudes can only be applauded.

Newby Moor stinted pasture has 602 sheep gaits; Ingleborough Fell is much greater in extent with correspondingly more gaits.[5] The number here varies, and reached its maximum of 2110 in 1946, but is currently around the 1200 mark. The size of individual stints varies enormously. The Fell currently has forty-six gaitholders, not all active, with the number of gaits per individual ranging from only one (five people have one gait) to 120 at the opposite end of the spectrum. The latter is exceptional and the average number of gaits per holder is twenty-seven. If statistics have any intrinsic value, the median number of gaits per holder is 20/21. In Austwick, Long Scar and Moughton have had a maximum of 571 and 668 gaits respectively. Clapham Bottoms, being relatively small, is no longer managed in the traditional way as a true stinted pasture, and does not have a chairman these days.

The month of March 2001 heralded a spell of untold misery for the inhabitants of the Dales. On 7 March the first incidence of Foot and Mouth disease was confirmed on a farm in Wensleydale and by May it had spread across much of the area though not to Ribblehead itself. It had crept up Widdale but did not cross the watershed; it sped up Ribblesdale but stopped at Horton; and it encroached from the Lake District into Barbondale and the Ingleton area but not to Chapel le Dale. Some would say our area had a miraculous escape; others would beg to disagree, as we shall see. By December of that year it was technically all over but the ramifications have lasted to this day and it is generally accepted that farming will never be the same again.

Not all farmers in this area lost their stock to the disease but they were affected in other dire ways. In February 2001 drastic restrictions were imposed on all stock movements. Even to transfer animals from this field to that one across the road was affected. Sheep which had been agisted for the winter in the Lancashire and Cheshire lowlands – and in one case far beyond there – could not be brought back to Chapel le Dale. Agisting means the individual farmer up here was paying a farmer down there to look after his stock over winter. Not being able to bring the sheep back had obvious and direct economic implications. In addition the restrictions meant the farmers could not despatch any stock to market that year, neither fat lambs nor ewes, so their income was slashed.

The ewes over-wintered in the area before Foot and Mouth hit produced lambs in the spring and all these animals had to be kept on the farm and, of course, fed. Stocking levels were consequently too high for the available pasture which had at least two knock-on effects. Firstly, more fodder had to be bought in than was usual, further hitting the farmers in the pocket; and, secondly, grass that would normally have been harvested as hay, silage or haylage was eaten off during the summer. In the winter of 2001–02 farmers had to buy in hay to make up the shortfall: yet again their financial position was worsened. Farmers who had stock culled, either because they had been directly hit by the disease or because their farm was contiguous to one that

Plate 10.3
Rebuilt Dry Stone Wall,
funded by the National
Park Authority's Barns
and Walls Conservation
Scheme.

had been, were compensated well. Those like the farmers of Ribblehead, who fell into neither category, received a paltry sum in comparison.

One positive outcome of this whole sad episode is an increased awareness of what form the relationship between people and the land should take. There has been an environmental awakening and a growing realisation and acceptance that farmers can benefit by farming in harmony with the natural way of things; and the general desire of people across the country for changing direction and running matters in a more sustainable, and organic, manner has been translated into schemes to make stock farming more compatible with this way of thinking.

Two schemes pre-date the disease. In the 1980s the government of the day brought in the Environmentally Sensitive Area (ESA) scheme and this was extended to the National Park in 1986 and to Ribblehead and the valley of Chapel le Dale in 1997.[6] In 1991 the Countryside Stewardship scheme was brought in to provide similar aid to farmers outside ESA areas. In both cases, payments were made to farmers in return for taking a more environmental approach to the business of farming, and to integrate stock management with regard for conserving biodiversity. These two schemes were effectively rationalised by being merged to form the Environmental Stewardship scheme in 2004.

In addition, the National Park Authority provided financial help through the 1990s to farmers in certain areas who wished to restore traditional and decaying field barns and walls (around 30 per cent of Dales walls are semi-derelict or worse) under its Barns and Walls Conservation Scheme (Plates 10.2 and 10.3), though funding for this programme has now ceased; and it also introduced its Farm Conservation Scheme in 1996. This was applied first in Kingsdale and near Chapel le Dale as a pilot scheme and help was given for preservation of and improvements to traditional farm buildings and walls, to maintaining traditional hay meadows and to improving neutral grasslands in a non-chemical manner. Restrictions were placed on fertiliser applications and on ploughing and draining while blanket spraying was outlawed. In the Chapel le Dale area and Kingsdale twenty farms joined the scheme, with a further five in Ribblesdale and Malham Moor. The Farm Conservation Scheme was phased out in 2003.

One scheme grew on the back of the impact of Foot and Mouth. The Limestone Country Project was initiated in 2003 for a five-year period in the Ingleborough (and Malham) area, partly utilising finance from the European Union.[7] The aims were twofold: to protect and enhance the natural environment while assisting participating farmers to develop an economically viable and sustainable business. It is basically turning the clock back to a time when land was not overstocked, when there was a balance between sheep and cattle numbers, when chemicals and 'intensivisation' did not rule the land.

Farmers who entered the scheme agreed to manage their holdings in an extensive way, by letting the animals range more widely at lower stocking densities. They were encouraged to reduce the number of sheep and to increase the number of cattle as sheep are more selective eaters than cattle, and natural plant diversity had been gradually reducing over the last four or five decades as flowering species are squeezed out. They were also helped to purchase hardy traditional breeds of cattle which will eat what sheep and modern selective breeds of cattle leave alone, and which are able to thrive in the harsh climatic conditions of the area. Breeds such as the Shorthorn, Welsh Black, Galloway and Blue-Grey are now making a welcome comeback to the area (Plate 10.4). The scheme's initial target was to involve fifteen farms across 1500ha of the Malham and Ingleborough areas with 500 head of traditional cattle.[8] By the beginning of 2007 the statistics were impressive: eighteen farms had signed up (four of them in our area), 400 head were grazing under the project (100 in our area) over 1850ha (500 in our area), and this situation has continued for the duration of the project's designated lifespan.

There are economic pros and cons of grazing in this way. The rare breeds can be left out on the fell for much of the winter, unless deep snow dictates otherwise, and they do not need the expensive supplementary feeds required to keep modern selective breeds in sound condition. This consequently saves costs. Other economies are made by not having to house the cattle indoors through the winter and by not having to provide straw bedding, and the time-labour input is also minimised. On the economic downside, these savings

Plate 10.4
Blue-grey cattle on Sulber, part of the Limestone Country Project.

need to be balanced against the longer period needed to bring these animals up to maturity. Selective, intensively-bred stock can be despatched to market within fifteen to eighteen months compared to thirty-six months for these extensively-reared rare breeds.[9] Economics are not the prime determinant here, though. The cattle are very much a conservation tool, not only here but elsewhere. For the latter part of each winter they have been be taken off Ingleborough and transported to Whitbarrow in the South Lakes to graze and 'manage' those, less exposed, upland pastures.

Further grants for sympathetic improvements have been made available to farmers through the Yorkshire Dales Millennium Trust. The stone-built field barn is one of the most iconic features of the Dales landscape, and there are estimated to be around 4500 across the National Park. Only fifteen are listed and thus protected. Results of a sample survey undertaken in 2006–07 made rather disappointing reading as only 55 per cent were found to be in a 'favourable' condition. This is not to cast blame in any direction: changing farming techniques and a ban on tethering animals by the neck have rendered barns redundant, and farmers cannot be expected to divert scarce resources to maintaining them for aesthetic reasons. Some grants have been made available for barn restoration but the scale of the overall task is daunting. Hodge Hole Barn (SD735 787) near Chapel le Dale has been fully restored and saved for the future (see Plate 10.2). Traditional field barns are an integral element in the Dales landscape and heritage and are surely worthy of preservation.

Farming had been in decline for decades; in 2001 it was knocked for six but, at last, there are signs of hope for the future, a future where farmers may end up truly being guardians of the countryside, where stock co-exist with wildlife to the benefit of both ... and where farmers and their families, too, are guaranteed a decent future.

A Sporting Estate

Today the red grouse (*Lagopus lagopus*) appears on Britain's Amber List of birds of 'medium conservation concern' owing to a decline in the breeding bird population over the last twenty-five years, though its fortunes have long been cyclical. The breeding season of 2005 was disastrous and 2006 and 2008 were disappointing while those of 2003 and 2004 were the best for many years.[10] Despite current concern about red grouse's long-term prognosis there are still around 250,000 breeding pairs in the country.[11] Preferred red grouse habitat is heather moorland up to 700m above sea level, though their optimum hovers around the 450m contour. Their dominant food source is young fresh heather shoots and flowers supplemented with bilberry in autumn and a range of insects in the summer months. For nesting they require older and more woody heather growth. All told 1km² of heather moor can support 30 pairs of grouse.

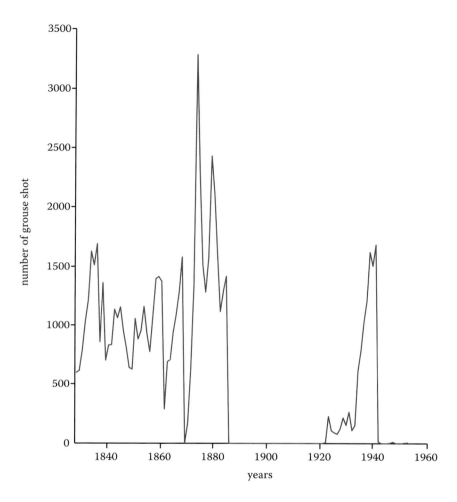

Figure 10.1
Ingleborough Estate:
Size of Grouse Bag,
1830–1948.
Source: North Yorkshire
County Record Office
ZTW III 11/120, 12/15,
11/5

It is often said that a healthy red grouse population reflects healthy moorland which in turn supports a healthy bird population in general, and surely no one can argue that moorland 'small' birds, grouse, raptors and vegetation biodiversity are inextricably interlinked, though some might argue that a managed heather monoculture has a negative impact on biodiversity. There is, however, a very different linkage with grouse and that is economic and, some might argue, cultural. Like it or not, the grouse is one of the country's prime game birds.

Grouse shooting in the Pennines was first recognised as a 'sporting' pastime in the time of Charles II and it became more widespread as an acceptable sporting activity in the late eighteenth century,[12] but strictly as the preserve of the aristocracy and landed gentry. This situation began to change with the repeal in 1831 of the game laws which gave farm tenants the right to shoot game birds within their tenancy, and to sell the shooting experience to those from outside.[13] Many of the increasingly prosperous body of urban industrialists saw this as a way of worming their way into a higher social order, and grouse shoots began to emerge as a new source of rural income. At a time of falling farm incomes and rentals, and an increasing realisation that income from upland mining was going to decline, any potential source of new income was welcome. It was not just the landowners and tenants who benefited in the pocket: part-time work was provided during the season for beaters and pickers-up; game dealers, transporters and local inns logged on to the phenomenon; and full-time employment was provided for a new class of game keepers and under keepers.

As the nineteenth century progressed moorland was increasingly seen as the exclusive preserve of the grouse.[14] For centuries they had been used for sheep grazing and it was common practice to periodically burn the heather to promote fresh growth and thereby ensure a supply of food for the sheep as winter approached. Burning also destroyed parasites which attacked and debilitated sheep. By the 1850s landowners had come to believe that burning the heather discouraged grouse and that the large numbers of sheep were discouraging grouse breeding.[15] Burning was stopped and sheep were removed from the moors, but it took only twenty years for them to realise they had been quite wrong. In the 1870s there was a serious grouse population crash, so sheep were brought back and burning was reintroduced, on a ten to fifteen year cycle, to destroy the parasitic threadworm that periodically devastates grouse stocks. In addition further impetus was provided by the publication, from 1853, of *The Field*, a magazine aimed at the shooting fraternity, which offered advice on all aspects of grouse moor and shooting management and regularly included records of how many birds had been shot on particular shooting estates.

The coming of the railway through Ribblehead made these grouse moors more accessible, attracting more 'customers', and (allegedly) royalty in the form of the future Edward VII, who made shooting an essential pursuit of any aspiring gentleman. Technological developments in the 1850s and 1870s had improved the efficiency and capacity of guns to the point that bags

Plate 10.5
Gayle Beck Lodge, a former shooting cabin, photographed in 2008.

were now frequently counted in the thousands and a typical shoot began to resemble a slaughter. The 'old' aristocracy blamed the 'new' (industrial) rich for spoiling their sport's image so the idea of driven shoots came in. Rather than having birds being shot as they took flight by being disturbed by dogs – invariably flying away from the guns which meant the birds were a proverbial sitting duck – beaters were now employed to drive the birds across the moors towards the guns making them harder to pick off. Integrity had been restored!

The industry went into a rapid decline after the First World War. The old social order began to break down, the heirs to many estates had been killed and the rural population depleted meaning fewer men were available or willing to work on the estates, and the introduction of death duties in 1894 (raised to 50 per cent in 1919) led to vast areas being sold off. Growing demands for public access to our fells and moors, as well as burgeoning sheep populations, had a negative impact on grouse populations. Overstocking led to a depletion of heather as the moors were overgrazed.

The scale of the sport – or perhaps one should say industry – around Ribblehead paled into insignificance compared with the southern flanks of Ingleborough. Newby Moor, Moughton and Ingleborough Fell were sections of a huge grouse moor that stretched from Crina Bottom in the west to the Horton parish boundary in the east. It was all part of the Ingleborough Estate, managed from Ingleborough Hall in Clapham by the Farrer family and their land agents.

The Farrers purchased the manor nearly two hundred years ago, not for its agricultural income or opportunities but because of the potential the moors held as a prime sporting estate. From that time onwards management of the estate focussed on preserving shooting rights to provide sport and, importantly, to generate income to support the upkeep of the estate, which farm rents alone could not do. Shooting was dominated by red grouse: an estate with a creditable record for returning large bags of grouse after a day of challenging shooting would draw in 'guns' from far and wide, boosting its reputation. Shooting rights were jealously guarded and the Ingleborough Estate widened its appeal by offering first-class shooting of other game birds such as pheasants in the wooded areas of Clapdale and Rayside, golden plover, partridge, snipe and woodcock, as well as ducks on The Lake in Clapdale and specially dug ponds.

Literature put out by the estate in 1912 to try and tempt a potential new tenant to take up the shooting lease for the south side of the mountain waxed lyrical asserting that the 'shooting affords the most sporting shots in the district and is one which holds the highest place in Yorkshire for the charm of its surroundings,'[16] though the thrust of this selling pitch was pheasant rather than moorland birds. The former claim may well have been true, and no one can doubt the latter, but shooting in the decades since the Farrers had purchased the manor had not been consistently successful. This was in large part due to a combination of factors (primarily disease, over-stocking with sheep, and inclement weather) and estate correspondence bears this out. The 1907 season was a comparative failure owing to the 'exceptionally severe' weather experienced during the rearing season[17] and 1912 was very similar with disease being induced by the cold, and damp conditions through the summer dramatically reduced the number of poults. A letter sent by the estate's land agent in 1935 lamented the impact of overgrazing on the shooting and expressed the (vain) hope that they 'could get the stint on all our Moors reduced to give the heather a chance to grow'.[18] Too many sheep translated very quickly into a despoiled habitat, too few grouse, and reduced estate income. The same agent had clearly felt very strongly for many years about what he considered to be unreasonable behaviour by gaitholders on the commons. He expressed disapprobation in a letter in 1908 over their exercising customary rights to shoot rabbits on the fells claiming that this caused disturbance to nesting game birds and occasional destruction of actual nest sites.[19]

Long before this, though, the estate had shown awareness of and concern about the state of the moors across Ingleborough. A letter from the agent in 1861 had noted that the moors had not been burned for some time to the detriment of sheep and grouse, and warned that mature, woody heather would take several years to regenerate if burnt too late in its life cycle.[20]

Grouse moors such as those above Clapdale and Austwick were at the twin mercy of natural forces and over-zealous graziers who, after all, also had a business to run. The size of bags and therefore income from shooting fluctuated markedly over the years in direct response to these variables (Fig. 10.1). Even in the 'good' days of grouse shooting on Ingleborough there were disastrous seasons, such as 1867 when only three birds were downed. Yet, only four years later, the bag on the entire estate totalled 3289. Over the period 1830 to 1882 nearly 65,000 shotgun cartridges found a living target across this entire sporting estate: rabbits fared worst (38,358), followed by grouse (21,241) with other mammal and moorland bird species, and woodland-based pheasants, accounting for the remainder.[21]

It also became increasingly difficult to find anyone willing to take on the shooting lease, even before the Great War. No one took on the lease for the four seasons 1907 to 1910 and, though it was let towards the end of that year, the rights were again being advertised just two years later.[22]

Grouse shooting had no long-term future and terminal decline was already apparent before the traumas of the First World War. By 1934 Newby Moor and Ingleborough Fell were considered to have 'practically no game at all' and it was said that it was no longer profitable to let the shooting,[23] given the running costs incurred by the estate in maintaining the infrastructure and grouse population.

Correspondence to the Ingleborough Estate's land agent in 1935 summed up the situation well by describing the Gearstones shooting business as a 'bad egg', which is odd given the size of recent bags.[24] In 1932, 396 brace had been shot, with 776 in 1933, and 1046 in 1934. The estimated bag for 1935 was 1200 to 1500 which on the surface might appear healthy but costs had risen so much that profit margins were severely squeezed. Had the 1935 bag been 1200 brace, the net return per brace would have been four shillings, or five at the higher estimate, which compared unfavourably with the average fifteen shillings in the heyday before the First World War. The Second World War sounded the death knell: predictably no tenants came forward to take on the shoot, and keepers and beaters had to be dismissed as there was nothing for them to do and no money to pay them.

An explosion of parasitic nematode worms in the 1970s was the final straw for some shooting moors, though the grouse moors of Ingleborough had not seen sustained activity for many years prior to that. Grouse have not been shot on Blea Moor since 1964. To minimise the effects of nematode infestation gamekeepers maintain dumps across the moors of medicated grit for grouse to eat.[25]

What impact has grouse shooting had on the Ribblehead landscape? Organised estates provided shooting lodges for their rich and privileged clientele. The old inn at Gearstones had been rebuilt in 1880, closed down in 1911, and developed as a shooting lodge for the Ingleborough Estate, while the youth hostel in upper Dentdale (closed in January 2007) was for many years an aristocratic shooting lodge. Individual moors needed lunchtime shelter for the shooting party so shooting cabins were erected, usually of stone. They tended to conform to a set pattern having two rooms, one for the 'guns' with its fireplace and supply of warming whiskey and a second for the beaters with their ale. One such cabin, Gayle Beck Lodge (SD791 814), is currently slowly collapsing by the roadside beyond Far Gearstones while two on the flanks of Ingleborough itself have all but gone (Plate 10.5). Driven shoots required structures for the guns to hide behind so lines of stone or turf butts were built, typically 45m apart, the remains of which now often provide the only reminder of this past activity. Two lines of butts, still shown on the Ordnance Survey 1:25,000 map, follow Dry Gill on the southern flanks of Blea Moor and Axletree Gill just north-east of Far Gearstones. Being within the gills both sets were ideally placed so that birds flying over would be high in the sky thereby providing the guns with a greater challenge and making the birds' flight slightly less of a suicide mission.

Until the 1930s the southern flanks of Ingleborough from Grey Scars to Moughton were purple with heather in the autumn: extreme overstocking to feed the nation during the war saw most of that swept away. Heather is still to be found on Thieves Moss at the head of Crummack Dale and across Moughton and Moughton Long Scar but it occurs only in isolated patches and much of it is not in a healthy state. Grouse have become an extremely rare species on the mountain because the spatial extent and quality of surviving heather cannot support them. The two shooting cabins (or luncheon cabins, as they were sometimes described) on southern Ingleborough, which stood roofed and intact into the 1980s, and one at the head of Crummack Dale, are now sadly decayed. The latter (SD7842 7193) was deliberately reduced almost to foundation level though its two-room plan is still clear amongst the pile of rubble; that above Sulber (SD7687 7349) is rapidly crumbling now that the roof has collapsed; and that on Wetherpot Heath (SD7342 7157) has lost one of its two rooms. This is to be regretted as these cabins have their own social story to tell, and the Sulber cabin tells it graphically. The southern room is larger than the northern; it had a larger, south-facing window and a splendid fireplace whereas the small room had a tiny north-facing window and a simple fireplace. The larger room was for the 'guns' who had paid a lot of money for the privilege of shooting and who thus expected to be cosseted; the other room was for the humble beaters. This social divide was mirrored by what each set consumed – whiskey and appetising food for the guns, ale or cordial and basic fare for the others. In the mid-1980s I had reason to be working near this cabin and, in an idle moment, two of us began rooting around in the midden, or rubbish tip, close by. We found two heaps of well-preserved glass bottles, one consisting mainly of spirits bottles, the other exclusively beer and lemonade!

The Ordnance Survey 1:25,000 map marks lines of grouse butts radiating out southwards and eastwards from the mountain, and other lines across Moughton. Those on Moughton stand like forlorn stone sentinels but the rest are either becoming archaeological features capable of misinterpretation or are being slowly swallowed up and naturally recycled within the landscape. Grouse shooting is firmly part of history on Ingleborough and Moughton, almost as distant in the collective folk memory as Robin Proctor or the packhorse drivers of yore, and the birds themselves had all but been consigned to the history books.

There are signs of hope, however. Reduced stocking levels on the commons following on from the foot and mouth disaster, and deliberate policies to over-winter fewer sheep on the fells, are beginning to bear fruit in terms of limited heather regeneration. South House Moor is now managed as a nature reserve with zero grazing and heather and bilberry are making a come back on the higher slopes towards the crest of Park Fell. Nature has a wonderful capacity to put right what we have disturbed and upset. Perhaps the next generation will be able to enjoy a purple-clad Ingleborough. A dozen or so red grouse over-wintered on South House Moor in 2007–08,[26] totally safe from the guns, but grouse are still shot on Burn Moor, across the Wenning valley in the southern extremity of Clapham parish. Here, the winter season of 2007 saw an upturn in the number of brace bagged after five or six seasons of mediocre performance. Those who oppose shooting would no doubt view this as a setback but there is the brighter side: a healthy grouse population ensures the moors will be properly managed and, in turn, this promotes habitat for non-sport moorland bird species. Every story has two sides.

Yet grouse on Ingleborough are again falling foul of man's work. As their numbers slowly recover, they range further afield for food. The post and rail fence along the scar top above Thieves Moss is on one of their main flight paths, and several have come to grief here by flying straight into the fence. Some are killed outright, others are injured, but most end up providing an easy meal for the resident fox population. Natural England are trying to solve this unexpected problem.

If we take the long view the picture may not be so rosy, after all. An influential report, published in January 2008, was flagged up by the Royal Society for the Protection of Birds (RSPB) because of the enormous effects global warming and climate change will have on the distribution of many key bird species.[27] Some will be wiped out in this country, others will move north where it will still be cooler, yet others will move in here from the increasingly balmy south; one species highlighted as of concern by the RSPB is the red grouse because its habitat range will shrink markedly. It is projected that, by 2075, red grouse will be restricted to Scotland.

Forestry

The Yorkshire Dales are not impressive in terms of tree cover, even when compared with the rest of the country. Europe as a whole has approximately 30 per cent under forest and woodland compared to England's 8.4 per cent and Yorkshire's 5.8 per cent.[28] The Yorkshire Dales National Park has only

Figure 10.2
Location of Commercial Quarries at Helwith Bridge, early nineteenth century.
Source: North Yorkshire County Record Office ZXF (M) 1/4/8

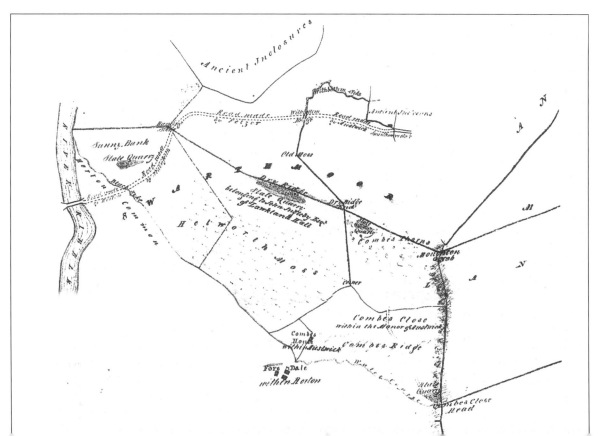

3.41 per cent under trees, equating to 3000 hectares, and much of this (2.14 per cent) is coniferous plantation rather than broadwood or semi-natural woodland. A large proportion of the plantations lie within spitting distance of Ribblehead, over large swathes of Widdale, much of Cam Fell, and Greenfield which has by far the most extensive continuous tract of plantation in the Dales.

These plantations extend up to the 500 metre contour and occur on what was previously wet bog or acidic grassland. The term 'blanket afforestation' has been applied to such forests and viewed from the air or from afar it seems an appropriate description. Most plantations were laid out with no regard for contour configurations, with ruler-straight edges marching up hill and vast stands of identical trees, mainly spruce varieties, being planted in a regimented fashion. To make the ground suitable for tree growth the hill slopes were first drained with a series of herringbone ditches, or 'grips', being cut leaving dry strips in between. These forests are uniform in plan, in species and in colour and mature forests support a limited range of bird and animal species.

Much of this plantation woodland was planted by the Forestry Commission in the 1960s during a concerted national drive to increase the level of self-sufficiency in timber: even now we import 85 per cent of our timber needs. Tax incentives made investment in new plantations an attractive prospect, but there was a basic and unseen long-term flaw in this policy. Ultimately forests need felling, or harvesting. If you plant huge areas at more or less the same time, you must harvest at roughly the same time and this creates problems. Firstly, too much timber comes on to the market at one time thereby possibly driving down prices, and therefore profits; and, secondly, there are severe logistical problems to be overcome at harvest time.

Large tracts of the forest in Widdale have recently been clear felled and here the logistics were not insurmountable as there is a decent road running through the dale from which the forests are accessible. Cam and Greenside are ready for harvesting now and the management company is keen to get the timber out, but an argument has been raging for a lengthy period over access. Neither forest has direct access to suitable roads. Those to the east are narrow, steep in places, and pass through very small settlements in the upper dales, and there are no roads to the west. The company applied to despatch timber southwards through High Birkwith and Horton in Ribblesdale but this caused an immediate outcry in the tiny hamlet of Newhouses and in Horton which has a difficult bridge crossing. An alternative proposal was mooted to construct a completely new road westwards from the plantations across the Ribble but, predictably, this has also met with sustained opposition. Yet another possibility is to bring it down Cam High Road to Far Gearstones. There is no simple solution but, say the forest owners, the timber has to come out soon, especially given the current high prices for raw timber. It still awaits resolution.

Then, of course, there arises the whole issue of what is left once the clear felling has been completed: an unsightly jumble of tree stumps and brashings. The jury is out as to the viability and rationality of 1960s policies.

Woodlands of the future hereabouts will be very different from these monotone coniferous forests. Planting will be of mixed broadleaved woodland: Natural England's predecessor had already planted a large part of South House Moor, with grant aid through the Yorkshire Dales Millennium Trust – around 10,000 mixed deciduous trees have already been planted here. A further planting of 500 trees has been completed at Hurtle Pot just outside the hamlet of Chapel le Dale, and part of the cleared Widdale forest is being put down to deciduous species.

Slate Quarrying

The Silurian strata that outcrop so prominently at Helwith Bridge have been worked by quarrymen since at least the eighteenth century, and possibly even earlier: occasional documentary references exist from 1739 onwards. Two commercial quarries still produce crushed roadstone, though both have a very limited future with planning consents running out for Dry Rigg in 2009 and Arcow by the end of 2011. Historically, seven quarries have been worked here, all but one exploiting the Silurian rock resource (Fig. 10.2).

Dry Rigg has the earliest confirmed reference, in the form of a seven-year lease dated 6 February 1739 of 'mines, delfs and quarries of blue slate'.[29] John Ingleby, a major local landowner who lived at Lawkland Hall, granted the right to quarry stone here to two local farmers, John Ridley, described as a yeoman of Lawkland parish, and Thomas Armitstead, a husbandman from nearby Studfold. At that time what is now Dry Rigg Quarry was two separate slate delfs,[30] one of which was called Combes Thorns Quarry and the other originally Coum Rig. Whether the lessees employed quarrymen to work the quarry or worked it themselves will never be ascertained, but it is known that rough-hewn slabs of stone known to the quarryman as blue slate[31] (though geologically it is not slate) were carted on the old road to Silloth, below Wharfe, to a water-powered stone sawmill where the slabs were refined into dairy slabs, door lintels, water cisterns, floor slabs, and a range of other finished products that can still be seen across the western Dales (Plate 10.6). Over the next century Dry Rigg passed through various hands but by 1880 both delfs had ceased working. It reopened in 1938 to produce crushed stone to meet the seemingly endless demand generated by road building programmes locally and regionally,[32] and it has continued thus ever since.

Not to be confused with Combes Thorns Quarry was the now long defunct Combs Quarry (see Plate 3.6), whose impressive working face looms large over Foredale Cottages. This was cited, in 1774, in promotional material for a proposed canal link from Langcliffe to Lancaster,[33] as one of the more significant potential sources of traffic for the canal, with its 'inexhaustible quarries of blue-flags, grit flags, excellent blue slate, and grit slate'. The quarry was worked through the nineteenth century, selling mainly high quality 'blue-flag' products that had been sawn onsite, between the quarry and the cottages, using a donkey engine as the power source. It is not known when Combs ceased working.

Arcow Quarry also produced similar blue slate products but its two delfs operated on a limited scale until the lease was taken up by the Ribblesdale Lime & Flag Quarry Company Ltd in 1878.[34] Initially at least, this company concentrated on producing burnt lime rather than blue slate or crushed stone products. Large-scale crushing really only got underway in the 1930s.

Two further quarries at Helwith Bridge exploited flagstone beds rather than the more slate-based mudstones. Studfold Quarry was worked from the mid-eighteenth century but operations ceased around 1880.[35] Various planning applications were unsuccessfully lodged in 1938 and 1951, and again in 1967, to create a completely new Studfold Quarry south of the earlier workings, again with roadstone in mind.[36]

Helwith Bridge Quarry – once known as Sunny Bank Slate Quarry – was worked on a much larger scale, not closing down until 1972. Like its neighbours, Helwith Bridge concentrated on roadstone from the 1930s but until then it had also turned out blue slate (Fig. 10.3).[37] From about 1938 to 1958 crushed stone was exported by rail: an overhead gantry system housed a conveyor belt from the quarry crushing plant over the railway line to a siding on the eastern side. Now flooded, this old quarry serves a very different commercial purpose as a fishery.

Quarrying at Ribblehead

Quarries were developed in the 1870s on Blea Moor for constructing Ribblehead viaduct. Both the Little Dale and Force Gill quarries were small-scale and the passing of the years has largely reclaimed them. It is possible now to walk past and not realise they were once quarries. Three other sites in the area have left a more permanent mark on the Ribblehead landscape: Ribblehead Quarry itself; Colt Park Quarry (SD773 785) and Salt Lake Quarry nearby (SD775 783), both of which are adjacent to the railway. These two quarries were established in the early 1870s for the building of the railway, not for the viaduct but for producing crushed stone as ballast to lay on the trackbed. Work there continued after completion of the railway project as, for example, mobile crushing plant was operational in Salt Lake through the 1880s. Colt Park Quarry is now a nature reserve managed by the Yorkshire Wildlife Trust while Salt Lake Quarry lies within the railway curtilage.

What happened to Ribblehead Quarry in the years after the railway was finished is unclear, and the date when it opened is not known, but it was certainly being worked by the Craven Lime Company by 1895.[38] This was a

Plate 10.6
'Blue Slate' Trough
at Thorns, now
cracked and no longer
watertight.

major player in the region with quarries and lime kilns at Mealbank Quarry in Ingleton and the Craven Limeworks between Langcliffe and Stainforth. In 1907 the company abandoned Ribblehead Quarry for economic reasons, and it was subsequently worked by others on a very spasmodic basis until 1943 when a Leeds-based company, Horace Austin & Sons, took over the lease to produce crushed stone and powdered limestone for agricultural use. In 1953 this company sub-leased the operation to Messrs Adam Lythgoe of Warrington which was heavily involved in the agricultural crushed limestone business. Three years later Lythgoes bought Austins out and invested heavily in new production plant and successfully applied for planning permission to extend the quarry's area.

Business remained buoyant for more than a decade but in 1971 Lythgoes put the site on the market, at first without success so it was mothballed. ARC (now Hanson) took it over two years later as a replacement for another of its quarries, outside the Dales, which was coming to the end of its life. Ribblehead's 23 million tonne reserves seemed an attractive acquisition. It was set to reopen on a grand scale in 1979 but negotiations for a massive long-term contract to supply the new Selby power station collapsed and work at Ribblehead did not resume.[39]

In 1998 Hanson voluntarily surrendered its planning consents on the quarry and in October 2000 handed the site over to English Nature, now Natural England.

The valley below Chapel le Dale has also seen major quarrying activity over a long period of time. Ingleton Granite Quarries (SD719 753) produced not granite but a rock known as greywacke from 1887 to 1955, selling it in crushed form. In that year production was transferred to the new (and still working) Ingleton Quarry (SD705 742) by ARC (Plate 10.7). New state of the art plant was installed here in 1993 making it one of North Yorkshire's most efficient quarries.

Ribblesdale Limeworks

Ribblesdale Limeworks was part of the large-scale operations of the Ribblesdale Lime & Flag Quarry Company (from 1910 shortened to the Ribblesdale Lime Company) Ltd at Foredale Quarry, along with Arcow Quarry (Fig. 10.4).[40] Both quarry and limeworks had stopped working by 1958 and very little now remains of the limeworks site, apart from some relict sections of reinforced concrete, and no one would know of the quarry's existence without prior knowledge as it is located high up above Foredale Cottages, well-hidden from the valley bottom.

This quarry is unique in the Yorkshire Dales in having the imprint of its working features fossilised on the quarry floor[41] – the incline from quarry to limeworks, the complex network of tramway tracks within the quarry, the compressed air system that fed the drills, the drumhouse, and a number of buildings, can all be clearly seen as 'footprints' on the ground (Fig. 10.5). It has been possible to reconstruct the story of this quarry from its inception in 1878, utilising archaeological evidence, documentary sources and oral history, and an impressive photographic archive has been built up. At every other limestone quarry in the Dales the historic features have been wiped away by modern quarrying operations, or buried under measureless volumes of landfill material or, in some cases, by being flooded deliberately or by default. Foredale is therefore particularly important as a preserved part of Ribblesdale's industrial heritage.

The limeworks consisted of two banks of large stone-built kilns, along with crushing plant to turn out roadstone, hydrating plant to produce powdered lime, and a whole range of ancillary workshops, stores and staff facilities (Plate 10.8). The combined quarry and limeworks was an impressive operation, for many years giving employment to nearly eighty men, but its outdated nineteenth-century quarry and limeworks technology were the causes of its downfall. The company had been subsumed within a larger company structure in 1939[42] and, over time, production was increasingly concentrated at the more accessible and more efficient

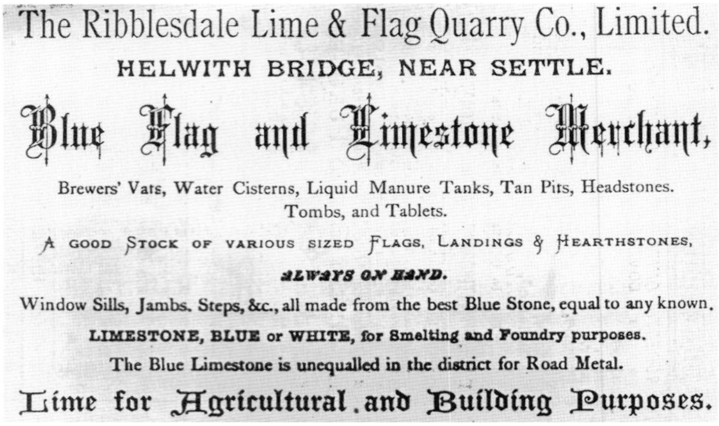

Figure 10.3
Advertisement for Christopher Ralph at Helwith Bridge Quarry, 1896.
Source: Settle Household Almanac 1896

Figure 10.4
Advertisement for Ribblesdale Lime & Flag Quarry Co. Ltd, 1885.
Source: Settle Household Almanac 1885

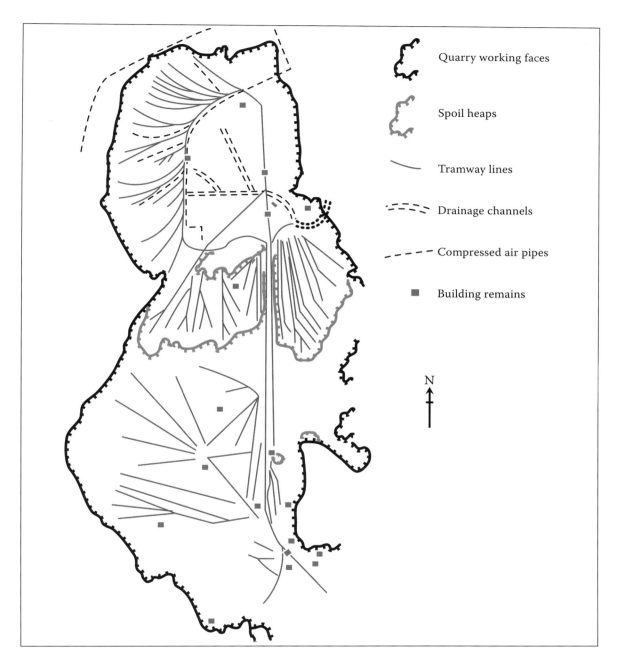

	Quarry working faces
	Spoil heaps
	Tramway lines
	Drainage channels
	Compressed air pipes
	Building remains

N

Figure 10.5 Plan of Features fossilised within Foredale Quarry Source: D. S. Johnson (2005) 'Foredale Quarry, Ribblesdale Limeworks', privately published report

operation at Horton in Ribblesdale. This larger company was bought up by the giant ICI in 1962[43] which expressed the intention to work Foredale by extending Horton Quarry southwards but, probably thankfully, these plans were abandoned and Foredale's planning consent was allowed to lapse in 1996. Had it continued, the present landscape between Horton and Helwith Bridge would be very different.

Plate 10.7
Loading stone in
Ingleton Quarry,
exploiting high-grade
roadstone.

John Delaney and Horton Limeworks

Stand in Horton or on Pen-y-ghent and look to the west and the view is dominated by the vast working faces of Horton Quarry eating into the rich limestone reserves of Moughton (Plate 10.9). With Swinden Quarry in Wharfedale, this operation is among the largest and most modern limestone quarries in the north of England. With planning consent valid until 2042 it is bound to have a further impact on this part of the Ingleborough massif as the annual target production level is 610,000 tonnes. Multiply that by the number of years remaining and it represents a staggering quantity of stone. Approximately seventy-five per cent of this is destined for concrete production, a further five per cent goes to a chemical plant in the North-East, and the balance is crushed as roadstone and construction base material.[44] It all goes out by road owing to short-sighted decision made decades ago which allowed the removal of the rail link into the quarry site. The quarry's operators had hoped to reinstate the link but the costs are probably financially unrealistic, and the Settle-Carlisle railway is so busy with passenger and through-freight traffic that it no longer has the capacity to absorb quarry traffic.

There are also tentative plans to reopen long-abandoned workings beneath the limestone, similar to those quarried at Helwith Bridge, when Ingleton Quarry closes in 2018, but this would have little obvious impact on the landscape seen from afar. The intention would be to quarry down rather than horizontally.

Horton Quarry was opened up by John Delaney. His is a real rags to riches story.[45] Of Irish parentage, he was born in 1846 and started his working life in Langcliffe cotton mill where he soon rose to the position of overseer. His inner drive and determination saw him dabble in business locally and in the 1881 census he was described as a coal merchant, operating from Settle station, and as a grocer in Langcliffe. By 1891 he had moved to Settle, was now a 'stone quarry owner and coal merchant' and had sufficient disposable wealth to employ a live-in servant. Somehow he had managed to attract the attentions of a philosophically minded financier who supported him on a course in geology at Manchester University.

Whether or not this was the catalyst for expanding into the quarry business is debatable and perhaps he had seen the opportunity to expand his coal business by working his own lime kilns. It made perfect economic sense: bring coal up from West Yorkshire using his own rail wagon stock to fuel his own lime kilns, and export burned lime and pulverised limestone to the Sheffield steel mills on the return journeys of his rolling stock. He was minimising his transport costs while maximising his sales' income. He had a sound business head, firmly screwed on.

This all came to fruition when he negotiated a lease in 1888 to develop Horton Quarry and Limeworks.[46] By the end of Delaney's life – he died on Christmas Day 1921 – he owned four other limestone quarries in the Dales and, for a short time, a coal mine at Threshfield in Wharfedale. Horton was his crowning glory and it rapidly grew into a major production unit, pioneering new methods of blasting, and with banks of the latest lime kilns. Delaney turned his business into two separate limited companies which, after his death, entered into an agreement with the Ribblesdale Limeworks at Helwith Bridge and the Craven Limeworks at Langcliffe to create a company that became Settle Limes Ltd. If the quarry had continued to grow across the entire extent of lands over which they had planning consent, today it would not only border the main road through Horton village but would also spread north-east up Harber Scar. There can be few regrets that planning consents were never taken up here and were eventually surrendered.

In one respect the limeworks in Delaney's time, and beyond, were greener than today as much of the stone and lime was despatched by rail. Nowadays only stone products are produced; the last lime kilns were spectacularly consigned to a tangle of scrap metal and rubble in the early 1980s (Plate 10.10). Now there would probably be calls to preserve them as part of our industrial heritage but only twenty-five years ago they were perceived as an eyesore to be eliminated.

Plate 10.8 Ribblesdale Limeworks, 1950s, showing the L-shaped kiln bank, the crusher on the left, workshops centre, rail link into Arcow Quarry top centre and the incline down from Foredale Quarry far left.

Plate 10.9
Horton Quarry, showing
the upper working face
in 2008.

For more than a century the quarry was an important element in the rural economy and Horton was able to support not only a range of small shops but also a Co-operative store. Before the age of mechanisation and automation Horton Limeworks employed over one hundred people, many of whom lived within Ribblesdale. Quarrymen and their families helped to keep the shops open, kept buses on the road and the railway profitable, and churches full, filled the schools and made sure the pubs kept going. What happened subsequently in Horton and Helwith Bridge? All but one of the shops has long since closed, the bus service is rudimentary, and Helwith Bridge school shut down many years ago. When the last quarry closes down, where will all the stone come from to build the new roads, new houses and new airport runways that the country seems to demand? And what will happen to the total road mileage incurred by bringing in stone from afar with the ineluctable increase in carbon emissions? Quarries do have a positive side to them.

Tourism

Visitors have been coming to the Ribblehead area for more than two hundred years and we owe it to early travellers and painters who popularised the Dales in print and on canvas. Late eighteenth century men of substance such as the Hon. John Byng, whom we met earlier at a drovers fair at Gearstones, and the Reverend John Hutton were not able to conduct their grand tours across the continent because of the French Wars so they toured the North instead, compiling diaries and travelogues as they went, invariably mentioning the area's caves and mountain scenery. Hutton's description of Weathercote Cave at Chapel le Dale church is evocative and accurate. Painters of the same period, such as J.M.W. Turner and his companion Thomas Girtin, made several visits to the Dales and painted atmospheric depictions of local scenes. One wonders if Turner had been moved to visit Weathercote Cave having read Hutton's earlier description. Ruskin, too, visited the area and noted the 'vague sense of wonder with which I watched Ingleborough stand without rocking.'

One of the first books aimed at potential visitors was written by William Dobson.[47] Published in 1864 it sold out and went to a second edition within the year, such was its popularity. Written before the coming of the railway,

Plate 10.10
Horton Limeworks.
Knibbs Kilns being
demolished, 1984.
© Hanson Aggregates,
Horton Quarry

Dobson's narrative encouraged visitors to visit and explore Chapel le Dale and the Ribblehead-Gearstones area.

Tourism today is broadly based on the Three Peaks and the National Park Authority has spent a small fortune over the past two decades repairing and renewing the various footpaths that ascend Ingleborough, Whernside and Pen-y-ghent, in a valiant attempt to cope with the thousands of walkers who are drawn to the summits. Estimates for the number of walkers scaling Ingleborough are put at 120,000 per year and 50,000 for Whernside (Pen-y-ghent gets about 80,000).[48] The annual Three Peaks race, first organised in 1954, attracts hundreds of hopefuls each year and the annual cyclo-cross race, first held in 1961, puts extra pressure on fragile environments. Natural England, and its predecessor, have laid out a series of walks around Ingleborough to cater for those walkers who want more than just a walk to the top. Birdlife and plantlife are important attractions for many of today's visitors.

For the more adventurous with a troglodytic bent there are caves aplenty. Between Ribblehead and Far Gearstones alone there are thirty-two known caves with many more down the valley of Chapel le Dale.[49] Some are short and dry; others involve challenging dry or wet crawls, squeezes, abseils and climbs, and are not for the faint-hearted. White Scar Cave, however, offers the visitor a long and exciting, but dry and safe, experience which is perhaps as much as most people require.

The viaduct and the archaeology associated with the navvy settlements are attractions in themselves, and not just for railway enthusiasts. The sheer scale of the viaduct and its dramatic backdrop bring in those who want to capture it on film as well as those who are content to sit and gaze. Last but not least we must not forget the myriad school groups that frequent the area on field trips studying at close quarters drumlins, river features and other aspects of local geomorphology.

Thankfully, Ribblehead is not scarred by caravan or camping sites. In fact tourist accommodation is limited. There are bunkhouses at Gearstones Lodge and the *Station Inn*; bed and breakfast is available at the two inns and at the odd farm, but that is about all. At busy weekends, especially when there is an organised Three Peaks event running, Ribblehead can seem a spot to avoid but most of the time it is quiet, atmospheric and empty.

Epilogue

I n the quarter of a century that I have lived in upper Ribblesdale there have been profound changes that have affected almost every aspect of life. The year of my arrival was not in any way a prophetic watershed: change had been underway for several decades prior to then. Some changes have been rapid, brought about by external events such as the Foot and Mouth epidemic in 2001; others crept up almost unnoticed. It is probably a pointless academic exercise to try and isolate which change has had the greatest impact or which might have been fundamental to all the rest.

No one can argue that farming has not been turned upside down, and not just by that dreadful outbreak. In my village, for example, five or six farms have ceased to exist as independent units. The land has been sold off and incorporated into larger units and the houses and barns have become residential property. In the longer term at least a dozen farms have disappeared from around Ingleborough. This has probably been an inevitable process as global economic forces and the laws of supply and demand have kicked in and, no less important, as the younger generations have sought work elsewhere. Such change should be regretted but can it realistically be decried? Dairying has all but vanished from the local farming scene around Ingleborough, haytime tends to be silage or haylage time now, and tasks formerly carried out on a cooperative basis are now more often than not handed out to commercial contractors who have expensive and high-tech machinery.

There has been social and demographic change, too. The point has already been made in this book that there have always been population movements into the Dales, that the purity of human stock, unsullied by incomers, is and always was a myth. There is nothing new about *offcumdens* (a local term of endearment for incomers!). After all, how did metal-working get here back in the Bronze and Iron Ages? Were the Romans not, arguably, the most organised set of incomers to inhabit our valleys? Nearer our own time were the many Displaced Persons not incomers – Germans, Poles and Italians who were billeted in the Dales and who were so vital in keeping our quarries, factories and farms running in the latter stages of World War Two, and for several years afterwards? Without demographic dynamism a population will stagnate and become inward looking. I do not believe anyone can accuse the western Dales of that.

What has changed demographically here, as in so many rural areas, are an ageing of the population as people choose to retire here, and an import of new skills as electronic communication allows people to work from home. In addition, many people starting out in life feel compelled to move away in search of career opportunities or affordable housing. There is nothing wrong with these changes *per se* but they do have a wider impact. House prices are driven upwards, beyond the reach of those starting out on life's ladder, primary schools close down through lack of children, and local services eventually succumb to attrition because there are not enough customers there to use them. Post offices are the latest to go under. In many areas the village pub is a likely victim but not here, even for those pubs that seem to have no obvious catchment area. Excluding the main settlements around Ingleborough, there are still three isolated hostelries, in Chapel le Dale, Ribblehead and Helwith Bridge, kept afloat no doubt by the tourist trade and by serving food but viable concerns nonetheless and, it must not be forgotten, important centres of local social activity.

There is, yet again, nothing new about young people having to leave their home area. Robert Southey's Daniel Dove, born and raised in Chapel le Dale in the early eighteenth century, was sent away by his father while still a boy to learn the medical trade in Doncaster.[1] The fictional father recognised that a remote upland farm held no appeal for, and offered no secure future to, his intelligent and ambitious son. That was fiction. The process has always been fact.

It is so easy in today's media-driven world to look for the negatives and to forget that so many changes are for the good and that so much just carries on as it ever did. The merchants of doom would have us believe that the environment is going to rack and ruin, that upland farming has no future, and that we should hark back wistfully to the glorious and always sunny days of yore. In the western Dales we do not need to do that. There are enough positive signs here and now, and in the offing, for us to look with optimism to the future. Let us consider a few examples.

Twenty or thirty years ago there were many traditional but redundant farm buildings that were rapidly decaying because their owners could not justify the expense of maintaining them. So many stretches of dry stone wall were crumbling and collapsing, yet both of these are so important to the integrity of the landscape and the identity of the area. Some have indeed been irretrievably lost but many have been saved and restored or consolidated by grants and subsidies. One can only applaud the sterling efforts of farmers such as those at Kingsdale Head and Spring Cote near Chapel le Dale who have reconstructed hundreds of metres of wall to a very high standard. This adds value to their farms but also to the landscape … and they deserve a medal.

So many farmers are in tune with the environment and have taken advantage of environmental schemes such as Stewardship, the Limestone Country Project, and the Hay Time Project. The first two of these have been discussed in an earlier chapter, so let us briefly examine the last one. Initiated in 2006, the Hay Time Project is managed in our area by the Yorkshire Dales Millennium Trust and the National Park Authority,[2] and its basic aim was to restore 140ha of flower-rich meadow across the Park by 2009. It is not just another funding body but harvests seed from existing species-rich meadows while the hay is still green and spreads it on meadows to be restored. As the hay dries out, the flower seed falls to the ground and, hopefully, takes hold ready for the following year's growth. There are no losers in this process. Seed donors receive welcome income, receptor farmers are entitled to a higher level of subsidy, we all benefit from an enhanced landscape, and nature wins hands down. Bird and insect species and numbers multiply. By the start of 2008 53ha across the Park had been treated in this way, including land at Ribblehead. Natural England, and its predecessor English Nature, have undertaken field trials at Colt Park in conjunction with Newcastle University and Defra since 1990, and it is this work that effectively paved the way for the Hay Time Project.[3] Thus far, one farm at Ribblehead has acted as a donor with the receptor being situated further down Ribblesdale.

Natural England is also closely involved in managing the Ingleborough National Nature Reserve, covering 1014ha on the north and east sides of the mountain, which is itself part of a much larger Site of Special Scientific Interest (SSSI) extending over most of the mountain, including Moughton. It is also recognised as a wildlife site of international importance by having been designated the Ingleborough Complex Special Area of Conservation and part of the European Union's Natura 2000 series of sites. Such international designations provide a higher level of protection than purely national-based ones. Heather regeneration on High Lot Pasture, between Braithwaite Wife Hole and Humphrey Bottom, is putting the purple back onto Ingleborough, and South House Moor is being actively re-wilded. No livestock is allowed on it and, with a little help from Natural England, there has already been a visible and impressive improvement in the diversity of plant, bird and invertebrate species. Even the former Ribblehead Quarry is being managed for nature. Much of Kingsdale and Whernside are also SSSIs in addition to Foredale and Swarth Moor at Helwith Bridge.

Dry Rigg Quarry at Helwith Bridge is due to close down in the not too distant future and the owners, Lafarge Aggregates, have already set in motion a restoration plan.[4] Much of the ugly bunding that surrounds the working quarry will be pushed back into the hole, and a raised bog, a fen system, and broadleaved woodland will be created, with the main hole being allowed to fill with water (Plate 11.1). This all lies in the future but a small and shallow open area of water has already been established, with careful planting of aquatic species to create a habitat attractive to wetland species.

In the most recent breeding season, sixteen species have bred here, over-wintered, stopped by on passage, or simply 'cased the joint out' (Table 11.1). Such diversity in a working quarry is marvellous. It raises the spirits and augers so well for the future.

Table 11.1 Breeding Bird Species at Dry Rigg Quarry

Species	Breeding pairs 2007	No. of chicks fledged
sand martin	200	?
swift	several	?
swallow	1	?
wheatear	1	?
meadow pipit	5	?
skylark	1	?
buzzard[a]	1	2
oystercatcher	5	?
coot	3	3
moorhen	1	4
redshank	1	unsuccessful
lapwing	4	unsuccessful
kestrel	3	4
peregrine falcon[b]	1 (2006)	eggs stolen
little owl	1	2
pied wagtail	1	

a nested on the scar above the quarry
b 1 pair overwintered here 2007–08
Source: Michael Cardus, Assistant Quarry Manager, Dry Rigg Quarry

In 2007 the Heather Trust was formed and a group of organisations – universities, the RSPB, the National Trust, national park authorities and government agencies – are co-operating in the newly-formed Sustainable Uplands project. The broad aims of the project are to anticipate and then to manage change in northern moorlands and to devise ways in which such areas can adapt to climate change. Initially it is focussed on the Peak District, the Yorkshire Dales and south-west Scotland, and current research programmes are investigating the viability of peat and habitat restoration, as well as the possible use of peat moors for carbon capture.[5]

As I write, a Local Biodiversity Action Plan (LBAP) is being formulated for Craven District, within which Ingleborough lies.[6] LBAPs are new and have the laudable aim of identifying local wildlife priorities and developing strategies for a range of iconic habitats and species. The Craven LBAP has placed special emphasis, in terms of non-plant forms, on all species of bat found in the Dales and on the small pearl-bordered fritillary butterfly (*Boloria selene*). The concept arose from the Earth Summit held in Rio de Janeiro in 1992 which required every government to come up with a national BAP. LBAPs are the means of ensuring the process is carried down to every corner of the country. They are not there to impose yet another layer of bureaucracy but to act as a stimulant and a point of contact for statutory and voluntary bodies involved in all aspects of wildlife. This is something we will surely hear more of as time passes.

In the same vein we also now have an LGAP[7] and are soon to have RIGS and DEGS, acronyms all connected with geology, and a logical extension of the LBAP programme. Within the National Park this is all under the umbrella of the 'Your Dales Rocks Project LGAP' that was launched in Ingleton in May 2007. GAP means Geodiversity Action Plan and a consortium of vested interests formed the North Yorkshire Geodiversity Partnership in 2005 to push it all forward. The fundamental aim of an LGAP is to conserve and enhance the geodiversity (geological diversity) of each designated area, to increase public awareness of geologically important sites, and to ensure they are protected and managed for the future.

An integral element of the LGAP approach is to designate RIGS (Regionally Important Geological Sites)[8] and, at the time of writing this, twelve such sites had been identified in the National Park, all of which lie within the Cumbrian sector. None had yet been finalised nor made public around Ingleborough, but it does not need much thought to suggest suitable candidates. The Basement Inliers between Ingleton and Helwith Bridge have long since been recognised as geologically important, and the Ingleborough SSSI formally includes points of geological as well as botanical interest, not least the exceptional exposures within past and present quarries. The whole process was set to move forward in our area late in 2008. Designating RIGS is not a mere academic exercise but is to have direct educational relevance at school and university level with some RIGS also becoming DEGS (Dales Educational Geological Sites).[9]

So, nature is covered and geology is well on the way to being covered, but what about archaeology? Should we not now have an RIAS and LAAP, the letter 'A' representing archaeology? There is so much work to do around Ingleborough, at the most basic level, recording the location of sites of archaeological or historic importance, and adding them to the Heritage Environment Record (HER), which is maintained by the National Park Authority. Beyond this there is a desperate need for detailed ground surveying and photography, and for synthesis of what is known. Too little has been achieved in the way of looking for patterns in the landscape, whether of fields, settlements or routeways. Too little dating evidence has been logged and too many stereotypical or dated snippets have become entrenched in the unofficial public record. The local archaeology group, based in Ingleton, has been doing sterling work, as have a few committed individuals, but Ingleborough's archaeological canvas is endless. At least, a small start is being made with the launch, by the National Park Authority, of the Traditional Farm Buildings Census in 2008, with an ambitious long-term aim of surveying every such building, whether still in agricultural use, converted to residential usage, or just a heap of stone in the middle of a field. Encouragingly, this census will draw on the skills and enthusiasm of local volunteers.

Tourism is a further positive aspect of the western Dales. Since the Romantic period people have been drawn here by Ingleborough's physical challenges and 'natural' beauty. The two show caves (White Scar and Ingleborough) are as popular as ever, even if the number of 'wet' cavers seems to have declined in recent years; Ribblehead viaduct is more of a magnet now than ever before; a series of nature trails has been laid out and publicised by Natural England and the Ingleborough Estate; and an experimental summer festival first organised by the Yorkshire Dales Millennium Trust in 2006 is hopefully set to become an annual event celebrating all that Ingleborough has to offer.

*   *   *

We can never know how prehistoric and early historic folk perceived this mountain but we do know it has been seen as a special place for more than two hundred years. The landscape we see here today has been shaped and re-shaped by people over thousands of years, and their responses to the mountain have been, to a greater or lesser extent, partly shaped by what it has to offer them. It is still a special place, no matter what angle one comes from, and it does have much to offer (Plate 11.2). Ingleborough will surely remain a special place for countless generations to come.

Glossary

Glossary of Place-names within the Ingleborough Area

Modern Place-name	Meaning
Arcow	ON hill
Arten Gill	OE /ON hart and OWSc ravine
Austwick	ON east and OE (dairy) farm
Backstone Gill	OE where bakestones occur and OWSc ravine
Batty Green	Batty is a local surname
Birkwith	ON birch and ON wood
Black Rake	ME bleak and OE sheep walk
Black Shiver	ME bleak and OE hollow place (poss.)
Blea Moor	OE blue (or dark) and OE moor
Broadrake farm	OE broad sheep walk
Brow Gill	OE brow or ON brow of a hill and OWSc ravine
Bruntscar	OE burnt and ON scar
Bullet Mire	OE cuckoo flower and ON swamp
Cam	OE ridge
Capple Bank	ON nag (and bank)
Cat Hole Sike	OE wild cat and OE hollow and OE small stream
Chapel le Dale	OF and OE chapel in the valley
Clapdale	OE noisy stream and OE or ON valley
Clapham	OE noisy stream and OE settlement
Cold Cotes	OE outlying settlement
Colt Park	OE the emparked place where horses were reared
Combe Scar, Combs	OE hollowed out area or ON ridge and ON scar
Cosh	OE cottage or hovel
Cote Gill	OE outlying settlement and OWSc ravine
Cragghill	ON rocky hill
Craven	Brit possibly where wild garlic grows; or stoney place
Crina Bottom	OE valley bottom and OIr Crin's (pers. name)
Crooklands	ON bend or corner
Crummack	Brit crooked hill
Douk Ghyll	local dialect for damp valley
Dry Lade	ON barn (and dry)

Dry Rigg	ON ridge (and dry)
Duttons Hull	OE shelter with a pers. name
Ellerbeck	ON alder trees and ON stream
Feizor	OIr/ON Fiach's (pers.name) and OIr/ON shieling
Force Gill	ON waterfall and OWSc ravine
Foredale	OE front and ON valley
Gauber	OE gallows and OE hill
Gavel Gap	ON gable (and gap)
Gayle	ON steep-sided valley
Gearstones	OE triangular place and OE/ON stone posts
Gragareth	ON grey and ON stones
Great Coum	OE hollowed out area or ON ridge (and great)
Great Douk	local dialect for damp or boggy place (and great)
Great Wold	OE high wooded area (and great)
Greensett	ON seat (and green)
Greta	ON stoney
Gunnerfleet	ON Gunnar's (pers.name) and ON stream
Hagg	ON deep valley
Harber Scar	ON oats and OE hill (plus ON scar)
Helwith Bridge	ON flat stones and ON ford (plus bridge)
High Birkwith	ON birch and ON wood (and high)
Hinkinshaw	OE hillside and OE copse
Holly Platt	OE holy and ME plot of ground
Horton	OE dirty or muddy area and OE farmstead
Humphrey Bottom	pers.name
Hunterstye	hunter's OE/ON path that climbs a hill
Hurnel Moss	corruption of Herning (meaning unknown) (and moss)
Ingleborough	possibly OE hill;[1] and OE fortified camp
Ingleton	OE farmstead and possibly OE hill[1]
Ireby	ON farmstead occupied by the Irish
Ivescar	OE ivy and ON scar
Jenkin Beck	pers. name
Keld	ON spring
Kingsdale	either king's valley, or ME cattle and OE/ON valley
Knoutberry	ON rocky hill and dialect for cloudberry
Know Gap	OE hill (and gap)
Laithbutts	ON barn and either OF mounds for archery practice or OF headland in arable open field
Langstrothdale	OE long and OE brushwood and OE/ON valley
Ling Gill	ON heather and OWSc ravine

Little Knott	OE rocky hill top
Lord's Seat	prob. suggesting a spot where the Lord God could sit to survey his kingdom. The view from here is encyclopaedic
Moughton	OE heaps of stones and OE hill
Moughton Nab	as above plus ON hill spur
Nan Bottom	Brit valley (poss.) and OE valley floor
Nappa	OE bowl-shaped hollow and OE enclosure
Nether Lodge	OE lower and OFr lodge or farm
Newby Cote	OE the outlying settlement to Newby
Norber	OE/ON north and OE/ON hill
Oddies Lane	possibly a pers.name
Oxenber	OE oxen and OE/ON hill
Park Fell	hill on or near the emparked land
Pen-y-ghent	Brit hill and possibly borderland. **Not** hill of the winds
Philpin Sleights	possibly pers.name and OE sheep pasture or ON level ground
Raven Ray	possibly ON bend or ON roe deer (where ravens were seen)
Rayside	OE roe deer or ON corner and ON shieling
Ribble	OE boundary (western boundary of ancient Craven)
Runscar	Brit headland or ridge (possibly) and ON scar
Scales	ON shieling or mountain hut[2]
Selside	ON willow trees and ON shieling
Shaw	OE wooded copse
Silloth	ON hut (possibly) or ON pers. name and ON laithe (barn)
Simon Fell	OE pers.name (and hill)
Skelside	OE shelf of land and ON shieling
Skirwith	ON bright headland or promontory
Slatenber	OWSc smooth field (poss.) and ON hill
Sleights	OE sheep pasture or ON level ground
Southerscales	ON Sutari's (pers.name) and ON shieling
Sowerthwaite	OE sour (acidic) and ON clearing
Spice Gill	ON spearman (nickname) and OWSc ravine
Stoops Moss	ON stakes (and moss)
Studfold	OE horse-breeding enclosure
Studrigg	OE herd of horses and OE ridge
Sulber	ON silver or ON sunny and OE/ON hill
Swarth Moor	ON black or dark-coloured (and moor)
Syke	OE/ON ditch or small stream
Thorns	OE/ON thorn bushes
Thornton	OE/ON thorn bushes and OE farmstead

Thwaite	ON woodland clearing
Twistleton	OE between rivers and OE farmstead
Trow Gill	OE tree-clad and ON ravine
Weathercote	OE wethers and OE outlying settlement
Wenning	OE dark coloured
Wharfe	ON bend
Whernside	OE quernstone and ON seat[3]
Whinney Mire	ON gorse and ON swamp
White Shaw	OE wooded copse (and white)
Widdale	ON wooded and OE/ON valley
Winshaw	OE/ON windy and OE wooded copse
Winterscales	OE winter and ON shieling
Yarlsber	ON earl and OE hill

[1] For an alternative explanation of 'Ingle', see Chapter 1.

[2] The word scales is also a former dialect word referring to an area with expanses of limestone pavement. Scales Moor probably has this origin.

3 Place-name elements 'sett' and 'side' could derive from ON saeti or ON saetre. The latter refers to a shieling, a settlement used during the summer grazing season away from the home village or farmstead. Place-names like Selside or Henside probably have this origin. Saeti on the other hand means 'seat'. This element is found in place-names accorded to prominent rocks or localities, such as Whernside or Greensett, or Lords' Seat on Ingleborough, and it is thought that whoever first named these features believed that God used them to survey his realm.

Brit	British (*ie* Celtic)
ME	Middle English (*ie* medieval)
OE	Old English (*ie* Anglo-Saxon)
OF	Old (*ie* Norman) French
OIr	Old Irish
ON	Old Norse (*ie* Danish or Norse)
OWSc	Old West Scandinavian

Further Reading

Full bibliographic references are provided in Notes and References and the intention of this guide is to point the reader in the direction of sources that are both accessible and likely to be of general interest though, inevitably, some recourse to specialist journals is necessary. The guide is not meant to be exhaustive. Where appropriate, the emphasis has been on recent publications.

Abbreviations

NCHT Jo.	North Craven Heritage Trust Journal
NYCRO	North Yorkshire County Record Office
Proc.Y.Geol.Soc.	Proceedings of the Yorkshire Geological Society
WYRO	West Yorkshire Record Office
YAJ	Yorkshire Archaeological Journal

Chapter 1

Much of this chapter was written from a personal perspective and is deliberately selective. It offers a synthesis of how Ingleborough was perceived by notable visitors in the past so it must follow that original sources are recommended, such as John Housman's *Topographical description* or John Byng's *Torrington diaries*. I hesitate to direct the reader to Robert Southey's *The Doctor*, despite its obvious local interest, simply because it is not an easy read and I would be loathe to hear of any newcomer to Southey being put off by starting with this his only novel.

For a very readable general treatment (despite the title!) of early tourism in the Ingleborough area, see K. Exton, 2007. 'Aestheticism and athleticism: the changing depictions, pursuits and visitors in North Craven, 1750–1900'. *NCHT Jo*, pp. 3–9. The Trust's work and interests can be examined at www.NorthCravenHeritage.org.uk.

Chapters 2 and 3

Geology is necessarily a technical subject and it is difficult to find up to date material that is aimed at the general reader while still being thorough. For one such general account see A. Wilson, 1992. *Geology of the Yorkshire Dales National Park* Grassington: Yorkshire Dales National Park Authority. Brumhead's *Geology explained* fits the bill, with its area-specific treatments, though it is now rather dated, while Scrutton's *Yorkshire rocks and landscape* provides an excellent – if somewhat technical – summary of areas perceived to have special geological interest. Those with a genuine interest in geology are directed to the two HMSO memoirs, *Geology of the North Pennine orefield* and *Geology of the country around Settle*, which are the key sources for these chapters as they are British Geological Survey publications. The Survey also produces excellent mapping, both of solid and drift geology, and they are essential to fully understand the complexities of local geology. Regrettably, full coverage of the Dales is still awaited.

As a contrast to recent work, the interested reader may wish to seek out Kendall and Wroot's pioneering detailed survey of Yorkshire's geology, now over eighty years old.

Chapter 4

Until very recently no author had produced a general treatment of landforms and landscape processes in the Yorkshire Dales, though Tony Waltham happily filled this void with a book published in 2007 and aimed at a general readership (*The Yorkshire Dales. Landscape and geology*, Marlborough: Crowood Press). Waltham has drawn on his professional and leisure experiences of limestone landscapes underground and on the surface to produce this readable introduction to the basic geology, limestone processes and land uses of the Dales as a whole.

For detail of specific landscape processes and landform types the reader will need to source articles in a range of academic journals, and there has been a pleasing resurgence of research interest in the Dales in recent years by leading names in their respective fields. The various papers cited in the Notes are thoroughly recommended for those requiring further detail, for example, those by Chris Clark and Wishart Mitchell on glacial processes; by Peter Vincent on loess deposits and karst landforms; and by Helen Goldie and Margaret Marker on erratics, dolines and limestone pavements. All are based on primary field research carried out in our area by these university researchers.

Chapter 5

There is a wealth of written material, at all levels, on the archaeology and history of the Dales. Discussion of how the Three Age System evolved can be found in P. Rowley-Conwy, 2007. *From genesis to prehistory*. Oxford: Oxford University Press. For accessible and up to date treatments of the subjects in general see R. Bradley, 2007. *The prehistory of Britain and Ireland*. Cambridge: Cambridge University Press.; M. Bell, 2007. *Prehistoric coastal communities: the Mesolithic in western Britain*. CBA Research Report 149, which gives an up to date and rigorous summary of Mesolithic archaeology, and J. Taylor 2007. *An atlas of Roman rural settlement in England*. CBA Research Report 151. For an excellent general study of monastic Yorkshire see B. Jennings, 1999. *Yorkshire monasteries. Cloister, land and people*. Otley: Smith Settle. For a specific study of the late prehistoric and Roman period in the area see A. King, 1986. 'Romano-British farms and farmers in Craven, North Yorkshire' in T. G. Manby and P. Turnbull, *Archaeology in the Pennines. Studies in honour of Arthur Raistrick*. BAR British Series 158, pp. 181–93.

Several books adopting a broad-brush approach have been written on the general history of the Dales, such as P. Gunn, 1984. *The Yorkshire Dales. Landscape with figures*. London: Century, and G. N. Wright, 1986, *The Yorkshire Dales*. Newton Abbot and London: David & Charles. Both provide a useful historical summary of the Dales through the centuries. Arthur Raistrick's work is now very dated, given advances in research techniques since his time, but still to be recommended, especially his *Pennine Dales*, published in 1968. A very useful and readable introduction to Dales' prehistory and history is *The Yorkshire Dales* written by the National Park Authority's senior archaeologist, Robert White. On a more academic level are two excellent publications of the Yorkshire Archaeological Society

– see *Archaeology and historic landscapes of the Yorkshire Dales*, edited by R. F. White and P. Wilson, and *The Archaeology of Yorkshire*, edited by T. G. Manby and colleagues.

The local community-based Ingleborough Archaeology Group has been carrying out – and publishing – ambitious research projects in the area, for example its *Excavation of Broadwood Enclosure, Thornton in Lonsdale*, edited by me and published in 2004, and the *Kingsdale Head Project* edited by A. and A. Batty in 2007. For details of the Group's work see its website at www.ingleborougharchaeologygroup. org.uk.

The Yorkshire Dales National Park maintains a useful website covering many aspects of the Park's archaeology and history, including a link to the Heritage Environment Record, and it can be searched at www.outofoblivion.org.uk.

Chapter 6

The general and specific works described for Chapter 5 are relevant here, too. For recent and detailed discussions of rock art in the north of England B. Brown and P. Brown's *Prehistoric rock art* and Stan Beckensall and Tim Laurie's similarly entitled book can both be thoroughly recommended; while Stephen Moorhouse's 'Anatomy of the Yorkshire Dales' is written by one of the foremost exponents of historical landscapes in the Dales.

Beyond these, the results of recent field research into aspects of the archaeology of the region await publication though very little work has been carried out across southern Ingleborough, despite the myriad opportunities, largely owing to the lack of funding for such studies. See www.northcravenhistoricalresearch.co.uk for details of current work in North Craven.

Chapter 7

The corpus of literature on routes and transport in the country is considerable but two recent books in particular are relevant to this chapter: for a general treatment of routeways through time see H. Davies, 2006. *From trackways to motorways*. Stroud: Tempus. D. Hey, 2001. *Packmen, carriers and packhorse roads*. Ashbourne: Landmark, provides an excellent survey concentrating on the South Pennines but with much of relevance to the Dales. G. N. Wright's *Roads and trackways of the Yorkshire Dales* is the only book devoted to the development of a route system within the Dales. It is full of local detail and is an essential source for those with a special interest in this topic.

Arguably the most reliable source on droving is K. J. Bonser's *The drovers*. It is rather dated now but nothing has been published since to effectively replace it. Similarly, Sir William Addison's *Old roads of England* has a wealth of useful material on coaching days, though not directly related to this part of the country. T. Bradley's *The old coaching days in Yorkshire* (1889, Leeds: S. R. Publishers) provides a highly detailed survey of coaches and coaching inns in the country. For more academic treatments, the *Journal of Transport History* must be an early port of call.

To appreciate the growth of the road network around Ingleborough it would be useful to consult contemporary maps, especially those produced by John Ogilby, published in 1720, Thomas Jefferys, published in 1771, and William Smith, published in 1815.

Chapters 8, 9 and 10

Much of these chapters has been written utilising either primary sources held in various archives within North Yorkshire and West Yorkshire, as well as the National Archives at Kew, as listed in the Notes, or detailed items in journals or academic monographs. Much of it, too, results from my own interest and work on the mountain and from discussions with those whose life and work revolves around it. No serious book has been published on the history of the Ingleborough area though, again, Robert White's *Landscape through time* provides a useful overview for the Dales as a whole.

Chapter 11

Like Chapter 1, this takes a personal view and the priorities outlined within it are recognised solely from my own perspective and background. Others with an interest in the area may well disagree and suggest alternatives which I am sure would be equally valid. Any factual elements of this chapter have been obtained from official websites or through informal discussions with those directly involved on the ground.

Notes and References

Preface

1 Rée, H. and Forbes, C. 1983. *The Three Peaks of Yorkshire*. London: Wildwood House.

Chapter 1: Setting the Scene

1 Daniel Defoe quotes Camden here. See Defoe, D. 1971 edition. *A tour through the whole island of Great Britain*, vol. 3. Harmondsworth: Penguin, p. 485. First published in 1726.

2 Westall, W. 1818. *Views of the caves in Yorkshire near Ingleton, Gordale Scar and Malham Cove*. London: John Murray.

3 Wood Warter, J. (ed.). 1848. *The Doctor etc by the late Robert Southey*. London: Longman, Brown, Green & Longmans, *passim*

4 Madden, L. (ed.). 1972. *Robert Southey. The critical heritage*. London and Boston: Routledge & Kegan Paul.

5 Quoted in Redding, Mr and Taylor, W. C. 1844. *The pictorial history of the County of Lancaster*. London: George Routledge, p. 217.

6 Note 1, p. 213.

7 Housman, J. 1800. *A topopgraphical description of Cumberland, Westmoreland* (sic*), Lancashire and a part of the West Riding of Yorkshire*. Carlisle: Francis Jollie, pp. 162–3.

8 Note 7, pp. 162–3.

9 Note 7, p. 216.

10 Note 7, p. 210.

11 Note 7, p. 222.

12 Note 7, p. 161.

13 Note 7, p. 205.

14 Note 7, p. 216.

15 Note 7, p. 23.

16 Fletcher, J. S. 1901. *A picturesque history of Yorkshire*, vol. 3. London: J. M. Dent, p. 166.

17 Note 14, p. 167.

18 Note 14, p. 175.

19 Note 14, p. 198.

20 Byng, Hon. J. 1970 edition. *The Torrington Diaries*, vol. 3, ed. Bruyn Andrews, C. New York: Barnes and Noble, London: Methuen, p. 89. First published in 1936.

21 Note 18, p. 90.

22 Note 18, p. 89.

23 Ruskin, J. 1892. *Modern Painters*, London: George Allen, vol. 5, p. xlix and vol. 5, part 7, p. 187.

24 Bibby, J. 1929. *A history of Bentham*, privately published.

25 See. for example, Metcalfe, P. 1992. *Place-names of the Yorkshire Dales*, Harrogate: North Yorkshire Marketing, p. 49.

26 This section results from fascinating recent discussions with Yvonne Luke, an archaeologist who has a close affinity with the mountain.

27 Farrer, J. 1853. 'Camp and huts on Ingleborough' in Phillips, J. *The Rivers, Mountains and Sea-coast of Yorkshire*, London: John Murray.

28 There is local disagreement as to whether the name Chapel le Dale should only be applied to the hamlet or to the entire dale, which some local inhabitants simply call The Dale. Historically the dale has been known as Weesdale with the variant spellings Wiersdall, Weysdale and Wyersdaile. For Wiersdall and Wyersdaile see Borthwick Institute, V. 1595–96, CB2, ff135v–136; V. 1595–96, CB3, f. 57. For Weysdale see National Archives SC2/211/68, Ingleton Court Roll 1506. In a manuscript 'Mapp of Twisleton (*sic*) Pasture', dated 1755 and in a private collection, the River Doe was named as the River Wees. I am grateful to Angus Winchester for bringing these references to my attention.

Chapter 2: Geology of the Western Dales

1 Zalasiewicz et al. 2008. 'Are we now living in the Anthropocene? *GSA Today* 18 (2), pp. 4–8.

2 Soper, N. J. and Dunning, F. W. 2005. 'Structure and sequence of the Ingleton Group, basement to the central Pennines of northern England' *Proc. Y. Geol. Soc.* 55 (4), pp. 241–61.

3 Tyson, L. O. 1986. 'Lead Mine Moss' *Dalesman* 48, p. 289.

Chapter 3: Geology of Ingleborough

1 Robinson King, W. B. and Wilcockson, W. H. 1933. 'The Lower Palaeozoic rocks of Austwick and Horton-in-Ribblesdale, Yorkshire' *Quarterly Journal of the Geological Society* 90 (1), pp. 7–31; Johnson, E. 1994. 'Lower Palaeozoic rocks of the Craven inliers' in Scrutton, C. (ed.). *Yorkshire rocks and landscape. A field guide.* Maryport: Ellenbank Press for the Yorkshire Geological Society, pp. 21–9.

2 Brumhead, D. 1979. *Geology explained in the Yorkshire Dales and on the Yorkshire coast.* Newton Abbot: David & Charles, pp. 38–43.

3 British Geological Survey, Hawes, Sheet 50, Solid Edition.

4 Scrutton. 1994. p. 29; pers.comm. D. C. Turner.

5 Dunham, K. C. and Wilson, A. A. 1985. *Geology of the Northern Pennine Orefield.* London: HMSO, p. 13.

6 Arthurton, R. S., Johnson, E. W. and Mundy, D. J. C. 1988. *Geology of the country around Settle.* London: HMSO, pp. 18, 20–32.

7 Note 6, p. 35.

8 Note 6, p. 97.

9 British Geological Survey, Hawes, Sheet 50, Drift Edition.

10 Note 6, p. 88.

11 Vincent, P. J. and Lee, M. P. 1981. 'Some observations on the loess around Morecambe Bay, North-West England' *Proc. Y. Geol. Soc.* 43 (3), pp. 281–94; Vincent, P. 2006. 'Problems associated with the loess of the Craven uplands' *Re-thinking Craven's limestone landscape.* Settle: Hudson History.

12 Atherden, M. 1992. *Upland Britain. A natural history.* Manchester: Manchester University Press, pp. 120–3.

13 Manby, T. G. 2003. 'The Bronze Age' in Butlin, R. A. (ed.). *Historical Atlas of North Yorkshire.* Otley: Westbury, p. 42.

Chapter 4: Landform Processes

1 Lee, J. R., Rose, J, Hamblin, R. J. O. and Moorlock, B. S. P. 2004. 'Dating the earliest lowland glaciation of eastern England: a pre-MIS12 early Middle Pleistocene Happisburgh glaciation' *Quarterly Science Review* 23 (14–15), pp. 1551–66.

2 Sissons, J. B. 1979. 'The Loch Lomond Stadial in the British Isles' *Nature* 280, pp. 199–203.

3 McManus, J and Oppo, D. 2006. 'The once and future circulation of the ocean' *Oceanus* 16 November issue.

4   Cox, J. D. 2005. *Climate crash: abrupt climate change and what it means for our future.* Oxford: National Academy Press; and see, for example, www.wunderground.com/education/abruptclaime.asp.

5   Clark, C. 2008. 'The last British ice sheet and was it culpable of Gulf-Stream shutdown?' Lecture delivered to a Yorkshire Geological Society symposium on 'Ice sheets: past, present & future', Sheffield, 23 February.

6   Clark, C. D., Evans, D. J. A., Khatwa, A., Bradwell, T. and Jordan, C. J. 2004 'Map and GIS database of glacial landforms related to the last British ice sheet' *Boreas* 33, pp. 359–75; Evans, D. J. A., Clark, C. D. and Mitchell, W. A. 2005. 'The last British ice sheet: a review of the evidence utilised in the compilation of the Glacial Map of Britain' *Earth-Science Reviews* 70 (3–4), pp. 253–312; Mitchell, W. A. 2006. 'The last glaciation in the Craven Uplands, Yorkshire Dales' *Re-thinking Craven's limestone landscape.* Settle: Hudson History; Mitchell, W. A. 2007. 'Reconstructions of Late Devensian (Dimlington Stadial) British-Irish ice sheet: the role of the Upper Tees drumlin field, north Pennines, England' *Proc. Y. Geol. Soc.* 56 (4), pp. 221–34.

7   Mitchell, W. A. 1996. 'Significance of snowblow in the generation of Loch Lomond Stadial (Younger Dryas) glaciers in the western Pennines, northern England' *Journal of Quaternary Science* 11 (3), pp. 233–48.

8   Mitchell, W. A. 2007. 'Reconstructions of Late Devensian (Dimlington Stadial) British-Irish ice sheet: the role of the Upper Tees drumlin field, north Pennines, England' *Proc. Y. Geol. Soc.* 56 (4), pp. 221–34.

9   British Antarctic Survey press release 2/2007. "Scientists observe drumlin beneath ice sheet", 23 January 2007.

10 See note 6, *Glacial Map of Britain.* 2004. Mapped at 1:625,000.

11 Pounder, E. 1989. *Classic landforms of the Northern Dales.* Classic Landform Guide No. 10. Sheffield: The Geographical Association, pp. 42–3.

12 Note 10; Arthurton, R. S., Johnson, E. W. and Mundy, D. J. C. 1988. *Geology of the country around Settle.* London: HMSO, pp. 88–90. Mitchell, W. A. and Riley, J. M. 2006. 'Drumlin map of the Western Pennines and southern Vale of Eden, Northern England, UK'. *Journal of Maps* pp. 10–16.

13 Shoemaker, E. M. 1995. 'On the meltwater genesis of drumlins' *Boreas* 24, pp. 3–10.

14 Cox, D. E. 1979. 'Drumlins and diluvial currents' *Creation Research Society* Quarterly 16 (3), pp. 154–62; de Schutter, P. 2005. 'On the surface. Drumlins' *Eurock* Open University Geological Society. http://ougseurope.org/rockon/surface/drumlins.asp.

15 Kendall, P. F. and Wroot, H. E. 1924. *The geology of Yorkshire.* Privately published.

16 Scrutton, C. (ed.). 1994. *Yorkshire rocks and landscape. A field guide.* Maryport: Ellenbank Press for the Yorkshire Geological Society, p. 27.

17 Goldie, H. S. 2005. 'Erratic judgements: re-evaluating erosion rates of limestones using erratic pedestal sites, including Norber, Yorkshire'. *Area* 37 (4), pp. 433–42.

18 2007. http://domino.lancs.ac.uk/info/lunews.nsf/r/5846.

19 Vincent, P. 1995. 'Limestone pavements in the British isles: a review' *Geographical Journal* 161 (3), pp. 265–74.

20 Note 19.

21 Vincent, P. 2004. 'Polygenetic origin of limestone pavements in northern England' *Zeitschrift für Geomorphologie* 48 (4), pp. 481–90.

22 Sweeting, M. M. 1972. *Karst landforms.* London: Macmillan, pp. 93–4.

23 Doughty, P. S. 1968. 'Joint densities and their relation to lithology in the Great Scar Limestone' *Proc. Y. Geol. Soc.* 36, pp. 479–512.

24 Goldie, H. S. and Cox, N. J. 2000. 'Comparative morphology of limestone pavements in Switzerland, Britain and Ireland' *Zeitschrift für Geomorphologie* NS122, pp. 85–112.

25 Goldie, H. S. and Marker, M. E. 2001. 'Pre-Devensian dolines above Crummackdale, northwest Yorkshire, UK' *Cave and Karst Science* 28 (2), pp. 53–8.

26 Brook, A, Brook, D, Griffiths, J. and Long, M. H. 1991. *Northern caves 2. The Three Peaks.* Clapham: Dalesman, pp. 152ff.

27 Murphy, P. J. 1999. 'Sediment studies in Joint Hole, Chapel-le-Dale, North Yorkshire, United Kingdom' *Cave and Karst Science* 26 (2), pp. 87–90; Murphy, P. J., Smallshire, R. and Midgley, C. 2001. 'The sediments of

Illusion Pot, Kingsdale, UK: evidence for sub-glacial utilisation of a karst conduit in the Yorkshire Dales' *Cave and Karst Science* 28 (1), pp. 29–34.

28 Craven, S. A. 2004. 'Ingleborough Cave, Clapham, North Yorkshire, England' *Cave and Karst Science* 31 (1), pp. 15–34.

29 McFarlane, D. A., Lundberg, J, and Cordingley, J. 2004. 'A brief history of stalagmite measurements at Ingleborough Cave, Yorkshire, United Kingdom' *Cave and Karst Science* 31 (3), pp. 113–18.

30 Note 29; Pentecost, A., Fifth Malham Tarn Research Seminar, 17 November 2007.

31 Pentecost, A. and Lord, T., 1988, Postglacial tufas and travertines from the Craven District of Yorkshire' *Cave Science* 15 (1), pp. 15–19.

Chapter 5: Archaeology: Ingleborough North

1 The Three Age system was introduced by C. J. Thomsen in 1836 to help in sorting and cataloguing the collections of the National Museum in Denmark.

2 The Stone Age was divided into Palaeolithic and Neolithic in 1865 by Sir John Lubbock, later Lord Avebury.

3 Cunliffe, B. 2001. *Facing the ocean. The Atlantic and its peoples 8000 BC–AD 1500.* Oxford: Oxford University Press.

4 Vyner, B. 2003. 'The Iron Age' in Butlin, R. A. (ed.). *Historical atlas of North Yorkshire.* Otley: Westbury, p. 44.

5 Raistrick, A. 1968. *The Pennine Dales.* London: Eyre and Spottiswoode, pp. 53–4.

6 Manby, T. G. 2003. 'The Late Upper Palaeolithic and Mesolithic periods in Yorkshire' in Manby, T. G., Moorhouse S. and Ottaway, P. *The archaeology of Yorkshire.* Leeds: Yorkshire Archaeological Society, Occasional Paper No. 3, pp. 31–3.

7 Spikins, P. A. 1999. *Mesolithic Northern England: environment, population and settlement.* British Archaeological Report Series 283.

8 Vyner, B. 2003. 'The Upper Palaeolithic and the earlier Mesolithic' in Butlin (ref.4), p. 31.

9 Excavations were carried out over several seasons directed by Randolph Donahue of the University of Bradford.

10 Batty, A. and Batty, A. 2007. *The Kingsdale Head Project.* Ingleton: Ingleborough Archaeology Group, p. 82–89.

11 Information provided by Network Archaeology Ltd.

12 Note 3, pp. 123–9.

13 Note 10, p. 82.

14 White, R. 2002. *The Yorkshire Dales. A landscape through time.* Ilkley: Great Northern, p. 19.

15 Swales, S. 1984. *The vegetational and archaeological history of the Ingleborough massif, North Yorkshire,* unpublished Ph.D. thesis, University of Leeds.

16 Note 3, pp. 153–4; Bell, M. 2007. *Prehistoric coastal communities: the Mesolithic in western Britain.* CBA Research Report 149, York: Council for British Archaeology; Scarre, C. 2007. *The megalithic monuments of Britain and Ireland.* London: Thames & Hudson, pp. 10–11.

17 This research is being undertaken by Timothy Taylor of the University of Bradford; for a preliminary view, see Taylor, T. 2006. 'From wildness to wildscape: questions from archaeological theory'. *Re-thinking Craven's limestone landscape.* Settle: Hudson History, pp. 27–8.

18 Gilks, J. A. 1976. 'Excavations in a cave on Raven Scar, Ingleton, 1973–5' *Transactions of the British Cave Research Association* 3 (2), pp. 95–9.

19 Gilks, J. A. 1995. 'Later Neolithic and Bronze Age pottery from Thaw Head Cave, Ingleton, North Yorkshire' *Transactions of the Hunter Archaeological Society* 18, pp. 1–11.

20 Manby, T. G., King, A. and Vyner, B. 2003. 'The Neolithic and Bronze Ages: a time of early agriculture' in Manby, T. G. et al., 2003 (Note 6), p. 101.

21 Huntley, B. 'The post-glacial history of British woodlands' in Atherden, M. A. *Woodland in the landscape: past and future perspectives*. Ripon: Leeds University Press for The PLACE Research Centre, p. 22.

22 See, for example, Raistrick, A. and Holmes, P. 1962. *Archaeology of Malham Moor. Field Studies* 1 (4).

23 King, A. 1978. 'Apron Full of Stones, a prehistoric cairn, Thornton in Lonsdale, North Yorkshire' *YAJ* 50, pp. 25–30.

24 Note 10, pp. 59–76.

25 For a general survey of burnt mounds in the Dales see, for example, Laurie, T. 2004. 'Burnt mounds of Wensleydale and Swaledale' in White, R. F. and Wilson, P. R. (eds.). *Archaeology and historic landscapes of the Yorkshire Dales*. Leeds: Yorkshire Archaeological Society, Occasional Paper No. 2, pp. 79–88.

26 Fairburn, N. 2008. 'The biggest dig in Welsh history' *Current Archaeology* 216, pp. 30–6.

27 Bowden, M. C. B., Mackay, D. A. and Blood, N. K. 1989. 'A new survey of Ingleborough hillfort, North Yorkshire' *Proceedings of the Prehistoric Society* 55, pp. 267–71.

28 Cunliffe, B. 1978. *Iron Age communities in Britain*. London: Routledge and Kegan Paul, p. 221.

29 Luke, Y. 2006. 'Rethinking Ingleborough' *Yorkshire Archaeological Society Prehistory Research Section Bulletin 2007*, pp. 18–24.

30 Wheeler, R. E. M. 1954. *The Stanwick fortifications, North Riding of Yorkshire* Report of the Research Committee of the Society of Antiquaries, London, No. 17, pp. 27–30.

31 Shotter, D. 2004. *Romans and Britons in North-West England*. Lancaster: Centre for North-West Regional Studies, p. 48.

32 Taylor, J. 2007 *An atlas of Roman rural settlement in England*. CBA Research Report 151, p.6.

33 Johnson, D. 2004. *Excavation of Broadwood Enclosure, Thornton in Lonsdale, North Yorkshire*. Ingleton: Ingleborough Archaeology Group.

34 *Cravescire* was mentioned as a wapentake in Domesday Book.

35 An eruption of Krakatoa in AD 535 may have been responsible.

36 Loveluck, C. 2003. 'The archaeology of Post-Roman Yorkshire, AD 400 to 700: overview and future directions for research' in Manby, Note 6, pp. 151–8.

37 Higham, M. 1992. 'The Regione Dunutinga – a pre-Conquest lordship?' *Bulletin of the Centre for North West Regional Studies* New Series 6, pp. 43–9.

38 Boulton, D. 1993. 'The ancient kingdom of Dent'. *Sedbergh Historian* 3 (2), pp. 2–5.

39 Graham-Campbell, J. 2001. *The Viking world*. London: Frances Lincoln, p. 10.

40 See Gelling, M. 1993. *Place-names in the landscape*. London: J. M. Dent, pp. 198–207; Whaley, D. 2006. *A dictionary of Lake District place-names*. Nottingham: English Place-name Society, pp. 409, 420–1 for a discussion of 'ley' and 'ton' place-names.

41 Abrams, L. and Parsons, D. N. 2004. 'Place-names and the history of Scandinavian settlement in England' in Hines, J., Lane, A. and Redknap, M. (eds.) *Land, sea and home*. Leeds: Maney, pp. 379–431.

42 Higham, N. 2004. 'Viking-age settlement in the North-Western countryside: lifting the veil' in Hines (note 40), pp. 297–311.

43 King, A. 2004. 'Post-Roman upland architecture in the Craven Dales and the dating evidence' in Hines (note 40), pp. 335–44.

44 Cottam, A. 1928. 'The granges of Furness Abbey, with special reference to Winterburn-in-Craven' *Transactions of the Historical Society of Lancashire and Cheshire* 80, pp. 58–85.

45 Dalton, P. 1994. *Conquest, anarchy and lordship*. Cambridge: Cambridge University Press.

46 Platt, C. 1969. *The monastic grange in medieval England*. London: Macmillan.

47 All sites have been entered on the Heritage Environment Record maintained by the Yorkshire Dales National Park Authority http://ads.ahds.ac.uk.

Chapter 6: Archaeology: Ingleborough South

1 White, R. 2002. *The Yorkshire Dales. A landscape through time* Ilkley: Great Northern, p. 23.

2 For a detailed treatment see Brown, B. and Brown, P. 2008. *Prehistoric rock art in the Northern Dales.* Stroud: Tempus.

3 Beckensall, S. and Laurie, T. 1998. *Prehistoric rock art of County Durham, Swaledale and Wensleydale.* Durham: County Durham Books, p. 112.

4 Note 3.

5 This work is being spearheaded by a group of academic archaeologists, notably Dr Timothy Taylor of the University of Bradford.

6 Brassey, J. 2002. 'Historic finds on a path between Austwick and Clapham' *NCHT Jo*, pp. 4–5.

7 National Archives MPC1/235, 'Map of Austwick by Richard Newby 1619'.

8 Moorhouse, S. 2003. 'Anatomy of the Yorkshire Dales: decoding the medieval landscape' in Manby, T. G., Moorhouse, S. and Ottoway, P. *The archaeology of Yorkshire*. Leeds: Yorkshire Archaeological Society Occasional Paper No. 3, p. 329.

9 Raistrick, A. and Holmes, P. 1962. 'Archaeology of Malham Moor' *Field Studies* 1 (4).

10 NYCRO ZTW MIC1655, frame 1603, letter dated 24 August 1929.

11 *Settle Household Almanac* 1885.

12 NYCRO ZTW XI. MIC2207, frame 397–99, Know Gap Estate.

13 Note 11, frame 411–20, Clapdale Farm.

14 Note 9.

15 Note 6.

16 National Archives DL44/653, 'Christopher Saxton map, 1603' in 'Plans and Letters 2 Jas 1 1604'.

17 Note 6.

Chapter 7: Routes through the landscape

1 For a general account see Bell, M. 2007. *Prehistoric coastal communities: the archaeology of western Britain 6000–3000 cal BC*. CBA Research Report 149; and Conneller, C. and Warren, G. 2006. *Mesolithic Britain and Ireland*. Stroud: Tempus.

2 Vyner, B. 2003. 'Prehistory. The Upper Palaeolithic and the earlier Mesolithic' in Butlin, R. A. (ed.). *Historical atlas of Yorkshire*, pp. 31–3; Manby, T. G. 2003. 'The late Upper Palaeolithic and Mesolithic periods in Yorkshire' in Manby, T. G., Moorhouse, S. and Ottoway, P. *The archaeology of Yorkshire*, pp. 31–2.

3 Manby, T. G. 2003. 'The Bronze Age' in Manby. 2003 (Note 2), p. 40.

4 Parker Pearson, M. 1994. *Bronze Age Britain*. London: BT Batsford for English Heritage, p. 95.

5 Shotter, D. 2004. *Romans and Britons in North-West England*. Lancaster: Centre for North-West Regional Studies, pp. 26–51.

6 Pers.comm. Arthur Batty.

7 Welch, M. 1994. *Anglo-Saxon England*. London: BT Batsford, p. 88.

8 Loveluck, C. 2003. 'The archaeology of Post-Roman Yorkshire, AD 400 to 700: overview and future directions for research' in Manby (Note 2), pp. 156–8.

9 Note 8, p.158; Faull, M. L. 1974. 'Roman and Anglian settlement patterns in Yorkshire' *Northern History* 9, pp. 1–25.

10 King Edwin of Deira (later to form part of Northumbria) defeated and expelled Ceredig, the ruler of the 'kingdom' of Elmet in battle in AD 616 or 617. See Note 9, Faull, pp. 24–5.

11 Graham-Campbell, J. 2001. *The Viking world* London: Frances Lincoln, p. 26.

12 Note 11, p. 28; Higham, N. 1985. 'The Scandinavians in north Cumbria: raids and settlement in the later ninth to mid tenth centuries' in Baldwin, J. R. and Whyte, I. D. *The Scandinavians in Cumbria*. Edinburgh: Scottish Society for Northern Studies, pp. 37–51.

13 Gerhold, D. 1993. 'Packhorses and wheeled vehicles in England, 1550–1800' *Journal of Transport History* 14 (1), pp. 1–26.

14 Johnson, D. 2002. *Limestone industries of the Yorkshire Dales*. Stroud: Tempus, p. 49.

15 Walker, G. 1814, *The costume of Yorkshire*. London.

16 Addison, Sir W. 1980. *The old roads of England*. London: BT Batsford, p. 97.

17 Bonser, K. J. 1970. *The drovers*. London: Macmillan, p. 19.

18 Note 17, p. 21.

19 Note 17, pp. 167–8.

20 Smail, J. (ed.). 2001. *Woollen manufacturing in Yorkshire. The Memorandum Books of John Brearley, cloth frizzer at Wakefield 1758 – 1762*. Yorkshire Archaeological Society Record Series 155. Woodbridge: The Boydell Press, vol. 1, f.55r, p. 103.

21 Note 17, p. 70.

22 Keighley Library. BK354. *An Act for repairing, amending, and widening, the Road from Keighley in the West Riding of the County of York, to Kirkby in Kendal in the County of Westmorland 1753*.

23 Byng, Hon. J. 1970 edition. *The Torrington Diaries*, vol. 3, ed. Bruyn Andrews, C. New York: Barnes and Noble, London: Methuen. First published in 1936, p. 88.

24 Note 23, p. 99.

25 Note 23, p. 91.

26 Note 23, pp. 88–9.

27 Wright, G. N. 1985. *Roads and trackways of the Yorkshire Dales*. Ashbourne: Moorland, p. 147.

28 Chambers, J. D. and Mingay, G. E. 1966. *The Agricultural Revolution 1750–1880*. London: Batsford.

29 Thomas Jeffreys' Map of Yorkshire, published in London in 1771, at a scale of 1:63,360, was the first detailed topographical map of the county.

30 William Smith was a pioneer geologist whose geological map of Britain, published in 1815, has been described as the 'first true geological map of anywhere in the world'. See Winchester, S. 2001. *The map that changed the world*. London: Penguin Books, p. 2.

31 Brigg, J. J. 1927. *The King's Highway in Craven*. Cross Hills: Dixon and Stell, p. 9.

32 Note 31, p. 14.

33 Note 31, p. 17.

34 Stated in the Preamble to the Act for repairing, amending, and widening the Road from Keighley in the West Riding of York, to Kirkby in Kendal in the County of Westmorland, 1753. Keighley Local Studies Library BK354.

35 John Ogilby's maps were fully published by Thomas Bowles in London in 1720 as *Britannia Depicta*.

36 The original Act of 1753 was repealed and replaced several times. The 1823 Act made provision for changing Clapham's toll bars.

37 Keighley Library. BK354. *A book for entering the orders made by trustees for putting in execution a certain Act of Parliament*.

38 Yorkshire Archaeological Society MD390/1, 'Plan of Crummack in the Township of Austwick, Parish of Clapham, 1806'.

39 NYCRO ZXF6/2, Lord MSS.

40 NYCRO CRONT 1808.

Chapter 8: Developing Landscape: Ribblehead

1 Whyte, I. 2003. *Transforming fell and valley*. Lancaster: Centre for North-West Regional Studies, pp. 7–8; Winchester, A. J. L. 2000. *The harvest of the hills*. Edinburgh: University Press, p. 68.

2 See http://commons.ncl.ac.uk, Ingleborough: historical overview, 1.3.2.

3 Note 2.

4 WYRO, Wakefield WYL.524/209. 'Agreement to stint Scales Moor, 6 January 1810'.

5 The original document is in a private collection. "The Tenth day of May 1656".

6 1791 award: Yorkshire Archaeological Society DD104; 1804 award: in private hands; 1847 award: WYRO, Wakefield A13.

7 NYCRO ZTW XI. MIC2234/3, frames 46–48.

8 Note 7, MIC2234/3, frames 54–59: Johnson, D. S. 2000. 'A nineteenth century upland estate' *NCHT Jo*, pp. 7–9.

9 Borthwick Institute. P.PROB.REG. MIC 1656.

10 NYCRO ZTW (ADD) Box 16/6, Newby Manor Court Rolls 1739–1810.

11 Collins, E. J. T. 2000. 'Rural and agricultural change. B. The Great Depression, 1875–96' in Thirsk, J. *The agrarian history of England and Wales vol. VII 1850–1914*. Cambridge: Cambridge University Press, pp. 138–207.

12 Census records 1841–1901.

13 Rée, H. 1983. *The Three Peaks of Yorkshire*. London: Wildwood House, p. 199.

14 Anon. 1949. 'Dick ... the tame trout of Brunscar' *Dalesman* 11, pp. 407–8.

15 Jackson, K. C. 2001. 'The construction works between Batty Moss and Dent Head on the Settle and Carlisle Railway' part 1 *Yorkshire History Quarterly* 6 (4), pp. 34–42; Mitchell, W. R. 2006. *The lost shanties of Ribblehead*. Settle: Castleberg, p. 71.

16 Cardwell, P., Ronan, D and Simpson, R. 2004. 'An archaeological survey of the Ribblehead navvy settlements' in White, R. F. and Wilson, P. R. *Archaeology and historic landscapes of the Yorkshire Dales*. Leeds: Yorkshire Archaeological Society Occasional Paper No. 2, pp. 195–202.

17 Fleming, H. W. 2004. 'The temporary township of Batty Green: 1870–1879', part 1 *Yorkshire History Quarterly* 9 (3), pp. 34–8; Jackson, K. C. 1997. 'The railway shanty towns at Ribblehead, North Yorkshire' *Yorkshire History Quarterly* 2 (4), pp. 133–8.

18 Fleming, H. W. 2004. 'The temporary township of Batty Green: 1870–1879', part 2 *Yorkshire History Quarterly* 9 (4), pp. 19–24.

19 Tyler, G. 2002. *Sheep, steam & shows. Farming life in Chapel le Dale*. Chapel le Dale: Committee of the Ribblehead Sheep Show, pp. 33–6.

20 Tyler, G. 2001. *Scripture and schools for the navvies of Ribblehead*. Private publication.

21 Note 16.

22 Johnson, D. 2007. *Ribblehead construction camps. Excavation of building n6*. Unpublished report by the Ingleborough Archaeology Group for the Yorkshire Dales National Park Authority.

23 Binns, D. *Railways in the northern Dales – the Settle Carlisle line*. Skipton: Trackside.

24 Mitchell, W. R. 2006, *The lost shanties of Ribblehead*. Settle: Castleberg.

25 Mitchell, W. R. and Fox, P. 2001. *The story of Ribblehead viaduct*. Settle: Castleberg.

Chapter 9: Developing Landscape: Ingleborough South

1 National Archives DL44/653, 'Christopher Saxton map, 1603' in 'Plans and Letters 2 Jas 1 1604'.

2 National Archives MPC1/235 'Map of Austwick by Richard Newby 1619'.

3 'A feigned issue to establish rights on Ingleborough' 1682 ... The original document is in a private collection.

4 NYCRO ZXF(M)1/4/8. No date. 'Austwick and Horton in Ribblesdale – map of disputed land'.

5 Sergeant, H. 2006. 'The witch of Clapham?' *NCHT Jo*, 26–27.

6 Cragg, R. B. 1905. *Legendary rambles. Ingleton and Lonsdale*. Privately published.

7 WYRO, Sheepscar, Leeds, WYL1977, 'Award for the division of Bullet Mire, Austwick, 30 July 1782'.

8 NYRO ZXF.6/2. Lord MSS. Austwick enclosure 1814 (Act).

9 NYCRO ZS Box27. Swinton Archive. 1808. 'The ancient customs of the Forest of Knaresborough. Verses on the intended Inclosure of the Forest of Knaresborough'.

10 NYCRO. ZTWIII 11/168. MIC1655, frames 2893, 2912–13.

11 NYCRO. ZTWIII 11/168, estate accounts.

12 Pers. comm. Ken Pearce; Craven, S. A. 2004. 'Ingleborough Cave, Clapham, North Yorkshire, England' *Cave and Karst Science* 31 (1), pp. 15–34.

13 Mitchell, W. R. 2002. *Reginald Farrer at home in the Yorkshire Dales.* Settle: Castleberg.

14 Johnson, D. 2006. *The sow kiln project. Excavation of clamp kilns in the Yorkshire Dales.* Ingleton: Ingleborough Archaeology Group, pp. 26–34; Johnson, D. In press. 'The archaeology and technology of early-modern lime burning in the Yorkshire Dales: developing a clamp kiln model' *Industrial Archaeology Review.*

15 NYCRO. ZTW (ADD), Box 16/6. Newby Manor Court Roll. 21 April 1748, 2 May 1758.

16 Note 15, 6 April 1774 to 8 April 1884.

17 Johnson, D. 2007. 'Lime-kilns, "improvement", and superstition' *Current Archaeology* XVIII (9), pp. 40–4; Johnson, D., note 14, in press.

18 Hudson, P. and Johnson, D. 2002. 'An introduction to Wharfe Mills, Austwick' *Yorkshire History Quarterly* 8 (2), pp. 12–21.

19 NYCRO ZTW/XI. MIC1653, frame 35, 'Tracing of Wharfe Mill and land', no date.

Chapter 10: Modern Land Use

1 Many of the data in this section were obtained from the Yorkshire Dales National Park Authority.

2 *Settle Household Almanac* 1885

3 Data supplied by a local agricultural estate agency.

4 Little Dale Stint Minute Book, 1927-, courtesy of Dr John Farrer.

5 Ingleborough Fell Stint Book, 1927-, courtesy of Dr John Farrer, Ingleborough Estate.

6 For an analytical discussion of environmental schemes, including these, see Van Huylenbroeck, G. and Whitby, M. (eds.). 1999. *Countryside Stewardship: farmers, policies and markets.* Amsterdam: Pergamon.

7 See www.limestone-country.org.uk.

8 Data obtained from the Yorkshire Dales Millennium Trust.

9 Pers.comm. Paul Evans, Natural England.

10 Pers.comm. Dr John Farrer, Ingleborough Estate.

11 Data obtained from the RSPB.

12 The first legislation was the Game Act 1671.

13 The Game Reform Act 1831. See Munsche, P. B. 1982. 'Gentlemen and poachers: the English game laws 1671–1831' *American Journal of Legal History* 26 (4), pp. 395–6.

14 Done, A. and Muir, R. 2001. 'The landscape history of grouse shooting in the Yorkshire Dales' *Rural History* 12 (2), pp. 195–210.

15 Atherden, M. 1992. *Upland Britain. A natural history.* Manchester: Manchester University Press, p. 97.

16 NYCRO ZTW III.11/36 MIC1654, frame 2742, 'Clapham shooting'.

17 Note 22, ZTW III. 11/36 MIC1654, frame 2741.

18 Note 22, ZTW III. 11/120. MIC1655, frame 1181.

19 Note 22, ZTW III. 11/120. MIC1655, frame 1211.

20 Note 22, ZTW III. 11/155. MIC1655, frame 2577–78.

21 Note 22, ZTW III, various entries.

22 Note 22, ZTW III. 11/36. MIC1654, frame 2741.

23 Note 22, ZTW III. 11/20. MIC1654, frame 1783.

24 NYCRO ZTW III. MIC1654, frame 1811–12, correspondence.

25 See www.gct.org.uk.

26 Pers.comm. John Osborne, Natural England.

27 www.rspb.org.uk/ourwork/policy/climatechange/index.asp; Huntley, B., Green, R., Collingham, Y. and Willis, S. 2007. *The climatic atlas of European breeding birds.* Barcelona: Lynx Edicions.

28 Note 1.

29 Johnson, D. S. 2006. 'Foredale Quarry, Helwith Bridge, a historical and archaeological survey' *Memoirs. British Mining* 80, pp. 111–34.

30 Note 29.

31 Advertisement in *Settle Household Almanac* 1885 for "Blue Flag and Limestone".

32 Note 31, p. 11.

33 Yorkshire Archaeological Society MS1186. 'Plan of a proposed canal from Parkfoot Bridge to Settle, 1780'.

34 Note 29, p. 16.

35 Note 29, p. 11.

36 Note 29, p. 11.

37 *Craven Herald* 30 June 1978; NYCRO ZXF(M)1/4/8, 'Plan of Swarthmoor'; National Archives Rail 491/599 'Midland Railway. Settle and Carlisle Branch. Settle-Carlisle Railway No. 1 Land Plan: Stainforth-Blind Beck Bridge.

38 Johnson, D. 2006. 'An introductory history of Ribblehead Quarry, Ingleton' *Industrial Heritage* 32 (1), pp. 18–24.

39 Information supplied by Hanson plc (now Hanson Ltd).

40 National Archives BT31/30976/16762, 'Ribblesdale Lime and Flag Quarry Co. Ltd Special Resolution 24th November 1910'.

41 Note 29, pp. 30–49.

42 Johnson, D. 2002. *Limestone industries of the Yorkshire Dales*. Stroud: Tempus, p. 97–8.

43 Note 42, p. 120.

44 Information obtained from Hanson Ltd at Horton Quarry.

45 Mitchell, W. R. 1988. *The changing Dales*. Clapham: Dalesman, pp. 102–3.

46 Note 42, p. 116.

47 Dobson, W. 1864. *Rambles by the Ribble*. Preston: W. and J. Dobson and London: Simpkin, Marshall & Co.

48 Note 1.

49 Brook, A, Brook, D, Griffiths, J. and Long, M. H. 1991. *Northern caves 2. The Three Peaks*. Clapham: Dalesman, pp. 235–65.

Chapter 11: Epilogue

1 Wood Warter, J. (ed.). 1848. *The Doctor etc by the late Robert Southey*. London: Longman, Brown, Green and Longmans.

2 See www.ydmt.org/haytime.html.

3 Pers.comm. Paul Evans, Natural England.

4 Information obtained from Lafarge Aggregates at Dry Rigg Quarry.

5 www.moorsforthefuture.org.uk.

6 For LBAPs in general see www.ukbap.org.uk/lbap. For the Yorkshire Dales see www.yorkshiredales.org.uk/wildlife.

7 See www.nygp.org.uk and www.yourdalesrocks.org.uk.

8 For RIGS in general see www.ukrigs.org.uk.

9 Once these are up and running, material for all Key Stages up to GCSE will be produced for use in Science and Geography.

Index

List of Subscribers

Mrs B. C. Abbott, Barbon
Mrs P. Abbott, Leeds
Mrs Alison Acland, Sutton Coldfield
Professor J. Charles Alderson, Lancaster
Keith Allard, Shefford
Mr & Mrs D. W. Altham, Cullingworth
John Asher, Stainforth
Mr J. P. Ashton, Bury
Russell Graham Atkins, Edinburgh
Mr Edward Atkinson, Harpenden
Mr P. Balchin, Ilkley
Mrs E. Bannister, Pinhoe
David, Alex & Hugh Barbour, nr. Shap
Sallie Bassham, Chapel le Dale
Bryan Beattie, Stainforth
M. G. Blamire, Great Chesterford
Mr C. J. Bonsall, Ingleton
Anita Bottomley, Burley-in-Wharfedale
G. R. Bowring, Lawkland
Christine Brown, Ossett
Anne Buckley, Tyldesley
Mrs Kay Burn, Paull
A. Butterfield Glusburn
Dennis Cairns, Barnoldswick
C. S. Caisley, Stainforth
P. & P. Carroll, Haworth
Mrs M. Carter, Horsford
Mr R. A. Chappell, Long Preston
P. Charlesworth, Batley
Geoff Cheetham, Wetherby
Brian Clark, Chapel le Dale
Dr D. J. Clarke, Wigglesworth
Mrs Cynthia Clifton, Huntingdon
Mrs F. Cooke, Kendal
Mr & Mrs Cowley, Whitworth
Christine Cramer, Slyne, Lancaster
Craven Museum & Gallery, Skipton
Ian Cross, Shelf
Kathy Cullingworth, Normanton
Mike Dagley, Wirral
Lorraine M. Davies, Guiseley
Marian Dean, Bolton-le-Sands
Mrs C. Dearman, Peakirk
Mrs P. Dodsworth, Allerton
Mrs J. Donaldson, Leeds
Mrs Jean Dooley, Burton Joyce
Mrs Joan B. Dutton, Giggleswick
P. J. Dyson, Richmond
Robert Dyson, Shadwell
Paul Evans, Fremington
Mr A. S. Fahey, Appleby
Mrs Audrey Foxcroft, Giggleswick
Richard Gant, Grear Wilbraham
Mr Jonathan Gaskell, Bridgwater
John & Sheila Geale, Settle

Miss Barbara Gibson, Lancaster
Mike Gill, Sutton in Craven
Mr Trevor Grange, Ben Rhydding
Mr D. C. Grant, Skipton
J. H. F. Green, Heathfield
Reverend Ian Greenhalgh, Austwick
Mr & Mrs H. Greenwood, Bretton
Alan Hackett, Fulwood
Stuart M. Haddock, Longton, Preston
Mr B. Haigh, Hamerton
Mrs B. Hammond, Eccleshill
Noel Harbage, Leeds
Tom Hargreaves, Brierfield
David Harrison, Drighlington
Steven Harrison, Ingleton
John & Sylvia Harrop, Austwick
A. H. Haupt, Cross Hills
John M. Heaps, Bradley
John & Christine Helliwell, Kirkby Lonsdale
Nick Hide, London
P. M. Higginson, Eldroth
Edward Hindle, Settle
B. M. Holmes, Thorlby
Rodney Hooper, Settle
The Hougie family
Mrs P. Houlton, Settle
Mrs A. M. House, Deal
Miss C. Howard, Leck
Ralph Howson, Silsden
R. J. Ireland, Silverdale
Mr David Jackson, Shipley
Dr R Jenkins, Clapham
Brian James Jenner, Leeds
Mr Stuart Jennings, Hampsthwaite
Kai Johanson, Harrogate
Mrs S. Johnson, Low Fell
Michael Joyce, Harrogate
Diana Kaneps, Wigglesworth
S. C. K. Keele, Glasgow
G. Keeler, Harrogate
Mrs A. Kirkwood, Shipley
Lancaster University Library
Rex Lanham, Tadley
Stan Lawrence, Austwick
Mrs B. Lockwood, Brighouse
Brian Longhorn, Ingleby Barwick
Jane Lunnon, Embsay
Steve Macaré, Harrogate
Julia Madelin, Chertsey
David Manners, Crofton
Mr M. D. Martin, Ripon
Master Sean Thomas Martin, Kingsley
Roger Martlew, Kettlewell
Mrs D. Maunders, Horsforth
Kathryn Mawson, Elloughton
Helen McKinlay, Clitheroe

Mr D. C. & Mrs P. J. Mellor, Hellifield
Ann Melly, Winchester
Malcolm Metcalfe, Stokesley
Mr & Mrs Michalowski, Halifax
Mrs B. Middleton, Settle
Audrey Mills, Bardsea
Mr B. R. Minnitt, Askrigg
Robert & Joan Mitton, Clapham
Garry Morrison, Twyning
Alan Mosey, Morecambe
Mrs M. Mottram, Sprotbrough
Mr P. R. Mussack, Letchworth Garden City
Paul Norman, Skipton
Carol Ann Ogden, Morecambe
Mrs Ann Ormrod, Barrowford
Mike Owen, Greater Manchester
D. J. Pack, Darwen
Sheila Parker, Redruth
Jane A. Parkinson, Ilkley
Janet Patten, Malton
W. N. Patterson, Knutsford
Mr K. Pearce, Clapham
Bernice & Jerry Pearlman, Leeds
Mr & Mrs S. Pears, Leicestershire
J. Michael Pearson, Allerston
Mrs A. R. Pemberton, Settle
Jan Penney, Chelmsford (ex Hull)
Mrs Joan W. Phillips, Bardsey
Mr D. Preston, Ilkley
David Procter, Keighley
Ian Procter, Rugby
Bill Quinton & Royanne Wilding, Giggleswick
Mrs J. Raine, Clapham
Jean Reinsch Caillich Ruadh, Grassington
Adrian K. Reinsch, U.W.F.R.A., Silsden
Gregory M. Reinsch, U.W.F.R.A., Greetland
Paul Reinsch, U.W.F.R.A., Greenhow
Dr J. T. Rhodes, Settle
Mr W. Rhodes, Grassington
Mr I. G. Roberts, Hellifield
Mr N. H. & Mrs G. E. Roberts, Rathmell
Mr T. I. Roberts, Sheffield
Anne & George Robinson, Austwick
Geoffrey Robinson, Dewsbury
Christine & John Rose, Giggleswick
G. V. Sale, Worcester Park
Mrs F. Sanderson, Baildon
Elaine Savage, Horsforth
Robert P. E. Savage, Horsforth
John Schofield, Otley
Mrs P. M. Scott, East Preston
Helen Sergeant, Sellside

Derek G. Sharpe, Elland
The Shaw family
Mr John H. Shepherd, Harrogate
Lord Shuttleworth, Leck Hall
Allen Simpson, Southam, Warwickshire
M. J. & E. M. Slater, Langcliffe
S. M. Slater, Ramsbottom
Kate Smith & Chris Ellison, Austwick
Rick & Lindsey Smith, Austwick
Colin Speakman, Ilkley
Martyn Speight, Otley
Mrs Ruth Spencer, Skipton
Mr Stephen Steptoe, Silsden
Gus & Ann Stewart, Clapham
Michael J. Still, Midsomer Norton
Robin Strange, Coniston Cold
D. Streets, Hitchin Boys' School
J. A. Swanson, Skipton
Jill Sykes, Austwick
David Tayler, Stainforth
Katharine Taylor, Grimsby
Mrs B. Teale, Sandbeds
Ralph Tomlinson, Ingleton
Graham Townsend, Ripon
Miss K. Townson, Settle
Veronica Trueman, Settle
Gerald Tyler, Chapel le Dale
Mr M. J. Waites, Forton
Frank Walker, High Westhouse
Dr Dianne Wall, Ingleton
Mrs D. A. Wallis, Great Easton
Richard Warham, Settle
Keith Watkinson, Bentham
Peter Watson, Ingleton
Mary Webb, Radnage
Mrs M. Wedderburn, Austwick
T. M. Wheelwright, Wath
Mrs Jean Whitaker, Harrogate
Justin White, Guildford
Mr K. G. Whittington, Stainforth
Professor I. Whyte, Lancaster University
E. C. Wilkinson, Hull
Mrs S. Wilkinson, Kilnsey
R. S. L. Wilks, Brockenhurst
Alan Williams, Stanbury
Mr S. Williams, Shoeburyness
D M Wilmot, Bath
Anne & Richard Wilson, Tatham Fells
Ron Wilson, Clapham
P. & S. Woods, Bournemouth
William Wray, Gargrave
Mr Michael Wren, Ely
Yorkshire Dales Millennium Trust, Clapham